INTRODUCING
ANTHROPOSOPHICAL MEDICINE

Rudolf Steiner with medical coworkers in Stuttgart (1924)

INTRODUCING ANTHROPOSOPHICAL MEDICINE

Twenty Lectures Held in Dornach, Switzerland
March 21 – April 9, 1920

Translated by Catherine E. Creeger
Introduction by Christopher Bamford
Foreword by Steven M. Johnson, M.D.

RUDOLF STEINER

SteinerBooks

CW 312

Copyright © 1999 by SteinerBooks
Foreword © 1999 by Steven Johnson
Introduction © 2010 by Christopher Bamford

SteinerBooks
Anthroposophic Press

610 Main Street
Great Barrington, Massachusetts 01230
www.steinerbooks.org

Translation from the German by Catherine E. Creeger

This book is volume 312 in the Collected Works (CW) of Rudolf Steiner, published by SteinerBooks, 2010. It is a translation of the German *Geisteswissenschaft und Medicin,* published by Rudolf Steiner Verlag, Dornach, Switzerland, 1985. Previously published as *Spiritual Science and Medicine* by Rudolf Steiner Press, London, 1948.

The lectures of this first course for physicians were recorded in shorthand by Helene Finckh, a professional stenographer, and later transcribed by her. Hans W. Zbinden, M.D. edited the first public edition (Basel 1937). The notes that Rudolf Steiner took while preparing for this course were published in the *Beitrage zur Rudolf Steiner Gesamtausgabe* [Articles on the complete edition of Rudolf Steiner's works], volumes 16 (Winter 1966-1967), 20 (Christmas 1967), and 35 (Michaelmas 1971). In 1985, the Ita Wegman Archive made additional pages of Rudolf Steiner's notes available for publication.

Library of Congress Cataloging-in-Publication Data is available.

ISBN: 978-0-88010-642-9

Printed in the United States

CONTENTS

Lecture 18

DORNACH, APRIL 7, 1920

Causes of illness. Bacillus theory. The balance of animalization and mineralization tendencies. The rhythm of waking and sleeping. Typhoid fever. Outward gesture an indication of internal state. Epidemiology. The unity of rhythmic activity. Metamorphosis. Salt, mercury, and sulphur processes at different stages of life.

Lecture 19

DORNACH, APRIL 8, 1920

Heredity. The role of male and female. Diabetes and mental illness. Hemophilia. Antimony. Blood clotting and protein formation. The effects of antimony. Oysters. Typhoid. Deadly nightshade.

Lecture 20

DORNACH, APRIL 9, 1920

The senses and the outer world. Ammonia salts. Excretion and secretion. Pulmonary activity. Tooth-forming processes. Peristalsis. Eurythmy, dance, knitting, crocheting. Nux vomica. The human being as a sevenfold metal. Acute and chronic illness. Depression. Assessment of schools of medicine.

INTRODUCTION

CHRISTOPHER BAMFORD

After the First World War, and indeed presciently, as it was already drawing to a close, in response to the widespread social-political chaos and the sense of profound psycho-spiritual and cultural rupture—civilization ending—Rudolf Steiner felt impelled to become outwardly and socially engaged in a new way. There were powerful practical reasons to do so. The collapse of the old social order made it seem possible to reorganize social, economic, and cultural life according to human reality and spiritual principles. There were compelling esoteric reasons, too. Above all, the moment was right. Cosmic and spiritual circumstances made it possible (even necessary) to infuse initiatory and mystery wisdom into the germination process of the coming civilization. The future evolution of humanity in some sense depended on it.

Thus, from 1918 onward, new initiatives flowed out of Anthroposophy into the world: first, the Movement for Social Renewal or "The Threefolding of the Social Organism" (1918), followed a year later by the founding of the first Waldorf School in Stuttgart (1919). Then, in 1920 businesses were founded and, most importantly, a major effort was made to refound the various disciplines of learning, the arts and humanities as well as the sciences, out of anthroposophical insight and research. At the head of Rudolf Steiner's list of sciences (and professions) potentially receptive to such insight and research stood medicine. This was a field of long-standing and passionate interest, with which he had always hoped to work.

At the beginning of the year, on January 6, as the second of three public lectures in Basel, Switzerland, on the topic "Spiritual Science and the Tasks of the Present," Steiner gave a talk titled "The Spiritual-Scientific Foundations of Physical and Psychological Health."

He stressed that while practitioners of modern science strive to exclude the human being from their picture of the world, to remove themselves from it and be as value-free and objective as possible in their concepts, anthroposophical spiritual science always strives to be holistic, moving from the wholeness of the healthy human being to the wholeness of the cosmos into which it is integrated and out of which it is organized. The field of spiritual science thus encompasses our whole being and is able to investigate the complex and continually metamorphosing relationships and connections between our soul-spiritual and physical aspects. He then turned to medicine, which most clearly demonstrates the "disadvantages" of the natural scientific approach for "it is the most striking example of what happens when science eliminates the human being from its methods."

> Mere intellectual knowledge of the laws of aesthetics does not make you an artist. By the same token, simply knowing the current natural laws does not make a person a healer. Physicians must be able to live in the activities, the ebb and flow of nature, with their whole being. They have to be able to immerse themselves completely in creative, weaving nature. Only then will they be able to follow with sincere, heartfelt interest the natural processes accompanying illness. At the same time, studying healthy people will help physicians to understand them when they are ill.

After alluding to some spiritual-scientific insights—such as the threefold thinking, feeling, and willing human being mirrored in the sensory-nervous, respiratory-rhythmic-circulatory, and metabolic systems—Steiner then concludes:

> Precisely when it comes to such an area as truly intuitive medicine, it would be the spiritual scientist's ideal to be able to speak before those who are specialists in the field. If they could find their way in and allow their expertise to speak without preconceptions, they would see how much spiritual science could enrich their specialty. Spiritual science, which is no unprofessional dilettantism, does not fear criticism from experts. It seeks to create deeper scientific sources than

those of today's conventional science and it knows that amateurism, not expertise, is what it might have to fear—had it not long since overcome fear for reasons that are easily understood. Spiritual science has nothing to fear from expertise or lack of preconceptions. It knows that the more expertise is brought to bear on its findings, the more positively they will be accepted. In considering what might be a perspective for an intuitive medicine, we might remember an old saying... [which] in a narrower sense is certainly applicable to the art of treating the sick human being. Wise folk of old said, "Like is known only by like." To heal human beings one must first know them. The part of the human being with which science today concerns itself is not the whole human being. When the whole human being is called to know the human being, then will like (a human being) be known by like (another human being). Only then will a human knowledge of the human being and a healing art arise that will, on the one hand, keep the human being as healthy as is possible in his or her social life and, on the other, treat illness in a way that is possible only if all the actual healing factors are considered together.

Clearly Steiner was issuing a challenge, or at least a call; but it was not one that was taken up by any of the physicians present. In fact, only a chemical engineer, Oskar Schmiedel, heard it.

Acting on what he heard, Oskar Schmiedel organized the first course in anthroposophical medicine. As he himself noted, this fact made anthroposophical medicine very different from all other anthroposophical initiatives (like eurythmy, Waldorf education, The Christian Community, and biodynamic agriculture), which *without exception* were undertaken by Rudolf Steiner in response to specific requests. Schmiedel wrote:

The first doctor's course was not given at the request of doctors or medical students, or in fact on the basis of any request at all. The reason why Dr. Steiner departed from custom probably has to do with the fact that he thought it important and timely to speak about medical questions without waiting for doctors to approach him with the request for such a course. Furthermore, this first doctors' course proved how much he could offer the doctors. *Everyone attending the course felt something like the opening of the floodgates.* The future was to show how important it was that the course was held at just this time. Preconditions were thus achieved that made it possible to start Dr. Wegman's Clinical-Therapeutic Institute in Arlesheim, as well as the one in Stuttgart. My own role was simply to create the outer conditions that enabled Rudolf Steiner to give the lectures he wanted to give. (Italics added)

Given the dire economic conditions in Germany, Schmiedel spent the months preceding the course organizing lectures and collecting money to make it possible for German physicians to come to Dornach. He also organized the course itself, which unfolded under beautiful spring weather. More than thirty doctors and medical students attended. Steiner was very strict about admission: he would allow only professionals. Otherwise, he said, he would have to give entirely different lectures. Natural healers, midwives, nurses, and even a Russian medical officer were banned. Only three exceptions were made (Marie Steiner, Walter Johannes Stein, and Roman Boos), and Steiner was apologetic about them! The course itself was a great success. Planned to comprise two weeks, at the request of the participants it was extended to three. Steiner lectured in the morning, and either he or someone else gave the evening lecture. At the same time as the medical course, another course, "Anthroposophy and the Various Branches of Science," was taking place. During this same period, a theology student from Basel, Gertrud Spörri, came to ask Steiner whether it would be possible to create an anthroposophically oriented movement of renewal within the church. Steiner replied that he would speak to young people on that topic quite differently than he spoke to the doctors, as in fact he did when a year later he gave the first theology course for priests. All of which is to say that things were moving very fast at this time.

The medical course, however, stands apart. The organization of the course was interactive and to some extent spontaneous. Steiner had a general program of what he wanted to accomplish, but within it he left himself open to improvisation based on the needs and questions of his audience. Before beginning, he asked those assembled to jot down specific wishes and submit them. He then undertook to integrate his responses with their requests as the lectures unfolded. Consequently, these lectures have the aliveness and excitement of a dialogue: the sense of dealing with living concerns, not theory. Another important consequence is that the course achieves a fullness, even as Steiner himself says, a "sort of completeness," unusual in such an "introductory" presentation. So much is covered: the meaning of sickness; the history of medicine; polarities in the human organism, in the cosmos, and in nature; the heart; the three systems (nervous, rhythmic, and metabolic); nature outside and nature within the human organism; soul, spirit, and body; diagnosis and the whole person; mineral, mercurial, and phosphoric processes; the therapeutic use of metals; the senses; homeopathy—the list is well-nigh endless.

As Schmiedel noted: *Everyone attending the course felt something like the opening of the floodgates.* Readers of this book will confirm for themselves how right he was. It is as if Rudolf Steiner had been waiting for the opportunity to engage these subjects: to talk to doctors, to address their concerns out of spiritual science, but in the language of medicine and healing. Rarely has he seemed so at home in his subject, so familiar with it, so passionate about it. Rarely, too, has he seemed to have so much enjoyment in giving a lecture course, feeling so much pleasure at being able to lay out a series of overlapping perspectives in the certainty of being understood. It is as if, here, he felt himself to be among those with whom he was completely at ease.

Though not a physician by training, as he stressed in his lectures, Rudolf Steiner's medical interests were clearly longstanding, deep, sophisticated, diverse, and far-reaching. A scientific education at the Technische Hochschüle in Vienna (the M.I.T. of its time), coupled with a lifelong passion for learning (reading all the latest books) meant that his knowledge of many fields—including mathematics, physics, chemistry, biology, anatomy, zoology, botany, and geology—was always detailed, professional, and up-to-date. Justifiably, therefore, he has been called a "Renaissance man." There are few disciplines of which he was not master from his own, special point of view. But medicine—healing—holds a special place in his biography and mission. Examining it will provide a background to the founding lectures of anthroposophical medicine collected here.

It must be said that the combination of the range and depth of Steiner's knowledge often seems hard to believe. Certainly, in many ways it was unique. To begin to understand it, we must imagine a person who, from a very early age, was single-mindedly dedicated to the pursuit of knowledge and understanding of the human condition, and used every available opportunity to deepen, test, and enrich his worldview. However, we must not imagine a person interested only in abstract or theoretical knowledge, or knowledge for its own sake. Rudolf Steiner's search for knowledge was always practical and existential. He sought to know because he wanted to act consciously and freely out of the truth of what it meant to be a human being. He did so in order to make human life truly and profoundly conformed to reality in all its details. In other words, he was a "detail" person for whom—as it was for Goethe before him—the phenomenon, that is, the given fact, must in the last analysis be the theory. For him, theory must be immanent in experience, not something super-added to it.

At school, his interests were threefold and interrelated. He loved geometry and mathematics, and was always deeply interested in what he could discover in the sciences, especially physics, chemistry, and astronomy. What united this diversity (and led to what we might call a "sub-interest" in world history and the evolution of consciousness) was a passion for thinking itself, for posing questions whose answers he would try to discover for himself through a disciplined process of meditation and study. Thinking for him was not a limited, skull-bound, private activity, but the essential human experience by which a person could begin to participate in those cosmic processes whose traces the various sciences try to parse and formalize. Thus, in parallel with his school courses, from adolescence on, he began to read what he could of philosophy, above all the German Idealist tradition of Kant, Hegel, and Schelling, whose influences could be felt everywhere in his environment. Thus, he struggled with the great questions, such as: Are there limits to knowledge?

What are space and time? What is matter? What is life? What is light?

Three signal, life-altering extracurricular events, really the three major influences in his life—which would not only prepare him for his later role as spiritual teacher and Anthroposophist, but also orient him, at least implicitly, toward medicine and healing—occurred shortly after Steiner entered the Hochschüle.

Officially, during his first year he was registered for classes in mathematics, natural history, and chemistry. Unofficially, he also attended other lectures and read deeply and widely in the library. Continuing his interest in philosophy, he attended lectures by the now-forgotten Robert Zimmerman and the still-celebrated Franz Brentano (who was Husserl's teacher, taught the only philosophy course Freud ever took, and inspired Martin Heidegger to investigate Aristotle's theory of being.) Most significant, however, was a course offered by the literary scholar Karl Julius Schröer on Goethe and Schiller and, what we might call, the consequences of Romanticism in German thought. Steiner and Schröer became very close. Steiner read Goethe's works (*Faust* 1 and 2) for the first time and passed many memorable evenings talking about Goethe with Schröer. As Steiner writes: "Whenever I was alone with Schröer, I always felt a third was present—the spirit of Goethe."

Schröer, however, knew little about Goethe's science. At first, Steiner likewise had little interest in it. He was more interested, as he says, "in trying to understand optics as explained by physicists." Trying to do so, however, was sheer agony for him. Physicists understood light as vibration and colors as specific vibrations, but Steiner intuitively understood light as an extrasensory reality experienced within the sensory world that revealed itself as color. Such thoughts prepared him for the task that would come to him through Schröer when, in 1882, on his teacher's recommendation, Steiner was asked to edit Goethe's scientific writings for a collected edition, adding his own introductions and explanatory notes.

Encountering Goethe's work (in honor of whom he would name the new mystery center of Anthroposophy the "Goetheanum") and spending more than fifteen years intensely studying it was certainly life-confirming and life-altering in many ways. Above all, we may say that it introduced Steiner to the alchemical Hermetic tradition, itself the growing tip or germ of that sacred science of the ancient Mysteries that Steiner would bring to modern consciousness and contemporary fruition in Anthroposophy. For Goethe, the great opponent of Cartesian-Newtonian mechanico-materialism, did not come to his scientific views unaided. He was, as R. D. Gray showed in his *Goethe the Alchemist* "profoundly influenced throughout his life by the religious and philosophical beliefs he derived from his early study of alchemy." Goethe's science in essence was alchemical and Hermetic.

Goethe was not alone in his interests, though he alone by his genius made a science out of them. In his era, the study of alchemy was still widespread; many people had alchemical laboratories. Alchemical language and philosophy, deriving from Jacob Boehme and Gottfried Arnold, had become part of the then-dominant spiritual revival called Pietism. Indeed, it was a Pietist friend of Goethe's mother's, Katerina von Klettenburg, who introduced him to alchemy during a severe illness at nineteen when he had a tumor in his neck, which could have been fatal.

As Goethe describes her, Katerina was an extraordinary woman: "a beautiful soul," that is to say, serene, graceful, patient, accepting of life's vicissitudes, intelligent, intuitive, imaginative, and above all a moral and religious genius. In their meeting, one genius discovered another. "She found in me," Goethe writes, "what she needed, a lively young creature, striving after an unknown happiness, who, although he could not think himself an extraordinary sinner, yet found himself in no comfortable condition, and was perfectly healthy neither in body nor in soul."

Katerina provided medical assistance in both body and soul. She found him a doctor, Dr. Metz, who prescribed, in addition the conventional remedies of the time, some "mysterious medicines prepared by himself of which no one could speak, since physicians were strictly prohibited from making up their own prescriptions." These medicines included "certain powders" as well as a "powerful salt"—"a universal medicine." To encourage their efficaciousness, Dr. Metz further recommended "certain chemical-alchemical books to his patients ...

to excite and strengthen their faith," and to encourage them to attain the practice of making the medicines for themselves.

Thus, as Goethe convalesced he and Fraulein von Klettenberg began an intensive study of certain texts: above all, Paracelsus, Basil Valentine, Eirenaeus Philalethes (George Starkey), Georg von Welling's *Opus Mago-Cabbalisticum et Theosophicum*, van Helmont, and the *Aurea Catena Homeri* (The Golden Chain of Homer).

At the same time, Goethe began laboratory work.

Goethe's alchemical work continued intensely for the next few years. He continued to study alchemical and Rosicrucian authors. Two years later, he still claimed "chemistry" was his "secret love." As he wrote to his mentor E. T. Langer: "I am trying surreptitiously to acquire some small literary knowledge of *the great books*, which the learned mob half marvels at, half ridicules, because it does not understand them, but whose secrets the wise man of sensitive feeling delights to fathom. Dear Langer, it is truly a great joy when one is young and has perceived the insufficiency of the greater part of learning, to come across such treasures. Oh, it is a long chain indeed from the *Emerald Tablet of Hermes Trismegistus*...." For a time, his alchemical studies occupied Goethe completely. In fact, until he met the cultural genius Herder and turned to more "acceptable" studies, they dominated him almost obsessively. As he writes, "My mystical-religious chemical pursuits led me into shadowy regions, and I was ignorant for the most part of what had been going on in the literary world at large for some years past."

Here a brief aside on the four-stage history of medicine—Greek, Monastic, Paracelsian, and Romantic—may be useful. The point is threefold. First, it was these studies that determined Goethe's worldview and especially his science, which is alchemy translated. Second, these "mystical-religious chemical pursuits" that provided the ground for an anti-materialist, living approach to nature and natural processes differed fundamentally from ordinary, "value-free," quasi-objective science in that their *raison d'être* was clearly *to heal: to serve humanity*. Many alchemical texts, in fact, were explicitly "medical" in orientation. Unfolding an alternative science, they also provided a theoretical and practical model for an approach to medicine. Third, in order for Steiner to understand Goethe and "translate" his world-view and epistemology for the last third of the nineteenth century Steiner would necessarily have had to study the Paracelsian and other alchemical-medical works that Goethe studied. Therefore Rudolf Steiner's encounter with alchemical medicine—represented by Paracelsus, Basil Valentine, and the Rosicrucians—began very early and was very deep, fired by the ambition and the intensity that his work with Goethe required.

Ancient Greek medicine, transmitted by Hippocrates, Aristotelian-ized, cast in stone by Galen (much in the same way as Euclid petrified Pythagoreanism), and passing through Islam (and Avicenna) reached the Middle Ages, where it in turn soon ossified. In parallel, through the triple confluence of traditional Western herbal knowledge, the transmission of alchemy from Islam, and esoteric Christianity, what we might call "monastic medicine" arose. The medical texts of Hilde-gard of Bingen and Albertus Magnus, for example, give some idea of what this meant. The Renaissance then witnessed the overthrow of the ruling medical paradigm, which, despite monastic medicine and the growing presence of alchemical approaches was still based on Aristotle, Galen, and Avicenna.

The revolution came through the turn to *experience*. Through anatomy and dissection certainly, but most significantly the Paracel-sian synthesis that combined the fruits of monastic and folk culture with the newly available Hermetic, Neoplatonic, and gnostic insights, and the flowering of Christianized alchemy in a *new, nature-based, experiential, existential spiritual science*. Paracelsus's influence was tremendous and continued through the end of eigh-teenth century, when Hahneman reformulated certain aspects of it as homeopathy. Hahnemann was, however, only one of those attempt-ing to create what we might call "Romantic" medicine, a living med-icine, a medicine of life, that would be the practical enactment of a true philosophy of nature (*Naturphilosophie*). At the heart of the Romantic moment—say 1770 to 1830—was an attempt to put medicine as the science of *life* at the heart of a general reformation such as the Rosicrucians had first announced. Such was the tip of the iceberg that Goethe's work presented Steiner.

In addition to his life-altering encounter with the works of Goethe, two other—yet strangely related—life-altering encounters helped form Rudolf Steiner's basic orientation. First, there was a meeting with a nature-initiate, a factory worker and herb gatherer, Felix Kogutski, "a simple man of the people."

> Once a week he was on the train that I took to Vienna. He gathered medicinal plants in the country and sold them to pharmacies in Vienna. We became friends and it was possible to speak of the spiritual world with him as with someone of experience. He was deeply pious and uneducated in the usual sense of the word… With him, one could look deeply into the secrets of nature. He carried on his back a bundle of healing herbs; in his heart, however, he carried the results of what he had gained from nature's spirit while gathering them…. Gradually, it seemed as though I were in the company of a soul from ancient times…. One could learn nothing from this man in the usual sense of the world. But through him, and with one's own powers of perception of the spiritual world, one could gain significant glimpses into that world where this man had a firm footing.

The meeting with Felix Kogutski, important as it was, was only preparatory to an even more significant encounter with the figure Steiner refers to only obliquely—in his autobiographical notes for Édouard Schuré— as the M. (or the Master). As Steiner puts it "…Then came my acquaintance with the agent of the M…. I did not meet the M. immediately, but first an emissary who was completely initiated into the secrets of plants and their effects, and into their interconnection with the cosmos and human nature…."

While the Master's identity must remain to some extent conjecture, it is nevertheless clear from Steiner's own indications that the teacher in question was Christian Rosenkreutz, the founder and guiding spirit of the Rosicrucians. However redolent of charlatanism the word "Rosicrucianism" may sound today, given how many different groups and persons have often evoked it for less than reputable purposes, in this instance it must be taken seriously.

Rosicrucianism first burst—there is no other word for it—onto the scene of history in the early seventeenth century with three surprisingly widely distributed texts, originating in Lutheran circles in Tübingen, Germany, and published sequentially in Kassel in 1614, 1615, and 1616. The first two texts—the Announcement of the Order (*Fama Fraternitatis*) and the Confession of the Order (*Confessio Fraternitatis*)—told the story of Christian Rosenkreutz (1378-1484) who, some two hundred years previously, had traveled the world in search of spiritual, scientific, and universal wisdom before returning home to Germany, where he gathered students around him and formed an order. The time was, however, not yet propitious for public work and so he decreed that, following his death, his mission and teaching were to remain hidden for one hundred and twenty years—that is, until 1604, the legendary date given for the opening of his tomb. The third text, *The Chemical Wedding*, an alchemical allegory of spiritual development, was obviously different in tone, but served the same purpose: to proclaim a "general reformation" of science, art, and religion, a revolutionary program of cultural transformation based on raising into modern consciousness and thoroughly "enchristing" the entire harvest of ancient and traditional mystery wisdom. The manifestos called for all like-minded people to join the movement. A *furore*—literally, frenzy—resulted. Paracelsian physicians, philosophers, alchemists, artists, and scientists from all over Europe began writing tracts and treatises to qualify them to join the movement. But no one knew who the Rosicrucians were, or where to find them! Chaos ensued. Reactionary and repressive forces from the church and materialist science arose to quell the revolt—unsuccessfully at first, but within a few years, what they were unable to do, the Thirty Years War (1620-1650) accomplished very efficiently, and the Rosicrucians disappeared from the exoteric world.

Rosicrucianism as a historical and cultural impulse is important for Steiner's approach to medicine above all in three ways. First, we may note the "rules" of the original brotherhood:

First, to profess no other thing than to heal the sick, and that *gratis.*

In other words, the primary orientation of the Rosicrucian is toward *healing* as an act of *service*. We may call this *the rule of love or compassion*, which, as Paracelsus wrote, is "the true physician's teacher." As service, it also implies an orientation *toward the world*— toward other beings, for we can love only other living beings—as well as the dedication to work selflessly and compassionately for *world evolution*. The Rosicrucian thus works for the sake of the world and from this point of view sees no difference between the healing of soul and body and the healing of the world. This dedication to heal affirms the primacy of action. If one is a true Rosicrucian, one walks, as Rudolf Steiner walked, "the true thorn-strewn way of the Cross," renouncing all egotism for the sake of the healing of the world.

Second, to wear no kind of special habit, but to follow always the custom of the country in their dress.

At its simplest, this second injunction has been taken to mean that Rosicrucians were called to live anonymously, unpretentiously, plying some ordinary trade. But at another, higher level, since chief among the customs of a country is its language, the rule invokes the "gift of tongues," possession of which enables one to address people in their own language, that is, in the way and at the level appropriate to their understanding. This implies, too, that a Rosicrucian is attached to no form or dogmatic belief and is able to translate wisdom into any form as circumstances may require. Rudolf Steiner's adherence to this second "rule" is manifest in his task and vocation—in fact, his "commission," for his encounter with the M. directly led to it—of adapting or translating (that is, restating on the basis of his own experience) Rosicrucian-alchemical wisdom into a form appropriate to modern scientific consciousness.

Third, to meet together at the house *Sancti Spiritus* every year at Christmas.

This rule affirms the primacy of communion in the spirit and of the unity of humanity through participation in the spirit.

Fourth, to seek to a worthy person to succeed them after they die.

That is, to teach, to create a lineage of friends.

Fifth, to make R.C. "their seal, mark, and character."

In other words, to have the Rose Cross, the union of love and knowledge, inscribed in their hearts, which is to say that to conjoin the Rose and the Cross, love and knowledge, in nature and human nature as one, to heal and unite nature and human nature in its center or heart, is the goal of the Rosicrucian work. (To complete the "rules," the *sixth* and final rule specified that these rules were to "remain secret for one hundred years" [more precisely, 120 years] after Christian Rosenkreutz's death.

The second way in which Steiner's Rosicrucian calling significantly determined his approach to medicine was the central role accorded Paracelsus in Rosicrucian lore. The *Fama* mentions him as a forerunner who, "though he did not enter our Fraternity," read carefully in the Book of Nature with great effect, failing however to bring about the revolution he desired because of his irascible temperament. Nevertheless, not surprisingly, his books were held in such high esteem that he is the only author mentioned by name as having his works stored for continual study in Christian Rosenkreutz's tomb. This Paracelsian emphasis carried two further associations, namely: the primacy of medicine (in the original documents paired with theology) and the importance of alchemy and its "universal medicine," despite the cheaters and quacks who confuse it with the search for material gold.

All these elements (Rosicrucian, Paracelsian, and alchemical), which are really one universal approach, contributed significantly to Rudolf Steiner's understanding of the ethics, philosophy, and practice of medicine and the art of healing, which may therefore be called "Rosicrucian-Paracelsian-alchemical." More generally, since this tradition is, in fact, heir to the entire Western mystery tradition, whose source, finally, as Steiner will repeatedly stress, is the ancient mysteries themselves, we may call what Rudolf Steiner brought into the world as anthroposophical medicine "traditional Western medicine" in the same sense that we speak of traditional Tibetan or Chinese medicine—but spoken anew out of contemporary experience and consciousness.

From the beginning of his professional career as a Goetheanist, philosopher, and man of letters, this tradition was thus Steiner's constant, if hidden, companion and study. It accompanied him as he wrote his books on, and introductions to Goethe, and as he hammered out an epistemology or theory of knowing appropriate to contemporary consciousness, one that could legitimize what we might call a "Paracelsian" approach to nature. It was not his task—nor was he yet ready—during this first period of his life to bring it into the open. For that, he had to wait until he had reached the necessary maturity (forty years of age) to stand forth as a spiritual teacher. Then, in 1900, as if foreordained, the opportunity arose when he was asked to give a course of lectures in the Theosophical Library in Berlin. "By means of the ideas of the mystics from Meister Eckhart to Jacob Boehme," he wrote later, "I found expression for the spiritual perceptions that in reality I decided to set forth. I then summarized the series in the book *Mystics after Modernism*." It was an important moment. As Paul Allen, in his introduction, puts it, "This book is significant in the life-work of Rudolf Steiner because it is a first result of his decision to speak out in a direction not immediately apparent in his earlier, philosophical writings."

For our purposes, the key chapter, which comes after three more or less epistemological chapters, is chapter 4: "Agrippa von Nettesheim and Theophrastus Paracelsus." Here Steiner shows that what the "mystics" Meister Eckhart, Johannes Tauler, Heinrich Suso, Jan Ruysbroek, and Nicholas of Cusa worked out as a way of thinking or path of consciousness, Agrippa first more tentatively and then Paracelsus more fully and thoroughly put into action as a "natural science" to the extent possible within the limits of their times: a new way of knowing and working with nature.

Steiner shows how Paracelsus, taking a stand on himself, on experience, seeks to ascend through his own cognitive powers to the highest regions. He does not want to accept any authorities, but to read directly in the Book of Nature for himself. But this does not come without a struggle, for he is faced by the mystery of human experience that feels itself the apex of, and woven into, universal nature, and yet is hindered from realizing the relation because one experiences oneself as a single individual, separate from the whole. Paracelcus understands that in the human being what is a reality within the whole feels itself a single, solitary being. Thus he knows he experiences himself at first as something other than he is. In other words: we are the world, but we experience our relation with the world as a duality. We are the same as the world, but as a repetition of it, as a separate being. Such for Paracelsus is the paradoxical relationship of microcosm and macrocosm.

Steiner goes on to explain that Paracelsus calls what causes us to see the world in this way our "spirit." This seems singular, individual: a repetition bound to a single organism. While the organism is part of the great chain of the universe, its spirit seems connected only to itself. The struggle is to overcome this illusion.

In reality our nature falls into three parts: our sensory-bodily nature as an organism; our hidden nature, which is a link in the chain of the whole world and is not enclosed within the organism, but lives in relation with the whole universe; and our highest nature, which lives spiritually. The first he calls the "elemental body"; the second, the "astral body"; and the third, the soul. Usually, we are locked within the elemental body and world with which our "individual" spirit is associated. But once this spirit is quieted or no longer active, "astral" phenomena and cognition become possible.

On the basis of his threefold division, Paracelsus, as Steiner describes it, then goes on to articulate a more detailed sevenfold division. There is first the *elemental*, or purely physical-corporeal body; within which there are the *organic* life processes that Paracelsus calls the "archaeus" or the "spirit of life." The archaeus makes possible the *"astral" spirit*, from which the *animal spirit* emerges. This in turn makes possible the awakening of the *"rational soul,"* within which, through meditation and reflection, the *"spiritual soul,"* able to cognize spirit as spirit, can awaken. Through immersion in the spiritual soul, a human being can experience "the deepest stratum of universal existence," and ceases to experience itself as separate. We may call the final level the *"universal spirit,"* which knows itself in us. As Paracelsus says: "This...is something great: there is nothing in Heaven and on Earth that is not in a human being. God, who is in Heaven, is in a human being."

Turning to Paracelsus's alchemical understanding of evolution, Steiner shows that his vision is monistic and developmental. The universe is in a state of becoming in, with, and through humanity, just as humanity becomes in, with, and through the universe—a relationship that unfolds and is perfected through human creativity, which is called to complete what nature begins. "For nature brings forth nothing into the light of day which is complete as it stands; rather, humanity must complete it." Completing by art and science what nature begins is what Paracelsus calls alchemy, which is the "third column of medicine" (the first two are philosophy and astronomy; the fourth is virtue.): "This method of perfection is called alchemy. Thus the alchemist is a baker, when he bakes bread; a vintner, when he makes wine; a weaver, when he makes cloth...[Therefore] the third pillar of medicine is alchemy, for the preparation of remedies cannot take place without it because nature cannot be put to use without art." Yet nature is always primary. Paracelsus learns endlessly from nature and from his own experience. Certainly he takes his understanding of the four elements (fire, air, water, and earth) and the principles of sulphur and mercury from traditional alchemical cosmology. But from his experience, he creates the new triad of sulphur, mercury, and salt—combustibility, vaporability (solubility), and fixability, the residue—so that each object and each condition thus has its own sulphur, mercury, and salt.

In this short account, Steiner merely introduces Paracelsus as an important precursor of the Anthroposophical (Theosophical) approach to nature, but he does not mention the two central ideals that inspired Paracelsus's life and work: the primacy of healing as the service to which we are called and the cosmic and earthly-human importance of Christ for this work. The time was perhaps not yet appropriate to do so. Yet these same two ideals, clearly and with a like primacy, inspired and motivated Steiner, too. For Paracelsus as for Steiner, every human being—thus every sickness, each patient—is individual and must be treated accordingly. For both, each individual arises out of and exists within a context: earthly-geographic, social, cosmic, and spiritual-karmic. (Not for nothing is Paracelsus known as the "father of environmental medicine.") For both, the triadic nexus of sulphur, mercury, and salt processes is ubiquitous. Both, too, were homeopathic, not allopathic, in orientation and understood the primacy of the law of similars. Both made considerable use of minerals, in preference to herbs, in creating remedies. Both understood the "spirituality" of disease. And for both, Christ was present in all things.

Thus as the years of Steiner's teaching unfolded we can observe these two ideals coming into ever greater focus. The centrality of Christ is self-evident; the devotion to healing perhaps less so. Yet reading between the lines it is equally clear. Throughout the next years, lectures on various aspects of health and illness, as wells as references to Paracelsus, Boehme, Basil Valentine, van Helmont, and those he calls "the old philosophers" (the alchemists) recur with regularity. At the same time, the depth of his research into the complex field of the spiritual, psychic, and physical-sensory interactions and relations that constitute the living human being increased from the lectures in the course *Occult Physiology* (1911) to the final hammering out of the understanding of the threefold human organism (1917). But these are only traces of a deeper, more passionate interest.

Confirming this interest, Rudolf Steiner sought contact with practicing physicians from the beginning, and there were always doctors among his students. Mention must first be made, of course, of Ita Wegman, later his close collaborator and in a real sense the co-creator of anthroposophical medicine. She first met Steiner in 1902, and in 1905 on his recommendation moved to Zurich to study medicine. Ludwig Noll and Felix Peipers, for whom in 1911 Steiner created the sequence of healing images of the Madonna, date from the same period. Later, other doctors would join the Anthroposophical Society and begin to work medically out of what they were learning. Here two facts must be borne in mind. First, that for Rudolf Steiner Anthroposophy was always simultaneously a path of spiritual research and a way of social and cultural ethical action. Research, although perhaps undertaken in a certain sense for its own sake, was never to be purely "theoretical." That was anathema. Steiner did not believe in research that did not bear concrete fruit in life. Therefore, he is always exhorting his students to live the path of Anthroposophy: to bring it into life, to manifest it for the sake of the greater whole. Second, that however cosmic and removed from human concerns Anthroposophy sometimes seems, Steiner's focus is always human beings in their concrete and in their specific individualities. While understanding human beings contextually as divine-cosmic-spiritual beings, his larger purpose is thus always to aid and further human-earthly evolution. He calls on human beings to know themselves not as "cosmic hermits," but as "cosmic citizens"—citizens of the cosmos—who at the same time embody this knowledge in their arts, sciences, and social life. Thus Steiner's research—even when focused on what appear to be the most arcane details of spiritual evolution—is always centered on the concrete human being. It follows from this that, as he was always pursuing a particular interest in healing, no matter what topic of research he was addressing, his findings would inevitably contribute toward the understanding of human health and illness.

All this came together in this first medical course—*Introducing Anthroposophical Medicine*. It was of course only a beginning. As Rudolf Steiner said in concluding:

> It was difficult to begin.... But now that we are at the end, I must say that it is even more difficult to stop! ...I am speaking out of truly objective, not subjective, heartfelt feelings when I say to you, whose attendance here has demonstrated your great interest in this beginning, "Until we meet again, on a similar occasion!"

Many more lectures and lecture courses followed. The movement grew. Clinics were established. Together with Ita Wegman, he co-wrote in the last year of his life (1925) *Extending Practical Medicine: Fundamental Principles Based on the Science of the Spirit*. Fittingly, it was his last book. Anthroposophical medicine was launched.

Foreword

STEVEN M. JOHNSON, M.D.

Like other great works, this book can be understood on many different levels. It may, for instance, be read as an exposition of the anthroposophical view of the human being in relation to health and illness; or as a contemporary restatement in the light of modern medical knowledge of, for example, the legacies of Paracelsus, alchemy, and homeopathy; or as an attempt to lay the foundation for a truly spiritual medicine that takes account of the human being as an integrated body, soul, and spirit. Given this complexity, one reader may very well interpret its descriptions of illness and therapy in a quite different way from another. Some would argue that a rational approach to medicine does not allow for such differences—that there is only one way to understand any given symptomatic phenomenon—and that, if two people understand the basis of illness differently, then one (or perhaps both) must be wrong. But the truth of medicine is never quite so simple. It is not surprising therefore that good clinicians often refer to the diagnosis of illness as the "art" of medicine. As experienced physicians have demonstrated throughout history, two doctors working from completely different views of illness and using unrelated treatments, can both achieve a "successful" healing.

This book presents Rudolf Steiner's first series of lectures on medicine to physicians and medical students. The lectures were presented as a stimulus to the development of "anthroposophically extended" medicine. This approach to medicine was revolutionary when it was introduced in the 1920s. Since that time, much of what Steiner had to say has been validated and put into practice in clinical settings around the world. His approach to diagnosis and treatment continues to stimulate new and startling ideas about the healing process, while it challenges our thinking about our current theories of disease pathology and our basic concept of wellness. Anthroposophically extended medicine is revolutionary, since it does not begin with the assumption that a human being is only the biochemistry of a physical body; rather, it attempts to heal the psycho-spiritual human being in relation to the material organism. Spirit, soul, and body are viewed as inseparable.

This poses the following question: How does the treatment itself affect the whole human being, including that human being's context (age, biography, personal relationships), of which the presenting symptom is only a part? The reader will find that each chapter in this volume answers this large question in a unique way. One of Steiner's greatest achievements is his presentation of this material as a "living" science that allows for the transformative and metamorphic nature of life, intended to be understood within the context of life's natural processes. Consequently, the context within which he evaluates health and illness honors continuing human change and evolution.

To observe the results of this method of healing, we need a clear phenomenological science that reveals the relationships between the human psycho-spiritual and the physical, biological organism. Considered holistically and in terms of the larger questions of human destiny, the reality of what constitutes health and healing is an elusive and ambiguous field. Spiritual science, or Anthroposophy (which means "wisdom of the human being") attempts to open a doorway for humanity toward developing the capacity for such a larger understanding or living science. Steiner tells us that faculties for greater consciousness and observation are dormant in us. He speaks of capacities of perception that we can gradually awaken through discipline, love, and artistry. But do such faculties have a place in a modern clinical medical practice? This question is at the very heart of the current debate in medicine. In fact, they are already being used, albeit unconsciously. Physicians are often amazed and confused by the fact that the patient's receptiveness to a medicine seems to influence the response to treatment—hence the whole vexing issue of the placebo effect. At the same time, outcome-based research is today validating many of the "alternative" therapies that have their origins in spiritually-based methods of healing. Nevertheless, the "active ingredients" of such therapies elude current research techniques. New thinking is needed to understand life as it really is, the interrelated whole, in which spirit and matter interplay with each other like the instruments of a symphony orchestra.

Today, the field of psychoneuroimmunology has validated the connection between the human mind and the bodily processes. But this field has yet to develop a clear concept and language that expresses what constitutes the mind (some say "soul"). Many ancient Eastern forms of healing, such as Tibetan and Ayurvedic medicine, offer frameworks for just such an understanding, and these healing modalities are becoming increasingly popular throughout the world. Unfortunately, these magnificent teachings do not lend themselves easily to our "modern" Western worldviews. They do not always give us a workable framework within which to integrate contemporary science and spiritual knowledge, regardless of their validity as healing modalities.

This text clearly demonstrates Steiner's sincere intention and brilliant capacity to integrate the results of spiritual research with that of twentieth-century science. In many instances, Anthroposophy helps to bridge the gap between Eastern spirituality and Western consciousness by translating the language of those traditions for practitioners educated within the context of materialistic thought.

Anthroposophically extended medicine has influenced the practice of many areas of medicine, both modern and traditional. In many countries (particularly in Europe), anthroposophical medicine has been successfully integrated into numerous community and academic hospitals. Furthermore, medical education as it emerges in the future is likely to have a tremendous impact on physicians in their capacity to extend their knowledge of healing into "alternative" modalities of medicine such as that presented in this volume. There are currently many well-known medical schools in the United States that are developing departments of "integrative medicine." This tendency toward a more integrative and holistic approach to healing represents an attempt to take what appears to be adaptable and functional from nonallopathic methods and seeks to define specific indications for its use.

Many such unconventional therapies are being researched using controlled trials. The notion that materialistically based thinking is the only path to knowledge of the human organism will come under increasing scrutiny as the results of these studies continue to challenge researchers and physicians to reexamine their ideas.

There are ethical dilemmas confronting medical practice today that explain, at least in part, the growing interest in anthroposophically extended medicine and other alternatives to conventional medicine. Abortion, biogenetic engineering, advanced life support, immunization, and modulation of the immune system have all led to increased debate within the medical community as well as in the larger context of society. For example, Dr. Leon Kass, wrote: "I cannot know with certainty what I would think, feel or do or want done, faced with the knowledge that my wife was carrying a child branded with Downs syndrome or Tay-Sachs disease. But an understanding of the issues is not advanced by personal anecdote or confession. We all know that what we and others actually do is often done out of weakness rather than conviction. It is all too human to make an exception in one's own case."[1] But where do we find the substantive knowledge that gives force and moral credibility to our convictions? Such knowledge is certainly not inherent in our understanding of the technology that produced the dilemma in the first place. Clearly, the courage needed to act in truly ethical ways when we affect human life can arise only from a deeper understanding of human life.

While this book may not address these issues directly, the ways in which Steiner explores the meaning of illness and therapy does suggest methods of investigation that lead to insight into the moral challenges that face contemporary medicine and society. Without the kind of deep understanding of health and illness presented here, one cannot think, feel, or act with real conviction in the great matters involved in treating human life.

Steiner assumes here the enormous challenge of investigating the deeper nature of various substances. He explores mineral, plant, and animal substances within a context much larger than our current understanding of their biochemical properties and effects. He elicits the

---

1. *Toward a More Natural Science,* p. 86. The Free Press. A division of Simon & Schuster, Inc. New York 1988.

basis for a new biochemical perspective that may be called a "new alchemy." Indeed, Steiner reclaims for modern medical practice our own Western tradition, one that reaches back to the mysteries of alchemy, and to this he adds his own spiritual insights to bring us a practice of medicine worthy of the whole complex, integrated human being.

In these twenty lectures, Rudolf Steiner challenges our very notions of illness and its causes as well as its diagnosis and treatment. As the twenty-first century proceeds, serious illnesses such as heart disease, cancer, and Parkinson's disease, for instance, will be viewed increasingly as chronic disorders with decreasing impact on human longevity. Nevertheless, as certain illnesses burden humanity less and less, new ones seem to arise with alarming regularity. As medicine tries to keep pace with a changing climate, it becomes increasingly apparent that we need a deeper understanding of the human being.

How important is it for a clinician to understand the spiritual realities of life? Medicine, it seems, has begun to move into the spiritual realms of life and death through biotechnology, pharmacology, and various interventions that alter the natural course of birth and death. The moral questions posed by modern medical technologies cannot be answered at the biochemical level but require insight into life's invisible aspects. The fact that physicians are playing a bolder, more assertive role in manipulating human destiny requires that spiritual science and medicine work together in ways described here by Rudolf Steiner. Serious students may find in this lecture course the basis for an entirely new approach to the science of life and medicine. At whatever level these lectures are read, if approached with an open mind, one's view of health and illness will be forever changed.

INTRODUCING
ANTHROPOSOPHICAL MEDICINE

Rudolf Steiner

LECTURE 1

DORNACH, MARCH 21, 1920

Iт is quite evident that this course will be able to touch on only a very small portion of your probable expectations with regard to the future of medicine, since you will all agree with me that any real, enduring work in this field depends on reforms in the actual education of physicians.[1] What can be communicated in a course of lectures cannot instigate such reforms, even in the remotest way, except possibly by inspiring a number of people to participate in the reform process. Any medical subject discussed today, however, always has as its other pole and background the way people are prepared to work in the field of medicine through their studies in anatomy, physiology, and general biology. This preparation gives the thinking of medical students a particular slant from the very beginning, and this slant, above all else, is what we must get away from.

I hope to achieve the educational purpose of these lectures by making the following programmatic divisions in our subject matter: First of all, I will give you a few indications of the obstacles that the modern, conventional study of medicine presents to a truly objective grasp of the nature of illness as such. Second, I will indicate where we must look in our search for an understanding of the human being that is capable of providing a true foundation for work in the field of medicine. Third, I will use an understanding of human connections to the rest of the world

---

1. This course was advertised as a "specialized spiritual-scientific course for physicians and medical students." Personal invitations were sent to physicians and medical students who were members of the Anthroposophical Society.

to suggest the possibilities of a rational system of healing. In this third section, I will answer the question of whether healing is altogether possible and conceivable.

Fourth—and I think this may perhaps be the most important component of our studies, although it will have to be intertwined with the other three viewpoints—I would like each of you to jot down your special wishes for me on a piece of paper and give it to me by tomorrow or the next day. Please write down whatever you would like to hear about in this course. These wishes can extend to all sorts of topics. What I hope to accomplish through this fourth aspect of the program—which, as I said, will be worked into the other three—is to avoid having you leave this course with the feeling that you have not heard something you particularly wanted to hear. For this reason, I will structure the course in such a way as to work in all the questions you have jotted down. So please give me your requests by tomorrow, or—if that is not possible— by this time the day after tomorrow. I think this is the best way to achieve some sort of completeness in the context of this conference.

Today I would like to give only an introduction of sorts, a few observations for purposes of orientation. Above all, I have been making an effort to assemble everything that can be made known to physicians as a result of spiritual-scientific research, and I would like to take this as my starting point. I do not want what I am going to attempt here to be confused with a medical course as such, although in fact it is one. We will focus on anything that can possibly be important to physicians, regardless of its origin. A true science or art of medicine, if I may put it this way, can be built up only by taking into account everything considered in the sense I have indicated.

I will begin today with a few observations for the sake of orientation. If you have reflected on your task as physicians, you will probably have stumbled frequently over the question of what illness actually is, what a sick human being is. Although explanations of illness and the sick person may be disguised by one or the other seemingly objective insertions, they are rarely anything other than this: that disease processes are deviations from the normal processes of life; that certain phenomena, which work on an individual and to which his or her normal life processes are not adapted, produce changes in these normal life processes and in the person's bodily organization; and that illness consists of these change-related functional impairments of parts of the body. You will have to admit, however, that this is nothing more than a negative definition of illness. It is nothing that can help you when you are dealing with actual diseases. This missing practical aspect is what I want to work toward here. To arrive at a definitive view on this subject, I think we would do well to look at certain views on disease that have arisen over the course of time—not so much because I find this absolutely essential for a modern understanding of disease symptoms, but because we will be able to orient ourselves more easily if we are able to consider the older views that have led to current ones.

You all know that when we consider the origins of modern medicine, we usually point to ancient Greece in the fifth and fourth centuries B.C., to Hippocrates. It can be said—or at least we have the feeling—that the view that first appeared with Hippocrates and later led to what is known as humoral pathology (which basically continued to play a role right into the nineteenth century) was the beginning of the development of Western medicine. The influence of this belief, which is actually fundamentally erroneous, persists even today and prevents us from achieving an unbiased view of the nature of disease. The first thing we have to do is to eliminate this fundamental error.

To an unbiased student, Hippocrates' views—which, as you may already have noticed, continue to play a role right into the nineteenth century, right up to Rokitansky—constitute not only a new beginning but also, to a very significant extent, the end of ancient views on medicine.[2] In what comes down to us from Hippocrates, we encounter the last filtered remnant, so to speak, of very ancient views on medicine that were acquired by means of atavistic clairvoyance rather than by taking the anatomical route, as is done today. The relative position of Hippocratic medicine might be characterized best by saying that it was the point in time when ancient medicine based on atavistic clairvoyance came to an end. Speaking superficially—but only superficially—we can say that Hippocratic physicians sought the origin of all disease states in

---

2. Baron Karl von Rokitansky (1804–1878), professor of pathological anatomy, author of *Handbuch der pathologischen Anatomie*, 3 vols., Vienna 1842–1846.

an imbalance among the fluid bodies that work together in the human organism. They pointed out that in a normal organism, these fluid bodies must stand in a definite relationship and that in a diseased body, their proportions deviate from the norm. Correct proportions were called *crasis* and incorrect proportions *dyscrasy*. Of course, these physicians looked for ways to influence the imbalance and reestablish the correct proportions. Four components in the outer world were seen as constituting all physical existence: earth, water, air, and fire (although fire was the same as what we now simply call warmth). As far as human and also animal bodies were concerned, these four elements were seen as being specialized into black gall, yellow gall, mucus, and blood. It was thought that the human organism needed the right mixture of blood, mucus, and black and yellow gall in order to function.

If modern, scientifically educated individuals approach a subject like this, their first thought is that when blood, mucus, and yellow and black gall mingle, they do so in accordance with intrinsic properties that can be determined by means of elementary or advanced chemistry. Seeing it in this light, people imagine this to be the origin of humoral pathology, as if the Hippocratic physicians had seen blood, mucus, and so on, only in this way. This was not the case, or rather, it was true of only one of these components, namely black gall, which seems most typically Hippocratic to modern observers. As far as black gall was concerned, Hippocratic physicians did indeed think that its ordinary chemical properties were the active factors. But with regard to all the rest—white or yellow gall, mucus, and blood—they were not thinking only of the properties that can be determined through chemical reactions. They thought that these other fluid constituents of the human organism—for the present, I will always restrict myself to the human organism, without considering the animal organism—possessed certain intrinsic properties in the form of forces or energies lying outside our earthly existence. Thus, just as they saw water, air, and warmth as being dependent on the forces of the cosmos beyond Earth, they also saw these constituents of the human organism as being imbued with forces coming from outside the Earth.

In the course of the evolution of Western science, we have completely ceased looking toward forces that come from outside the Earth.

Today's scientists would find it downright peculiar if they were expected to think that water, when it influences the human organism, supposedly possesses not only those properties that can be confirmed through chemistry, but also others it possesses by virtue of belonging to the supra-earthly cosmos. But according to ancient views, the effects of forces originating in the cosmos itself are introduced into the human organism through its fluid constituents. Although the effects of these cosmic forces gradually ceased to be taken into account, medical thought into the fifteenth century continued to be based on remnants of the filtered view we encounter in Hippocrates. This is why it is so difficult for modern scientists to understand medical texts written before the fifteenth century, for it must be said that most of the authors of that time did not have any real understanding of what they were writing. They talked about the four basic constituents of the human organism, but their reasons for describing these constituents in one way or another were derived from a knowledge that had died with Hippocrates. In talking about the properties of the fluids that build up the human organism, people were simply talking about the aftereffects of Hippocratic knowledge.

Galen then contributed a compilation of old traditions that worked on into the fifteenth century, although they were becoming more and more incomprehensible.[3] But there were always single individuals capable of recognizing and pointing to the existence of something whose possibilities are not exhausted by the purely earthly element, by what can be ascertained chemically or physically. These individuals acknowledged the need to point to something in the human organism that makes its fluid substances work in ways other than those that can be confirmed through chemistry. Although others could also be mentioned, these opponents of the prevailing school of humoral pathology included Paracelsus and van Helmont who brought a new quality into medical thought in the sixteenth and seventeenth centuries simply by trying to formulate a concept that others were no

---

3. Claudius Galenus (ca. A.D. 129–199), Greek physician to the gladiators in Parganum and at the court of Marcus Aurelius. Considered the founder of experimental physiology, he demonstrated the function of arteries. He is responsible for about 100 treatises on physiology and medicine.

longer formulating.[4] Their formulation, however, contained thoughts that could be followed only by those who were still somewhat clair-voyant, as Paracelsus and van Helmont very definitely were. If we are not clear about all these matters, we will not be able to communicate understandably with each other about certain remnants that still cling to modern medical terminology, although their origins are no longer recognizable. Thus Paracelsus—and later others who were influenced by him—assumed the *archeus* to be the basis of the action of fluids within the organism. He assumed the *archeus* to be similar to what we speak of as the human etheric body.

The terms "*archeus*" as Paracelsus uses it and "human etheric body" as we use it actually sum up something that does indeed exist, but with-out tracing its actual origins. Doing so would oblige us to proceed as follows: we would have to say that the human being has both a physical organism, which consists essentially of forces that work out of the Earth, and an etheric organism, which consists essentially of forces that work out of the periphery of the cosmos [see drawing, "red"].

red

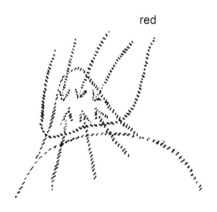

4. Phillippus Aureolus Paracelsus Theophrastus Bombastus von Hohenheim (1493–1541), Swiss physician and alchemist. He investigated problems and diseases related to mining. He was forced out of mainstream medical practice because of his unorthodox ideas and methods. He emphasized a phenomenological approach to medicine and helped to establish chemistry as a part of medical practice. Johann Baptist van Helmont (1579–1644), Flemish physician and chemist who coined the term *gas* (suggested by the Latin and Greek *chaos*) to designate aeriform fluids. He was the first to distinguish gases from air, such as carbon dioxide, and considered water a "pure chemical." He also sug-gested the use of alkalies to balance acidity in the stomach.

Our physical organism is a portion of the entire organization of the Earth, as it were. Our etheric body, and also Paracelsus's *archeus*, is a portion of something that does not belong to the Earth, something that therefore works into the earthly element from the cosmos from all directions. Thus, in his view of an etheric organism underlying the physical organism, Paracelsus summed up everything that had been described earlier as simply the cosmic aspect of the human being—a concept that came to an end in Hippocratic medicine. Although he indicated details here and there, he did not investigate further into the supra-earthly forces connected to what was at work in the *archeus*.

We might say that Paracelsus's meaning has become ever more incomprehensible. This is especially evident if we jump forward into the seventeenth and eighteenth centuries, where we encounter Stahl's school of medical thought, which no longer understood anything of how the cosmic aspect works into the terrestrial.[5] Stahl's school of medicine enlisted the help of all sorts of unfounded concepts—concepts of a life force, of life spirits, and so forth. Whereas Paracelsus and van Helmont still spoke with some degree of consciousness about what lay between the soul/spirit and the physical organization of the human being, Stahl and his followers spoke as if it were simply a matter of another form of the consciousness soul playing into the structuring of the human body. Of course, Stahl's view elicited a strong reaction, because anyone who carries on in this way, hypothesizing about some sort of vitalism, is entering the realm of purely arbitrary constructs. And, as you know, the nineteenth century then rose up in arms against these arbitrary constructs. It can be said that only very great minds like Johannes Müller, who died in 1858 and was the teacher of Ernst Haeckel, managed to overcome some of the harm that resulted from this unclear way of speaking that addressed life forces as if they were soul forces at work in the human organism, but had no clear idea of how they were supposed to work.[6]

---

5. Georg Ernst Stahl (1660–1734), an advocate of animism.
6. Johannes Peter Müller (1801–1858), German physiologist and comparative anatomist. Ernst Heinrich Philipp August Haeckel (1834–1919) became professor of zoology at the University of Jena. He was a prolific writer and, by the age of sixty, had published forty-two works.

At the same time, however, a totally different trend was emerging. We have traced the declining trend to its last vestiges. But more recent times saw the dawning of an idea that then became definitive in a different way in terms of the formulation of medical concepts, especially in the nineteenth century. Basically, this idea was derived from a single, unusually authoritative eighteenth century work, *De sedibus et causis morborum per anatomen indagatis* (1761) [On the bases and causes of diseases through anatomical investigation], by the Paduan physician Morgagni.[7] This book saw the emergence of a totally new view that essentially introduced the materialistic trend into medicine. We need to characterize these things completely objectively, without sympathy or antipathy, because what came to light in this book directed people's attention to the consequences of disease in the human organism. Autopsy became definitive. Only from this time onward can it be said that autopsy became definitive. It was possible to tell from the corpse that if a certain illness—regardless of what it was called—was present, a particular organ must have undergone a specific change. These changes began to be studied during postmortem examinations. This practice constitutes the actual beginnings of pathological anatomy, while everything that had previously existed in the field of medicine was based on certain persistent effects of ancient clairvoyance.

It is interesting to note how this great shift finally took place in one fell swoop. Interestingly enough, it is possible to point precisely to the two decades in which this transformation came about, when any remainders of the ancient legacy were abandoned and the atomistic and materialistic view of modern medicine was established. If you take the trouble to read through Rokitansky's handbook on pathological anatomy, published in 1842, you will still find traces of the old humoral pathology, remnants of the view that disease is based on the abnormal interaction of fluids. Rokitansky very ingeniously incorporated this view—which can be maintained only by legatees of the old view of the supra-earthly qualities of fluids—into his observations of

---

7. Giovanni Battista Morgagni (1682–1771), Italian physician and considered the founder of pathological anatomy.

changes in organs. Thus his book, although based on postmortem observations of organ changes, also suggests that particular organ changes came about under the influence of abnormal fluid mixtures. There you have, in 1842, the final appearance of the legacy of ancient humoral pathology. In the next few days we will talk about how forward-looking attempts (such as Hahnemann's) to consider more comprehensive concepts of disease were introduced into the decline of the old humoral pathology.[8] Hahnemann's and similar attempts are too important to be presented in a mere introduction and will have to be discussed later in greater detail.

At this point, however, I would like to draw your attention to the fact that in the two decades following the publication of Rokitanksy's book on pathological anatomy, the foundations were laid for the atomistic, materialistic view of medicine. In a very strange way, old views still played into the ideas that developed in the first half of the nineteenth century. It is interesting to observe that Schwann, for example, who might be said to have discovered that plants have cells, was still of the opinion that cell formation was underlain by the development of some sort of shapeless fluid (he called "blastema") and that the cell nucleus condensed out of this fluid formation, gathering cell protoplasm around it.[9] It is interesting to note that Schwann still posits an underlying fluid element possessing attributes whose tendency to differentiate brings about the cells as such. It is also interesting to trace the gradual subsequent development of a view that can be summed up in these words: The human organism builds itself up out of cells. This idea approximates today's customary view that the cell is a type of building-block for organisms and that the human organism is built up out of cells.

At heart, the view that was still evident between the lines (or even more pervasively) in Schwann's work is the final remnant of the old

---

8. Christian Friedrich Samuel Hahnemann (1755–1843), founder of homeopathy. His chief work, *Organon der rationellen Heilkunde* [Organon of medicine], Dresden, 1810.
9. Theodor Schwann (1810–1882), professor of anatomy and physiology in Liege and Louvain. His chief work was *Mikroskopische Untersuchungen über die Übereinstimmung in der Struktur und dem Wachstum der Tiere und der Pflanzen* [Microscopic investigation of the agreement between structure and growth in animals and plants], Berlin 1839.

system of medicine, because it does not lead to atomism. It sees an atomistic phenomenon—cells—as emerging from something that, if considered rightly, can never be thought of as atomistic, namely, a preexisting fluid essence that possesses inherent forces and gives rise to the atomistic element through differentiation. Thus, in the two decades of the 1840s and 1850s the older, more universal view was coming to an end and the atomistic view of medicine was dawning. It was fully present by the time Virchow published his book on cellular pathology in 1858.[10] We must recognize that an enormous leap, an enormous shift in the direction of modern medical thinking, took place between the publication of Rokitansky's book in 1842 and Virchow's in 1858. Virchow's book deduces all pathological phenomena in the human being from changes in cellular functioning. Ever since its publication, the ideal official view has been to study changes in cells in organ tissue and to understand all illness as resulting from such cellular changes. This atomistic view simplifies matters because it makes them very clear and lays them out in a way that is easy to understand. And more recent science, in spite of all its advances, always aims to understand everything in the simplest possible terms, without considering that it is the character of nature and the cosmos to be extremely complicated.

It is very easy to demonstrate experimentally, for example, that an amoeba in water changes its shape, extending and retracting its arm-like processes. Then, if you warm the liquid it is floating in, you will see that its processes extend and retract more quickly, at least until the temperature reaches a certain point. Then the amoeba contracts and is no longer able to respond to changes in the surrounding medium. You can also introduce an electric current into the liquid and observe how the amoeba assumes a spherical shape. It eventually bursts if the current running through the liquid becomes too strong. In this way, the changes an individual cell undergoes under the influence of its

---

10. Rudolf Virchow (1821–1902), professor of pathological anatomy in Würzburg and Berlin; cofounded the Archive for Pathological Anatomy and Physiology and Clinical Medicine; explained cellular pathology in his *Vorlesungen über Zellularpathologie in ihrer Begründung auf physiologischer und pathologischer Gewebelehre* [Lectures on cellular pathology: its basis in tissue physiology and pathology], Berlin, 1859.

environment can be studied and used as the basis of a theory of how disease gradually develops through alterations in the character of the cell.

What is the essence of the results of that great shift that took place within two decades? What emerged then lives on and now permeates all of official medical science. It is none other than the general tendency that has developed in the age of materialism—the tendency to grasp the world in atomistic terms.

Please take note of the following. I began by drawing your attention to the fact that anyone working in the medical field today is absolutely obliged to consider the question of what diseases are. What kind of processes are they, and how do they differ from the human organism's so-called normal processes? We need a positive conception of this deviation in order to be able to work with it at all, but the usual descriptions supplied by official science are exclusively negative and serve only to point out that such deviations exist. Then attempts are made to eliminate the deviations. But there is still no comprehensive view of the nature of the human being, and our entire philosophy of medicine suffers from the absence of such a comprehensive view.

What are disease processes, really? You will not be able to avoid calling them natural processes. Suppose you trace the consequences of some external process in nature. It is not so easy to make an abstract distinction between that process and a disease process. You call the natural process "normal" and the disease process "abnormal" without pointing out why the process taking place within the human organism is an abnormal one. You cannot develop practical applications until you can at least explain to yourself why the process is abnormal. Only then can you investigate how to do away with it, because only then will you be able to discover which corner of the cosmos makes it possible to eliminate such a process. Ultimately, even calling something abnormal is an obstacle, for why should any process in the human being be considered abnormal? Even if I cut my finger, that is only abnormal as it relates to the human being, because if I cut a piece of wood into a particular shape, that is a normal process. But if it is my finger that gets cut, I call that an abnormal process. The mere fact that we customarily engage in processes other than finger-cutting tells us nothing; it is merely playing with words. From a certain perspective, what happens when I cut my finger follows a course similar to that of other processes and is just as normal as any other natural process.

Our task is to discover the real difference between those processes within the human organism that we call disease processes—which are basically quite normal natural processes, even though specific causes must precipitate them—and the everyday processes that we usually call "healthy." We must discover this radical distinction, but we will not be able to do so if we cannot take up a way of looking at human beings that really leads us to their essential nature. In this introduction, I would like to sketch for you at least the first elements of this way of looking at the human being, with the intention of elaborating on them later.

I am sure you understand that in these lectures, which are necessarily limited in number, I will be giving you primarily what you will not find in books or other lectures, and I will assume a knowledge on your part of what is available elsewhere. I do not think it would be especially valuable to present a theory to you in constructs that you could also find somewhere else. For this reason, let us turn now to what you can discover by simply comparing what you can see in a human skeleton and the skeleton of one of the so-called higher apes—a gorilla, for example. If you compare these two skeletons on a purely superficial level, the main thing you will notice in the gorilla is the exceptional development of the entire lower jaw, simply in terms of mass. The lower jaw weighs heavily on the skull. When you look at the head of a gorilla with its massive lower jaw, you get the feeling that the lower jaw weighs heavily on the entire skeleton in some way, pushing it forward, and that the gorilla makes a considerable effort to remain upright in spite of this burden.

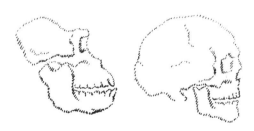

You will find the same distribution of weight, in contrast to the human skeleton, when you look at the gorilla's forearms and the lower part of the hands. They seem heavy. In the gorilla, everything is massive. In contrast, in the human being everything is refined and delicately jointed; weight moves into the background in the human being. In these particular parts of the body—the lower jaw and the forearms and fingers—the element of weight moves into the background in the human being, while it is prominent in the gorilla. Anyone who has cultivated a sharp eye for these proportions will be able to find them again in the bones of the feet and legs. There, too, an element of weight is present in the gorilla, which is pushing in a certain direction.

I will use this line [arrows] as a schematic indication of the force that can be seen in the gorilla's lower jaw, arms, and legs:

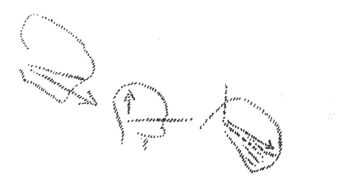

In the human being, this force is counteracted by an upward-striving element. This conclusion is inevitable if you observe a human lower jaw, which no longer weighs down the skeleton, and the delicate shaping of human arms and fingers.

The difference between a gorilla skeleton and a human skeleton is evident to the naked eye. You will have to deduce the form-creating element in the human being from a kind of parallelogram of forces, which results from the same upward force to which gorillas adapt only outwardly, as you can tell by the effort required for them to maintain uprightness. Here is the resulting parallelogram with its lines of force:

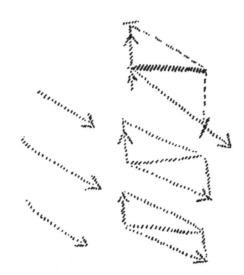

The very strange thing about this is that nowadays we usually restrict ourselves to simply comparing the bones or muscles of higher animals to those of humans and fail to place enough emphasis on this morphological transformation. In observing it, we must look for one essential aspect. You see, in the human being the forces that counteract those determining a gorilla's form must actually be present. Those forces must exist; they must be at work. If we look for them, we will rediscover the aspect of ancient medicine that was abandoned or filtered out by the Hippocratic system. We will rediscover that the original forces in the parallelogram are earthly in character. The other forces, however, must be sought outside the Earth. They unite with the original forces, and the resultant owes its origin to supra-earthly, extraterrestrial forces rather than to earthly ones.

We must look for forces that pull human beings into the upright position. This is not the same as the upright position higher animals assume from time to time, because the forces active in bringing about human uprightness are also formative forces. It makes a difference whether we are dealing with apes, who walk upright but still possess forces that weigh them down in the other direction, or with humans, whose skeletal development works in the direction of forces that are non-earthly in origin. If we simply look at the form of the human skeleton in the right way, tracing the dynamics at work in building it up instead of restricting ourselves to describing the individual bones and comparing them to animal bones, we will realize that what we see there is not to be found anywhere in the other kingdoms of nature. We must unite the specifically human forces with the original forces in the parallelogram. The resultant cannot be accounted for by considering only forces that exist outside the human being. It will be important for us to make a careful study of this leap from the animal to the human. When we do, we will be able to discover the origin of disease in both humans and animals. I can show these elements to you only little by little, but when we pursue them further we will be able to make many discoveries.

In connection with what I have just presented to you, I would like to mention the following. If we move on from the skeletal system to the muscular system, we discover significant differences in the character of muscles. A muscle at rest is alkaline in reaction, if we take its typical chemical effect into account. But we can actually say only that its reaction is alkaline-like, because in a resting muscle the reaction is not as clear-cut as alkaline reactions otherwise are. Similarly, in an active muscle a somewhat indefinite acid reaction occurs.

As you recall, in a metabolic sense muscles are composed, of course, of what human beings ingest. Therefore, in a certain respect, they are a result of the forces present in earthly substances. But when human beings become active, it becomes increasingly evident that what their muscle tissue contains as a result of being subject only to ordinary metabolism is being overcome. The changes appearing in active muscle tissue stand in contrast to ordinary metabolic changes and can ultimately be compared only to the forces bringing about the formation of the human skeletal system. These latter forces, which transcend what humans acquire from outside, imbue themselves with terrestrial forces, uniting with them to bring about a resultant force. Similarly, we must also see muscle metabolism as containing something chemically active that is working into the Earth's chemistry. You might say that in the skeleton, something we can no longer find within the earthly element is working into earthly mechanics and dynamics. Similarly, in our metabolism we have non-earthly chemistry working into earthly chemistry to produce effects different from those that can appear under the influence of earthly chemistry alone.

These observations about morphology on the one hand and quality on the other will have to constitute our point of departure if we want to discover what actually lies within the human being. This approach will reopen the way back to something that has been lost but is obviously still needed if we are not willing to accept a mere formal definition of disease that is useless in actual practice. You see, a very important question is emerging. Earthly remedies from our surroundings are all we have available to work on the human organism when it undergoes changes. Non-earthly forces, however, are at work in us—or at least forces that turn our processes into non-earthly processes. This gives rise to the question of how we can bring about an interaction between the sick human organism and its physical earthly environment, an interaction that leads from illness to health. How can we call forth a reciprocal relationship of this sort that will really also be able to influence those forces active in the human organism that are not encompassed by the realm of processes from which we select our medicines, even if these processes are dietary prescriptions and so forth?

You see that what can ultimately lead to a specific therapy is intimately related to an appropriate understanding of the essential nature of the human being. These first rudimentary elements of what is intended to enable us to rise to a solution to this problem have been derived from distinctions between humans and animals. I am fully aware of the very facile objection that animals and even plants can also become ill (lately there has even been talk of diseases in minerals!) and that therefore no distinction should be made between humans and animals as far as illness is concerned. We will deal with this objection later. These distinctions will become evident once you see how little physicians stand to gain in the long run from investigating the animal kingdom with the goal of making headway in human medicine. To be sure, animal experimentation does have something to offer with regard to human healing—and we will find out later why this is so—but only if the radical difference between animals and humans, a difference that persists right into the details of their organization, is fundamentally clear to us. For this reason, it will be important to find appropriate ways to continue to clarify the significance of animal experimentation for the development of the field of human medicine.

As we continue, I would like to draw your attention to the fact that when we are obliged to point to such supra-earthly forces, the personality of the individual is involved to a much greater extent than it is if we can always point to so-called objective rules or objective laws of nature. Admittedly, it will be important to work toward the intuitive element to a much greater extent in the field of medicine. We need to realize that an intuition trained to observe forms—the gift of drawing conclusions from morphological phenomena about the character of an individual human organism that may be sick or healthy in some respect—must play an ever greater role in the future development of medicine.

As I said, these things were intended to serve only as an introduction and orientation of sorts, because the important point for today is to show that medicine must once again turn its attention to something that cannot be accomplished through either chemistry or conventional comparative anatomy, something that can be achieved only if we move on to consider the facts from a spiritual-scientific viewpoint. Several errors are still prevalent in this regard. The main issue in the spiritualization of medicine is thought to be replacing material remedies with spiritual ones. This approach may be justified in particular areas, but it is totally unjustified on the whole, because what is most needed is a spiritual recognition of the healing value that may be present in a material remedy—that is, using spiritual science to evaluate material remedies. That will be the task of the portion of this course that I described as searching for healing possibilities by recognizing the connection between the human being and the rest of the world.

I want all the things I will say about specific therapeutic processes to be as well founded as possible and to help in acquiring a view, in each single illness, of the connection between the so-called abnormal process, which is of necessity a natural process, and so-called normal processes, which are also nothing other than natural processes. I would merely like to add a brief postscript: Whenever the fundamental question has arisen of how to come to terms with the fact that disease processes are also natural processes, attempts have always been made to evade the issue. For example, I was interested to learn that already in the first half of the nineteenth century, Troxler, who taught in Bern, was very emphatically pointing out that illness needed to be investigated as a normal phenomenon.[11] He claimed that this view would ultimately lead us to acknowledge the existence of a certain world that is connected to our world but forces its way into it through illegitimate channels, as it were, and that the results of such an investigation could have something to do with disease symptoms.

I want to touch on this only superficially at this point. Just imagine, however, a world existing in the background whose governing principles are very justified processes that happen to bring about disease symptoms in our world. If that were the case, if these laws that are totally justified in a different world were to break through into our world through certain gaps, they could cause all kinds of damage. This was what Troxler was aiming at. In spite of the fact that he expressed himself without clarity in some respects, it is still possible to see that he was on a path that was leading toward a certain healing for medical science.

Since Troxler had lectured at the university in Bern, a friend there once helped me investigate how he was regarded by his colleagues and what came of his suggestions. In the encyclopedia that documents many incidents in the history of the university, we were able to find only that Troxler had been the cause of a great many arguments! We found nothing in particular about his importance to science.

As I said, my intention today was only to point out these things. Please do write down all of your wishes for me by tomorrow or the next day so that I can weave them into what I myself intend to present. The form that these lectures will take will be based on these wishes of yours. I think this will be the best way to proceed, so please make extensive requests.

---

11. Ignaz Paul Vital Troxler (1780–1866). Published works: *Blicke in das Wesen des Menschen* [Glimpses into the essential nature of the human being], Aarau 1812; *Naturlehre des menschlichen Erkennens oder Metaphysik* [Natural history of human knowledge, or metaphysics], Aarau 1812; *Vorlesungen uber Philosophie, uber Inhalt, Bildungsgrenze, Zweck und Anwendung derselben aufs Leben* [Lectures on philosophy: its content, delineation, purpose, and applicability to life], Bern 1835.

LECTURE 2

DORNACH, MARCH 22, 1920

OUR points of departure today will be similar to yesterday's, but we will move on and gradually delve further into the essential nature of the human being by observing certain polarities that govern it. You will recall from yesterday that in the case of the human being, the downward-directed forces predominating in animals were combined visually into a parallelogram with forces that act vertically. We also saw an analogue of this in muscle activity. If we pursue these two ideas as we study the human skeleton and muscular system, enlisting the help of everything experience can provide at present, it should soon be possible to make the study of bones and muscles more significant for medicine than it has been thus far.

If we take cardiology as our starting point today, however, the connection between knowledge of the human being and the needs of medicine becomes especially difficult. I could say that something present as a mere potential in the study of bones and muscles has emerged fully in the view that has developed with regard to cardiology. (Let us restrict ourselves to the heart for the time being.) And what is the general view of the human heart? It is seen as a pump of sorts, pumping the blood into the various organs. All kinds of interesting mechanical constructions have been invented in the attempt to explain the heart as a pumping machine. In reality, these mechanical constructions completely contradict embryology, but people have not been attentive enough to really question this mechanical theory of the heart, so it has not been tested, or at least not in the generally accepted scientific way. I will first sketch the situation for you, and what I present in the next few days will confirm, bit by bit, what I can initially present only as a point of view. The main thing to consider in looking at the heart is that the heart absolutely is not, and cannot be, a so-called active organ. The activity of the heart is not a cause; it is a consequence.

You will understand this last statement only by bearing in mind the polarity that exists between the human organism's metabolic activities and its respiratory activities. Look at all the activities involved in taking in and processing nutrients and channeling them into the bloodstream (either directly or via the vessels). Here you trace the transformation of nutrients in the organism as they move upward from below; you trace this right up to the point of interaction between the blood, which has taken up the nutrients, and the respiratory process, which takes in air.

If you take a very good look at the processes under consideration here—and all you really need to do is look at them properly—you will find a certain contrast between everything belonging to the respiratory process and everything belonging to the metabolic process in its broadest sense. These processes want to balance each other out; they are "thirsting" after each other, in a manner of speaking, longing to satisfy themselves with each other. (Of course other ways of expressing this could be chosen; however, as time goes on we will understand each other better.)

Initially, liquefied nutrients interact with what is taken up by the organism in gaseous form through the respiratory process. This interaction must be studied precisely. It consists of forces that play into each other, but before doing so they are dammed up in the heart. The heart comes about as a damming-up organ between what I would now like to call the organism's lower activity—the intake and transformation of food—and its upper activities, of which I would consider respiration to be one of the lowest. A damming-up organ is inserted between these activities. The most important point about this situation is that cardiac function is a consequence of the interaction between liquefied food and air taken in from outside. Everything that comes to expression in the heart, everything we can observe in the heart, must be considered a consequence. To begin with, we must even consider it a mechanical consequence.[12]

The only promising attempt that has been made to reconsider at least this mechanical basis of cardiac function—but nothing more—was made by an Austrian physician, Dr. Karl Schmidt from North Styria, who published a paper entitled "Pulse Curves and the Beating of the Heart" in the *Vienna Medical Weekly* (1892, no. 15–17).[13] Although this treatise is somewhat short on content, an active medical practitioner has at least noticed that we must deal with the heart as if it were a damming-up apparatus rather than an ordinary pump. To Schmidt, the beating motion of the heart resembles the action of a hydraulic ram, which is flow-activated. Here, implicit in Dr. Schmidt's descriptions, lies the actual truth of the matter.

When we see all cardiac function as the consequence of these interpenetrating flows (as I can now symbolically term them) of fluid and of gas, we are still viewing matters only on the mechanical level.[14] But ultimately, what is the heart? It is a sense organ. And ultimately, even if we are not directly conscious of the heart's sensory function, even though this is one of our subconscious sensory activities, the heart nonetheless exists so that our upper activities may sense and perceive our lower activities. Just as you perceive color processes in the environment with your eyes, you also perceive with your heart, although in the dimness of the subconscious. You perceive what is taking place in the lower part of your body. Ultimately, the heart is an organ of inner perception, and it must be addressed as such.

We will understand the actual polarity within the human being only if we acknowledge that a human being is a dual being, built up in such a way that the lower portion is perceived by the upper portion. I must add the following, however: We can take the lower activities—

---

12. In the most recent German edition, these last two sentences constitute a single sentence, which was altered after reexamining the stenographic record.

13. Originally a lecture at the monthly meeting of the Styrian Physician's Association in Graz, October 26, 1891.

14. This sentence has also been altered on the basis of the original stenographic record of the lecture.

that is, one pole of the total human being—as given if we study the intake of nutrients and their transformation in the wider sense up to the point where they are balanced out against respiration. The balancing of nourishment with respiration takes place through our rhythmical activity, the significance of which we will still have to discuss. But we must see sensory and neural functions—everything related to outer perception and how it is taken further and processed by neural activity—as being entwined with respiratory functions. If you add together these two things—respiratory activity and sensory/neural activity—you have some notion of one pole of the human organization. On the other hand, if you add together the intake and transformation of nourishment—that is, metabolism in the ordinary sense of the word—you have the other pole in the human organization.

Essentially, the heart is the organ whose perceptible movement expresses the balance between these upper and lower poles. On a psychological—or perhaps it would be better to say sub-psychological—level, the heart acts as the organ of perception that mediates between these two poles of the human organization. You will see that only this principle, if kept in mind while studying everything that anatomy, physiology, and biology have to offer, is capable of shedding light on the human organization. As long as you do not differentiate between these upper and lower poles with the heart mediating between them, you will be unable to understand the human being, because there is a fundamental difference between all of the lower organizational activity of the human being and the activity of the upper organization.

If we want to express this contrast in a simple way, we might say something like this: Everything taking place down below has its negative image or counterpart up above. We can always find a corresponding image in the lower region for everything that is involved in the upper region. The most significant point here, however, is that there is no material transfer of substance between the upper and the lower, but only a correspondence. We must always understand how to relate something from down below to something else up above, without insisting on a material transfer. Let us take a very simple example—the cough reflex and actual coughing—in the context of what is up above, or to the extent that these things belong up above. Their counterpart down below is diarrhea. We will always find that anything in the upper region has its counterpart below. We understand the human being correctly only when we are able to grasp these correspondences correctly, and we will encounter many of them in this lecture course.

These are more than just abstract correspondences. At the same time, in any healthy organism, an intimate association is taking place between the upper and the lower. In a healthy organism, this association of pairs is such that any particular upper-body function—perhaps a respiration-related activity or one related to the sensory-neural apparatus—must overcome another activity down below and run its course in complete harmony with this lower counterpart. An irregularity immediately occurs in the organism if a process from below somehow gains ascendancy or precedence so that it is far too strong for its corresponding activity above, or vice versa. (Later, this will lead us to a true understanding of the disease process.) Upper functions must always correspond to lower ones in a specific way—overcoming each other, taking place in ways that reflect their orientation toward each other, as it were. This orientation is very specific and is individually different in each person, but in every case there is a very specific correspondence between how upper processes and lower processes run their course.

It is important to be able to make the transition from this healthily functioning organism, in which the upper and lower aspects are in correspondence, to a diseased organism. Let us begin with signs of disease in what Paracelsus called the *archeus*, and we call the etheric body. If you want to disguise it so that outsiders who want to know nothing of these things do not object, you could also say that you want to talk about the very first functional or dynamic signs of illness. If we begin with these, if we talk about what is disclosed first in the etheric body or in the merely functional dimension, we can again speak of a polarity, but a polarity that encompasses the non-correspondence or irregularity. This comes about in the following way.

Let us assume that down below, in food intake and in the digestive system in the broader sense, the inherent chemical and/or organic forces of the ingested food predominate. In a healthy organism, all of these forces that are active and inherent in the food itself, all the forces we study externally in the laboratory, have to be overcome by the upper element to such an extent that they become irrelevant to any internal activity of the organism. No outer chemistry or outer dynamics or the like continues to function. It is all completely overcome. It can happen, however, that the correspondence is not strong enough for the upper element to really grasp and pervade its lower counterpart completely. In a sense, the upper element cannot completely "cook" the lower or—as I might also put it—etherize it through and through, which would be a slightly more accurate description. In such a case, the process that predominates in the human organism really does not belong there. It is a process just like those taking place in the outer world, and it should not be taking place within the human organism.

Because irregularities do not immediately engulf the physical human being, processes such as these first become evident in what could be described as the functional aspect—in the etheric body, the *archeus*. If we were to choose a colloquial expression derived solely from certain specific forms of this irregularity, we would have to choose the term "hysteria." In fact, as we shall see later, this is not a bad choice, so we will use hysteria as an expression or technical term for excessive independence of the metabolic processes. Actual symptoms of hysteria in the narrower sense are nothing but metabolic irregularity driven to a climax state. In reality, even hysterical processes that have reached the stage of sexual symptomatology are nothing more than such metabolic irregularities, which by nature are outer processes that should not be present within the human organism, lower processes that the upper processes are too weak to overcome. This is one of the two poles.

Whenever such symptoms of hysteria appear, we are dealing with an excessively strong nonhuman or extra-human activity in the lower parts of the human organization. But the same irregularity in the interaction between upper and lower can also occur because an upper process fails to run its proper course, taking place in a way that is too demanding on the upper organization. This is the opposite, the negative image, of the lower process. It demands too much of the upper organization. It reaches its conclusion before it connects with the lower organism via the heart. It is too strongly spiritual, too strongly intellectual on an organic level, if I may use that expression. In such cases the other one of these polar irregularities appears, namely, neurasthenia. Above all else, it is important to look at these two irregularities of the human organism, irregularities that lie within the functional sphere, since these are the defects that express themselves above and below. We will gradually have to understand how the polarity in the human organization succumbs to one or the other of these deficits. In neurasthenia, we have an upper function that demands too much of the upper organs; as a result, something that should have been transmitted from above via the heart in order to take place down below instead takes place prematurely up above and reaches its conclusion there. The activity in question is not transmitted through the damming-up process in the heart and thus does not extend down into the lower flow, the flow of liquefied nutrients.

You can also see that it is more important—far more important, I might say—to study a syndrome's outer manifestations than to study defective organs postmortem. An autopsy of defective organs merely reveals consequences. The essential thing is to grasp the overall picture, the phenomenon of the illness, which in some way will always tend more in one direction or the other, toward neurasthenia or hysteria. (Of course, we have to stretch the usual meanings of these terms.)

Once we have pictured the collaboration between upper and lower clearly enough to take it as our starting point, we will gradually come to recognize how something that is initially apparent only as a functional element taking place in the etheric, as we would say, is then able to take hold of the organic/physical element by becoming denser in its forces. At that point it can be said that what was initially present as a mere suggestion of hysteria is then able to assume physical form in various abdominal diseases. Similarly, in the other direction, neurasthenia assumes an organic form in diseases of the throat and head. For the medicine of the future, it will be extremely important to study these "imprints" of what are initially functional/physical symptoms in neurasthenia and hysteria. The consequence of hysteria that has become organic, if I may put it this way, will be irregularities occurring anywhere in the digestive system or in abdominal processes in general. But what takes place in one such system of organs works back into the organism as a whole. We must not ignore the fact that irregularities occurring here work back on the entire organism.

Imagine it like this: something that would simply be a hysterical symptom if it initially appeared on the functional level fails to come to any kind of functional expression at all. It is absolutely possible for it never to be expressed on the functional level. Instead, the etheric body immediately forces it into the physical body, where it is present within the abdominal organs, although it does not appear there as any definite illness. We might say the abdominal organs are imprinted with a stamp of hysteria. Because this tendency is imprinted on the physical element, it does not come to expression on the psychological level as a symptom of hysteria, but neither is it strong enough to be a troublesome physical illness. It is strong enough, however, to influence the entire organism. Now we have the peculiar phenomenon of something that hovers between disease and health and works upward from below. It works back on what is up above, infects the upper aspect, and appears in the form of its negative image. The first physical consequence of hysteria appears in parts of the body that would usually be subject to neurasthenia if they became unbalanced and irregular. This phenomenon predisposes the person in question to tuberculosis.

This is an interesting connection. Predisposition to tuberculosis is a consequence of the activity that was just described as working back on the upper parts of the body from below. This very extraordinary interaction comes about because an unfinished process, as I described it, works on the upper part of the body. This gives rise to a predisposition to tuberculosis. It will prove impossible to discover any rational means of dealing with tuberculosis without going back to this archetypal tendency of the human organism, as I would like to call it. That parasites gain ground within the human organism is simply a consequence of the archetypal tendencies I have just described. This does not contradict the fact that, given the necessary prerequisites, an illness such as tuberculosis is contagious. Of course, the necessary prerequisites must be present, but unfortunately this predominance of lower-body organic activity occurs in a terribly high percentage of the population today, so predisposition to tuberculosis is frighteningly widespread.

Contagion is still a valid concept here, however, because people who are gravely ill with tuberculosis do affect their fellow human beings, and exposure to a tubercular patient's environment can indeed make it possible for what is otherwise a mere consequence to once again become a cause. I always attempt to use an analogy or comparison to clarify this relationship between the primary genesis of a disease and contagion. Let us assume I meet a friend in the street whose personal relationships normally do not concern me. This friend is sad, and with good reason, because one of his friends has died. I have no direct connection to the deceased person, but upon meeting my friend and hearing about his grief, I begin to feel sad with him. His sadness, however, is due to a direct cause, while mine is due to contagion. But it remains true that only the relationship between myself and my friend supplies the necessary prerequisite for this contagion.

In this way, concepts of primary occurrence and contagion are both fully justified, especially with regard to tuberculosis. These concepts, however, really need to be applied rationally. Tuberculosis sanatoriums are sometimes actual breeding grounds for tuberculosis. If tubercular patients have to be crammed together in sanatoriums, then at least these buildings should be torn down periodically and replaced with new ones whenever possible. After a certain length of time, tuberculosis sanatoriums always ought to be replaced. The strange thing about it is that tubercular patients themselves have the greatest predisposition to infection, which means that otherwise curable patients with the illness may become worse if they are in the proximity of those who are more seriously ill.

For the present, however, my intention is simply to indicate the nature of tuberculosis. This disease is a particularly good example of how the different processes in the human organism need to interweave. As you can imagine, these processes are inevitably influenced by the fact that we are dealing with an upper and a lower organization whose correspondence is like that of a positive image and its negative. If we study the further course of the most obvious symptoms that

pave the way for tuberculosis—namely, the presence of a bodily constitution such as I have described—these symptoms can serve as an
example of how we should view the nature of illness in general.

Consider the typical symptomatology of a person with incipient
tuberculosis. Perhaps we will observe that this person is coughing and
has a sore throat, chest pains, or pains in the limbs. We will note that
the person suffers from fatigue, and night sweats will also be especially evident. Well, what is all this? If we investigate these symptoms,
what are they really? Each of them is a result, at least initially, of the
irregular inner interactions described earlier. But at the same time,
each symptom also represents the organism's battle against the
underlying deeper foundations of the illness. Let us look first at simple things like coughing; we will get to the more complex issues soon
enough. You see, coughing should not always be suppressed regardless of the circumstances; that is certainly not a good idea. Sometimes
the organism may even need artificial stimulation to induce coughing. When a person's lower organization is such that it cannot be controlled by the upper organization, the cough reflex is a healthy
reaction on the part of the body, an attempt to prevent certain things
from getting in. Simply preventing coughing by direct means under
any and all circumstances may cause damage, because harmful factors
will then be able to enter. The body coughs because in its present
condition it cannot tolerate these harmful factors and wants to eliminate them. The cough reflex is just a sign of something happening in
the organism that makes it necessary to prevent the entry of invaders
that could otherwise easily gain access.

But the other symptoms we mentioned are also a defense, the
body's fight against incipient tuberculosis. Sore throat and limb pain
simply indicate that the organism will not permit the occurrence of
lower processes that cannot be controlled from above. Again, if the
predisposition to tuberculosis is recognized in time, it might be a good
idea, for example, to support the organism by provoking moderate
coughing and especially by inducing fatigue. (In subsequent lectures
we will see how this can be done; it can also be accomplished through
certain dietary measures). And if weight loss occurs, for example, this,
too, is only a means of defense, because the process that takes place if

weight loss does *not* occur may be the specific lower process that cannot be controlled from above in this case. In other words, the body is defending itself by losing weight, so that this uncontrollable factor is simply absent for the time being. It is therefore extremely important to study such issues in detail, rather than simply trying to fatten up someone who is losing weight without giving any further thought to the matter. There may be a very good reason for that person's weight loss in the context of what is being expressed in the organism at the time.

Night sweats are particularly instructive in the case of a person who does not yet have tuberculosis but is predisposed to the illness. These night sweats are nothing less than a bodily activity that takes place during sleep when it should take place during waking hours and when the person is fully spiritually and physically active. Something that ought to happen by day in full wakefulness does not take place then, but comes to expression during the night. It is simultaneously a consequence and a defense. While relieved of its spiritual activity, the organism creates the activity that comes to expression in night sweats.

In order to do full justice to this subject, we must know a bit about the intimate connection between all excretory functions, including sweat formation, and the aspect of our nature that includes psychological and spiritual activity. Building-up processes, the vital anabolic processes, really constitute only a basis for the unconscious, while excretory processes, wherever they may take place, correspond to the awake and conscious activities of the ensouled organism. Our thinking, too, corresponds to the brain's excretory or catabolic processes rather than to its anabolic processes. Night sweats constitute an excretory process that normally ought to parallel an activity of the soul and spirit, but because the upper part of the body is not interacting with the lower in the right way, this process waits until night, when the organism is freed from activity of spirit and soul.

So you can see how a careful study of all the processes that are connected with the overall growth and development of the human organism, be it well or ill, leads to the conclusion that interaction between disease symptoms also occurs. Weight loss is first of all a sign of disease. But weight loss is something that is appropriate in the context of incipient or early-stage tuberculosis. The symptoms of an illness are united in a functional structure, a nonmaterial organization, as it were. In a certain sense, one symptom belongs with another. As a result, if other conditions in the organism ought to provoke some sort of reaction—let us stick to incipient tuberculosis here—but the organism itself does not have the strength to accomplish this, then the rational thing to do is to assist the reaction just at that point, causing one illness to follow on another. Ancient physicians stated this as an important rule in the education of physicians. They said that the danger in being a physician lies in being able to induce illness as well as drive it away. Physicians are able to induce illnesses to the same extent that they are able to cure them. Thus, the ancients, who knew more about such connections because of their atavistic clairvoyance, realized that a malicious physician would be able to make people not only well but also ill. This ability to induce illness maliciously, however, is related to the need to induce certain disease states in order to bring them into the correct relationship with other disease states. But these induced disease states are illnesses in their own right. And coughing, sore throat, chest pain, weight loss, night sweats—all of these are real symptoms of illness. It may be necessary to induce them, but they remain real symptoms nonetheless.

Of course it is easy to realize that, having half cured a person—that is, having induced these symptoms—we cannot simply abandon the patient to his or her fate. At this point, the second part of the healing process must set in. We must take care not to stop with inducing reactions to ward off the disease; something must then ensue that cures these reactions and sets the whole organism back on the right track. We would have to ensure, for instance, that when coughing or a sore throat either develops naturally or is artificially induced as a defense against incipient tuberculosis, the digestive process, which in such cases always shows signs of constipation, is set straight. In one way or another, we will notice that this digestive process needs to be guided in the direction of an elimination process—diarrhea, for example. It is always necessary to allow diarrheal processes to follow coughing symptoms, sore throats, and the like. This points to the fact that a symptom appearing in the upper part of the body must not be seen in isolation.

We must often look to lower-body processes to cure upper-body symptoms, even though there is no material connection between them, but only a correspondence. This is a prime consideration.

When the metabolism is not controlled from above, severe symptoms of fatigue set in. I would not call these merely subjective symptoms; they are symptoms wholly determined organically and always based on a preponderance of the metabolism. Such symptoms of fatigue really do need to be induced in the tuberculosis patient, but they would have to be counteracted later, at the appropriate time, by means of a special diet (the details of which we will still have to discuss), so that digestion predominates in such a way that the patient digests food better than normal, and nutrients are more easily assimilated through digestion. Weight loss will later have to be counteracted through a diet leading to the disposition of fat formation in the organs and their tissues. We will have to deal with the induced night sweats by steering our patients toward an activity in which fully conscious, spiritualized exertion makes them sweat, so that they settle back into a healthy sweat-formation process.

You see, once a real understanding of cardiac function enables us to grasp correspondences between the upper and lower parts of the human being, and once we also understand the first signs of disease on the functional or etheric level, as in neurasthenia and hysteria, we can then move on to an understanding of their imprints on the organic and physical level. By studying the outer manifestations of symptoms that belong together—including symptoms we ourselves have induced—we will discover how to guide the course of an illness in a certain direction, deflecting it to a greater or lesser extent in order to lead the entire process back toward health at the right moment.

Of course, social considerations are the greatest impediment to the type of treatment I have begun to describe here. That is why medicine is definitely also a social issue. The patients themselves often present the greatest obstacles because they naturally insist that we "get rid" of their illness, as they put it. But if we immediately get rid of it, they may easily become even sicker than they were before. We must also consider the possibility that we will make them much sicker than before, and that they will then have to wait until we are in a position to make them well again. By then most of them—as I'm sure many of you will confirm—will probably have taken to their heels!

Correctly observing the human being in sickness and in health makes it imperative for the physician to have control over the post-treatment period as well, if the entire course of therapy is to be as effective as it should be. We will simply have to agitate publicly for such things. In our age, with all its faith in authority, it should not be difficult to make people aware of essential factors like this, if only the appropriate popular movements can be set in motion. Of course, it is not always only the patients or social considerations that make it inconvenient to see an illness through to its conclusion. Excuse me for saying this in your presence, but sometimes this is the fault of physicians, who are more or less satisfied with having "gotten rid" of an illness.

You will see that accurately elaborating on the heart's role in the human organism gradually leads us to the essential nature of illness. You will need to consider, however, the radical contrast that exists between the functions of the lower [and upper parts of the] body. Although the lower functions have certainly overcome mere external chemical activity in a certain respect, in some ways they also still resemble the upper functions, which are their complete opposites. It is extremely difficult to adequately define this duality within the human organism because our language has almost no means of alluding to factors that counteract physical and organic processes. Perhaps you will understand me well enough for the time being (and I do not shy away from the prospect of encountering one bias or another in any of you) if I attempt an analogy to clarify the character of this dualism between lower and upper processes.

If you call to mind the properties of any substance, the properties that make its effect apparent to us in any way, you have what is absorbed into the human being's lower functions once it has been overcome by the organism, as happens in digestion. It is also possible, however, to homeopathize substances (if I may put it like that), to eliminate the substance's internal cohesiveness. This happens when we dilute the substance in any way or prepare homeopathic doses. The resulting phenomenon has in no way been given due consideration by our modern science, and in any case people tend to consider everything abstractly.

Thus, light is said to spread out in all directions from its source—the sun, for example—until it vanishes into infinity. But this is not true. No such activity ever vanishes into infinity. Instead, it goes only as far as the limits of a definite sphere and then snaps back on itself as if it were elastic. Admittedly, however, its qualitative aspect is then often different from the quality of the original outgoing force. Only rhythmical processes exist in the natural world. There are no processes that lose themselves in infinity; there are only processes that rebound on themselves in a rhythmic way.

This is true of both quantitative and qualitative expansion. When you begin dividing a substance, it possesses certain properties from the outset. These properties do not decrease into infinity as you continue the divisions. Beyond a certain point, they swing back and turn into the opposite properties. This inner rhythm is also the basis of the contrast between our lower organization and our upper organization. Our upper organization is a homeopathizer. In a certain way, it immediately counteracts the ordinary digestive processes, forming their opposite, their negative image. It could be said that when homeopathic pharmacists produce their dilutions, they are really transforming properties that otherwise relate to the lower human organization into properties that then relate to the upper human organization. This is a very interesting inner connection, and we will have more to say about it in the next few days.

LECTURE 3

In the course of the lectures to come, I will make use of all of the requests that have been presented to me. Some of these requests may duplicate one another, so I need to have collected at least most of them before I begin. It will also make a difference whether we discuss them before or after a certain foundation has been laid. Today, therefore, I will attempt to create such a foundation for everything that will follow, taking into account what I have noted from your requests thus far.

As you have seen, I attempted to take the morphology and inner function of the bony and muscular systems as the starting point for what we considered in the first lecture. Then yesterday we progressed at least far enough to give examples of the disease process and the requirements of therapy, taking the circulation of blood in the cardiac system as our example and point of departure. Now today I would like to present a few additional introductory thoughts about a way of looking at the overall possibility and general character of healing, a view that can be acquired through a more profound consideration of humankind. We will go into the details in later lectures, but I would like to discuss these fundamentals first.

If you think about the character of modern medical education, you will find, for the most part, that therapy is taught parallel to pathology without any clearly understandable connection between the two. Especially with regard to therapy, a merely empirical methodology is often the only approach and totally dominates the scene, and we find almost no rational principles that could form the basis for practical therapeutic work. We know that in the course of the nineteenth century, these deficits in medical thinking even led to the nihilistic school of medical thought, which emphasized diagnosis almost exclusively. Its practitioners were actually content to identify illnesses and generally took a very skeptical view of any rational basis for healing. If we were to make purely rational demands on the medical profession, we would actually have to say that an indication of a cure ought to be inherent in the diagnosis. A mere outer connection between therapy and pathology cannot be allowed to prevail. Our understanding of the nature of an illness must be able to lead to insight into the process of curing it.

A related question, of course, is: To what extent are therapeutic substances and processes present in the overall context of natural processes? Paracelsus is often quoted as saying something very interesting, that physicians must pass the test of nature. It cannot be said, however, that the modern literature on Paracelsus knows what to do with an aphorism like this. If it did, it would be intent on discovering healing processes by listening to nature. Admittedly this search is indeed attempted in the case of disease processes that nature can cope with. But as a result, nature is observed only in exceptional cases, when damage has already set in and nature knows what to do about it, whereas a true study of nature involves observing its normal processes. This study ought to give rise to the question of whether it is actually possible to observe so-called normal processes in nature in a way that yields insight into healing processes.

You will notice immediately that this question is connected to another, somewhat dubious question, since healing processes in nature can obviously be studied in a normal way only when disease processes are normal occurrences in nature. So the question arises, are disease processes present in nature as such, so that we can learn to heal by passing nature's test? Although the answer to this question will emerge completely only as we continue with these lectures, we will attempt at least to get a bit closer to it today. But we can say immediately that the conventional scientific basis of medicine obstructs the path we are setting out on here. Current assumptions make it extremely difficult to go this route because—strange as it may seem—nineteenth-century materialistic tendencies have led to a complete misunderstanding of the functions of the nervous system, which is the next system I will discuss in addition to the skeletal, muscular, and cardiac systems.

It has gradually become customary to saddle the nervous system with everything that is soul-like in character. All the processes of spirit or soul taking place in the human being are thought to be subsumed by parallel processes found in the nervous system. Now you know that in my book *Riddles of the Soul*, I found it necessary to object to this way of studying nature.[15] In that book, I made an initial attempt to demonstrate that only perceptive processes as such are connected to the nervous system, while all emotional processes connect directly rather than indirectly to the organism's rhythmical processes. Our studies here will yield a great deal of empirical confirmation of these truths. Today's scientists normally think that emotional processes have nothing to do with the rhythmic system directly, except inasmuch as these rhythmical processes are transmitted to the nervous system; they think that emotional activity is played out in the nervous system.

Similarly, I attempted to show that all of our volitional activity is connected to the metabolic system directly, rather than indirectly via the nervous system. With regard to volitional processes, all that is left for the nervous system to do is to perceive them. The nervous system does not stage acts of will; it simply perceives what takes place in us as a result of volition. Everything I stated in *Riddles of the Soul* can definitely be confirmed by the relevant biological facts, whereas the opposing view that attributes psychological activity to the nervous system alone cannot be confirmed at all. It is possible for a so-called motor nerve to be severed and then allowed to grow back together into a single nerve. For once, I would like to see how healthy reason can connect this fact with the other assumption that there are nerves that serve both sensory and motor functions. Such nerves do not exist. What we call motor nerves are nothing other than sensory nerves that perceive the movements of our limbs—that is, they perceive what is

---

15. *Riddles of the Soul*, (CW 21), Mercury Press, Spring Valley, NY, 1996.

going on in the metabolism of our limbs *during an act of will.* Thus, in reality, motor nerves are sensory nerves that perceive only what is going on inside us, while what we ordinarily call sensory nerves perceive the outer world.

Moving in this direction, we encounter something that is enormously important for medicine but can be given its due only when we take a good look at the actual facts of the matter. Especially if we are faced with the symptoms I took as our starting point yesterday in developing the example of tuberculosis, it is difficult to make do with the assumption that separate sensory and motor nerves exist. Sensible researchers have therefore assumed that each nerve conducts impulses in both directions rather than only from the periphery toward the center or vice versa. Similarly, then, each motor nerve would have to lead in two directions, which means that if we take the nervous system as our basis for explaining any phenomenon such as hysteria, we find it necessary to assume that two lines of conduction exist, running in opposite directions. Thus, as soon as we get down to facts, we are already forced to assume that nerves have properties that totally contradict current hypotheses about the nervous system. Through having learned to think about the nervous system in the prevalent way, we have actually obstructed everything we ought to know about other things that take place in the organism below the level of the nervous system—what happens in hysteria, for example. Yesterday, we characterized what happens in hysteria as metabolic processes that are simply *perceived* by means of the nerves. More careful attention should have been paid to this in the past, but instead, the origins of hysteria were sought only in some kind of instability of or shock to the nervous system, and the entire responsibility was mistakenly laid on the nervous system.

Something else then happened as a result. It cannot be denied that some of the more distant causes of hysteria are psychological ones—grief, disappointments, inner urges that may or may not be able to be fulfilled—that then turn into symptoms of hysteria. By separating the rest of the organism from the nervous system and directly associating the soul's activity exclusively with the nervous system, we are forced to hold the nervous system responsible for everything.

This has led to a view that no longer corresponds in the least to the facts and also leaves us with no means of linking the soul to the human organism as a whole; we can link it only to the nervous system. The soul aspect cannot be linked to the human organism as a whole, except possibly by inventing motor nerves that do not exist and then expecting motor nerve functions to influence circulation, and so forth, all of which is hypothetical in the extreme.

What I have presented here has led even the most intelligent people astray in cases of autosuggestion and hypnosis and the like. These cases, which occurred some time ago, involved hysterical ladies misguiding the cleverest physicians, and leading them around by the nose. This could happen simply because it was impossible to investigate what was going on within the body; consequently, people fell for all kinds of behavior that such patients put on for the benefit of their doctors. In this context, it may be interesting to point out Dr. Schleich's error, although this case involves a hysterical man rather than a hysterical woman.[16] In spite of being accustomed to thinking quite clearly about such matters, Schleich committed an unavoidable error. He was consulted by a man who had pricked his finger with an inky pen point and said that this would surely lead to his death that same night—blood poisoning would set in, so his arm needed to be amputated. It is obvious that Schleich, a surgeon, could not amputate under such circumstances. He could merely reassure the man and do what was necessary—clean out the wound, and so forth—but of course he could not amputate simply because the man claimed he would develop blood poisoning that same night. The patient in question then went to some other expert, who also did not amputate his arm, of course. But Schleich felt somewhat uneasy about the situation. The next morning he inquired immediately, and in fact his patient really had died during the night. Schleich put forward a diagnosis of death by autosuggestion.

---

16. Carl Ludwig Schleich (1859–1922), the discoverer of local anesthesia. This incident is described in his memoir, *Besonnte Vergangenheit* [The happy past]. Other works are: *Vom Shaltwerk der Gedanken* [The switching mechanism of thoughts], *Bewußtsein und Unsterblichkeit* [Consciousness and immortality], and *Von der Seele: Essays* [Essays on the soul].

Diagnosing death by autosuggestion is obvious in this case, terribly obvious. But if we have any insight into the human being, it is simply not acceptable to think of this as death by autosuggestion in that sense. If we do, we are fundamentally confusing cause and effect. Results of the autopsy showed that blood poisoning had not set in, so the man in question had died—so it seemed—of a cause that remained unknown to the doctors. Someone capable of understanding this situation clearly, however, would conclude that the patient must certainly have died of a cause that was deeply rooted in his organism. On the previous day, this cause had made the man somewhat shaky and unsteady, so that he pricked his finger with the inky pen. This was a consequence of his shakiness, something that would not have happened otherwise. But while outwardly he became physically unsteady, his inner perceptive abilities were somewhat heightened; under the influence of his illness, he had a prophetic premonition of his death the following night. This death had nothing at all to do with the fact that he had pricked his finger on an inky pen. Instead, his imminent death was the cause of what he was feeling, and the entire incident was only superficially connected to the actual inner processes leading to death. There is no question in this case of "death by auto-suggestion." The man's belief that he was going to die had deeper roots and had nothing to do with actually bringing about his death. However, he did foresee his death and interpreted everything that happened in the light of this premonition.

This example will show you immediately how incredibly careful we must be if we want to arrive at an objective assessment of the complicated processes going on in nature. We cannot afford to take the very simplest assumption as our starting point. But now we will have to ask the question, do sense perceptions and similar processes offer us a clue to the effects of a somewhat different sort that medications are meant to have on the human organism?

You will agree that there are three ways of influencing the human organism in its normal condition: via sensory perceptions that are taken further by the nervous system, via the rhythmic system of respiration and circulation, and via the metabolism. These three normal relationships must have analogues of some sort in the abnormal relationship we bring about between therapeutic substances, which must also be derived from outer nature in some way, and the human organism. Admittedly, what takes place between the outer world and the human organism is most clearly apparent in the nervous system. We must therefore ask ourselves how we can rationally conceive of the connection between the human being and the nonhuman external nature that we want to utilize, either in the form of processes or in the form of therapeutic substances, in order to bring about healing in the human being. We must achieve a clear view of the interrelationship between the human being and external nature, the source of our medicines. Even if we apply only cold water treatments, we are using something external to the human being. Everything we use is taken from outside the human being and then applied to human processes, and we must achieve a rational view of the nature of the connection between the human being and outer, nonhuman processes.

Admittedly, we are now coming to another chapter of conventional medical education that is governed by pure aggregation rather than by any organic connection among its parts. Although medical students listen to preparatory scientific lectures, their later courses on general and specialized pathology and general therapeutic methods are then based on this preparatory science, and so on and so forth; by the time the actual medical courses begin, not much more is heard about how the processes and especially the therapeutic methods covered in their medical lectures relate to processes in outer nature. I believe that physicians who have undergone modern medical training will not only experience this outwardly and rationally as a deficit but will also carry it with them as a strong feeling that will force itself upon them when practical intervention in a disease process is called for—a feeling of uncertainty as to whether to use one medication or another. In actuality, they very seldom have any real knowledge of how the chosen remedy relates to what is going on in the human being. This is a case in which the very nature of the matter points to a much needed reform in the education of physicians.

Today I would like to make use of specific processes in outer, nonhuman nature to illustrate how they differ in many respects from the natural processes occurring in the human being. I would like to begin with processes that can be observed in plants and lower animals, and from there we will find our way to those that can be induced by substances we extract from nonhuman nature in general, whether from the plant or animal kingdoms, or particularly from the mineral kingdom. But we can approach the essential character of pure mineral substances only by taking very elementary scientific ideas as our point of departure and then proceeding to what happens, for example, if we use arsenic or tin or any other substance as a remedy that is introduced into the human organism.

The first thing that needs to be pointed out is that the metamorphoses taking place during growth in nonhuman organisms are completely different from those within humans. We will not be able to avoid formulating the different principles that apply to living growth both in human and nonhuman beings. The difference that appears here is of fundamental significance. For example, observe the common black locust, *Robinia pseudacacia*. If you cut its leaflets off at the petioles, something interesting happens: the petioles metamorphose somewhat, and then these transformed knobby petioles take over the function of the leaves. To begin with, we will hypothesize that what is so highly active here is a force that is present throughout the plant and that comes to expression when we prevent the plant from using one of its normally developed organs for specific functions. A remnant of what is markedly present in a plant (which is simpler in its growth patterns) becomes evident in a human being who is prevented for some reason from using one arm or hand for some purposes—the other hand develops more strongly, becomes physically larger, and so forth. We must make the connection between such things, because that is the route to recognizing a possible method of healing.

Now, in outer nonhuman nature, this phenomenon is taken to great lengths. For example, if we observe plants growing on a cliff, we may find that certain petioles of the plants develop without ever forming leaves; the leaves are absent. Instead, certain petioles bend over in order to support the plant. The leaves remain undeveloped; and instead, the plants have these leafless, transformed petioles that serve as organs of support. [See drawing below.] This is indicative of the plant's inner formative forces, which make it possible for the plant to adapt to a great extent to the mode of life demanded by its environment. Especially in lower organisms, we encounter very interesting forces like this.

For example, if you take any embryo that has advanced to the gastrula stage, you can cut it in half down the middle, and each piece will close up and be able to develop the three parts (upper, middle, and lower) of its own intestinal tract. If we cut a gastrula in half, we discover that each half behaves the way the uncut whole would have behaved. You know that this experiment can be carried further with lower animals, even earthworms, and that pieces cut off of certain lower animals will regrow. That is, the animal's internal formative forces replace the parts we have cut off. These formative forces must be pointed out objectively—not merely by hypothesizing about some sort of life force, but really objectively. If we observe more closely, if we really follow what is actually going on, we can see, for example, that if we cut off part of a frog's body at a very early stage of its development, the rest of the organism puts out a new part. If your way of thinking is materialistically inclined, you may say that there are forces of tension present in the wound that will replace what used to grow there. But that cannot be the case. If I cut an organism here [see following drawing], and a new part developed through forces of tension at the site of the wound, what grew back would have to be what is immediately adjacent to the wound.

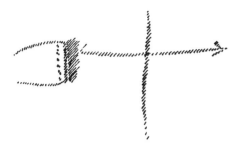

But in reality that is not the case. In reality, if you cut off a frog larva's terminal organs, such as the tail or even the head, or the antennae in other animals, what grows back is not the same as the adjacent part; it is the part that the organism needs. This means that it is totally impossible for forces of tension intrinsic to the wound site to put forth what develops there. On the contrary, we must assume that the whole organism is involved in some way.

We can actually trace such things as they occur in lower organisms. Now that I have shown you how to pursue a question like this, you can expand it to all the empirical reports that have accumulated in the literature to date, and in each instance you will see that this is the only path leading to insight into the matter. Of course you will say that this is not the case in human beings. It would be nice if we could cut off someone's finger or arm and it would simply grow back. But it doesn't, so the question is, what happened to the formative forces of growth that are so evident in lower animals? What has happened to them in the human organism? Have they been lost? Are they simply not present?

Anyone who knows how to observe nature objectively will understand that this is the only path to a natural view of the connection between the spiritual and physical aspects of the human being. In the human being, the forces that we recognize here as sculptural forces, as it were, forces that create forms directly out of substance, have simply been lifted out of the organs and are present only in the human soul and spirit. That is where they are. By being lifted out of the organs, by not remaining organ-forming forces, they are available to human beings for other purposes and are present in the functions of the human soul and spirit. Whenever I think or feel, I think and feel with the same forces that are sculpturally active in the plant kingdom or in lower animals. I would not be able to think, feel, or will without these same forces that I have extracted from matter. When I look at lower organisms, I must realize that their sculptural forces in place there are the same as those I also carry within myself; I, however, have taken those forces out of my organs and possess them. I think and feel and will with the same forces that are sculpturally active out there in the world of lower organisms.

Anyone who wants to become a psychologist whose constructs have some substance and are not mere words—which is how psychology is construed today—would have to trace the processes of thinking, feeling, and willing in a way that reveals them to be the same forces that appear in lower sculptural formations, but taking place on the level of spirit and soul. Just look at how our inner psychological processes can accomplish a task that we can no longer perform on the organic level: Trains of thought that have escaped us can be finished with others, which we bring in from far away rather than from what is nearest at hand. This function is actually similar to the regrowth of necessary parts of the organism that I mentioned yesterday.

What we experience on the inner psychological level completely parallels the natural formative forces and principles that are present in the outer world. There is a true parallelism between them. We need to point this out and to show that in essence the formative principle for us human beings in the outer world is our life in soul and in spirit, which we have extracted from the organic level so that it no longer constitutes the formative basis of matter or substance in our own bodies. But we have not extracted it from all parts of the body equally, and we have withdrawn it in different ways. We can approach the human organism in the appropriate way only when we are equipped with the knowledge that we have now developed.

If you look at everything constituting our nervous system, you will discover the peculiar fact that neurons, nerve tissue, and so forth are not usually described as very highly evolved structures. They have remained behind at relatively early stages of evolution. We might expect these so-called nerve cells to demonstrate the character of earlier, primitive cell structures. But in certain other respects they do not do that at all—for example, they are not capable of reproduction. Neurons, like blood cells, are incapable of self-replication from the moment they are formed. Thus, at a relatively early stage an ability that is the common property of nonhuman cells is taken away from them. They remain behind on an earlier developmental level. To some extent, they are paralyzed at this evolutionary stage. The part that is paralyzed takes on a separate existence as the human being's soul-spiritual aspect. In reality, our soul-spiritual processes harken back to what formerly assumed organic, material form. We achieve this, however, only by incorporating nerve tissue that we kill off or at least paralyze at a relatively early stage.

In this way, we can approach the essential character of nerve tissue. We then discover the reason for its idiosyncratic character, why it looks so similar to primitive structures on the one hand, even in its further developments, while on the other hand it serves what we usually call the highest aspect of the human being, namely spiritual activity. I believe—although this is just an aside and is not meant as part of our considerations—that even on superficial examination, the human head, which encloses the different nerve cells within a solid suit of armor, is more reminiscent of lower animals than of highly evolved species. I would go so far as to say that although it has been transformed, the human head is reminiscent of prehistoric animals. In speaking of lower animals, we usually say that they have external skeletons, while higher animals and humans have internal skeletons, with the exception of our heads. Our most highly developed part has an external skeleton. This is something that could at least be a leitmotiv of sorts for what has just been described.

Now imagine what can happen to these formative forces—forces that are present in outer, nonhuman nature, but that we ourselves have taken from our organism in order to use them for our spirit and soul. What happens when something we call an illness makes it necessary for us to guide these forces back into the organism by using a remedy such as a plant or the like? This is a topic I will still speak about later in more detail, but essentially we link the organism to something it is lacking. We help it by supplementing it with something that we withdrew from it by becoming human.

Here you can already see the dawning of what can be described as a healing process. We call on the help of forces in nature that we ourselves, as normal human beings, do not possess. We use them when we need to make an inner part of us stronger than it is in a normal human being. If we take one of our organs—the lungs, perhaps—as an example, just so we can talk about this matter in concrete terms, we will find that we have withdrawn formative principles from organs such as this in order to have them available for our soul and spirit. Suppose we discover, somewhere in the plant kingdom, these same forces that we have withdrawn from our lungs. If we then administer them to a person with a pulmonary disorder, we are coming to the aid of that person's pulmonary functions. You see, the question now arises, which forces in outer nonhuman nature are similar to the forces that underlie our human organs but have been withdrawn to serve soul-spiritual functions? This route leads away from merely experimental methods toward a rational approach to therapy.

In addition to the errors people fell into with regard to the nervous system, which are errors about something inside the human being, a very significant error was committed with regard to nature outside the human being. I will simply point out this error today and elaborate on it later. In our materialistic age, people have gradually come to think of the beings of outer nature as having undergone an evolution of sorts from the so-called simplest to the most complicated. After first extending their view to include lower organisms, they studied morphological transformations right up to the most complex organisms, also taking into account nonorganic forms such as those in the mineral kingdom. In looking at the mineral kingdom, they realized that it is simpler than the plant kingdom. This eventually led to all those strange questions about how life emerged from the mineral kingdom, about the one-time event that made substances come together and abandon their mere inorganic activity for organic activity. The idea of *generatio aequivoca* [spontaneous generation] stimulated many discussions.

To an unbiased observer, it not at all clear that this view is correct. On the contrary, it must be said that, in a certain respect, it is just as possible to imagine that minerals evolved from living organisms when life was withdrawn from plants as it is to imagine an evolution that proceeds from plants through animals to humans. As I said, I simply want to point this out today; it will be clarified as we continue our studies. We can come to terms with the issue of evolution only if we do not imagine it as proceeding upward from minerals to plants to animals to humans. Instead, we must choose a starting point in the middle and imagine one upward line of evolution, which moves from plants through animals to humans, and another downward evolution that leads to the minerals. That is, instead of taking the mineral kingdom as the starting point, we must begin in the middle so that some forms result from an ascending line of evolution, others from a descending line. If we do this, we will come to the insight that the forces that appear in the downward evolution from plants to minerals—and especially to metals, which are an exceptionally important mineral type—bear a special relationship to their mirror image in the ascending line of evolution.

In short, the question that comes to mind is, what are these special mineral forces that we can study only when we examine—as indeed we did—the formative forces in lower organisms? In the minerals, these forces become visible in crystallization. Crystallization very definitely shows us something that appears when we consider downward evolution. It is somehow related to, but not the same as, the formative forces that become apparent when we consider upward evolution. So, if we introduce the forces in minerals into a living body, a new question arises. We answered a similar question: What happens when we supplement the human organism with formative forces from the plant and animal kingdoms, forces that our soul and spirit have withdrawn from our own organization? We help the organism. But what happens when the forces we introduce into the human organism are different in quality? What if we use forces that are present in downward evolution, that is, in the mineral kingdom? That is the question I want to pose today. It should be thoroughly answered in the course of our studies here.

But we have still not reached the point of being able to make any real contribution to the question we highlighted at the beginning of today's lecture: Can we discover a healing process by listening to nature? In posing such questions, it is always important to approach nature with the appropriate insights—and we have been attempting to acquire at least a sketchy insight into such matters—so that certain processes will reveal their essential character. This is the important point.

As you know, there are two distinct processes in the human organism that are also present in animals, although we are less interested in that at the moment. In a certain sense, if we observe these processes equipped with the ideas we have now acquired, it becomes apparent that they are opposite or contrasting functions. I must make a point of emphasizing that this is not entirely true; please keep this in mind so that you do not misunderstand what I am now going to present. But to a considerable extent, they are polar opposites. These two processes are blood formation and milk formation as they appear in the human organism. Even outwardly, they differ in very significant ways. Blood formation occurs in the hidden depths of the human organism, while milk formation takes place closer to the surface. If we are considering the human being, the most essential difference between blood formation and milk formation is that blood formation possesses a very strong capacity for developing formative forces. In the overall "economy" of the human organism (if I may use such a materialistic expression) blood is the element to which formative forces must be attributed. Thus, in some respects blood still possesses the formative forces that we perceive here in the lower body; they are still present in the blood.

Modern science, in particular, would discover a very important support if it would study the blood, but at present it is not taking up this study in any truly rational sense. It would find support in the fact that the red blood cells, which are blood's main component, are not capable of reproduction. They do not have the ability to self-replicate. This is a feature they have in common with neurons. But when we emphasize a shared characteristic such as this, it is always important to know whether the reason for it is the same in both cases. The reason cannot be the same because we have not withdrawn formative capacities from the blood to the extent that we have withdrawn them from nerve tissue. Nerve tissue, which forms the basis of our conceptual activity, lacks internal formative capacities to a great extent. In human beings, nerve tissue continues to develop during life after birth, but this development is largely dependent on outer impressions. That is, internal formative capacities give way to the ability to simply adapt to external influences. The situation is different with blood, which retains internal formative capacities to a great extent. In a certain sense, as you know from experience, these internal formative capacities are also present in milk. If they were not, milk would not be a healthy food for infants, and we would not be able to give it to them. What infants need is milk, which contains formative capacities similar to those in blood. Thus, with regard to formative capacities, there is a certain similarity between blood and milk.

There is also a considerable difference, however. Milk possesses this formative capacity, but it has very little—only minimal amounts—of one substance blood needs in abundance in order to exist, namely, iron, which is the only metal whose compounds in the human organism show a significant ability to crystallize. Thus, although milk does contain small amounts of other metals, the difference is that blood needs iron, a pronounced metallic factor, in order to exist. Milk, which also possesses formative capacities, does not need iron. So the question is, why does blood need it?

This question is actually of cardinal importance for medical science as a whole. We know that blood needs iron. We will now gather material evidence to support the facts that I have outlined today. First of all, I will substantiate the statement that blood is the one substance in the human organism that is ill by nature and must constantly be cured by iron. This is not the case with milk. If milk were ill in the same sense as blood, it could not serve—as in fact it does—as a formative agent for human beings, a formative agent that is introduced from outside.

When we consider the blood, we are considering the factor in the human being that is constantly diseased for the sake of the human constitution. It is simply the nature of blood to be diseased and to be constantly cured through the addition of iron. That is, the process that takes place in our blood is an ongoing internal healing process. If physicians want to pass the test of nature, it is most important for them to consider one of nature's normal processes rather than one that is abnormal. And the process taking place in blood is certainly a normal one, although it is also one that nature must constantly cure by supplying a mineral, namely, iron. In a graphic representation of what happens to the blood, we might depict what blood possesses by virtue of its own constitution (but without the addition of iron) as a downward curve or line that would end in the total dissolution of the blood [see drawing]. Meanwhile, what iron accomplishes in the blood, constantly leading it back upward and healing it, could be represented by this yellow line.

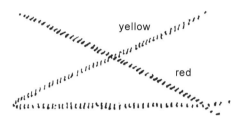

In actuality, we have here a normal process that must be emulated if we are to think about healing at all. In this instance we really can pass the test of nature, because we see the processes that nature carries out by introducing a nonhuman factor, a metal and its forces, into the human being. And at the same time we see how a factor such as blood, which wants to remain within the organism at all costs, requires healing, while a factor such as milk, which strives to leave the organism, does not and is able even to transfer formative forces (if, like milk, it contains them) to another organism in a healthy way. Thus, a polarity of sorts exists between blood and milk—not a total polarity, but one that we must look at carefully because there is a great deal that we can learn from it. We will continue with this topic tomorrow. I had to present all this first because I realized that your questions will be answered very differently after we acquire the right concepts as a basis for answering them.

LECTURE 4

OUR discussion yesterday afternoon was certainly extremely interesting. In connection with the question I see before us now, however, I must once again emphasize, as I have done before, that an adequate means of discovering the connection between individual remedies and individual disease symptoms can be supplied only after we have conclusively considered certain preliminary questions. Only then can we assess the implications of insights into the connection between the human being and the outer, nonhuman world that serves as the source of our remedies.

Without dealing with these initial questions, it is especially impossible to talk about the connection between individual remedies and individual organs, for the simple reason that this connection is not an entirely simple one. On the contrary, it is somewhat complicated, and we can gauge its actual significance only after dealing with the preliminary questions. That is what we will be doing today and possibly also for part of tomorrow. After that, however, it will become possible to really explain concrete connections between individual remedies (or, more particularly, therapeutic methods) and diseases of individual organs.

Today, however, there is something more I would like to say by way of introduction. I hope you will simply accept it for the moment because it may be able to shed a certain light on a number of issues. And because of the initial shock of such matters, I must emphasize that they simply *are* somewhat shocking. Taking up what was mentioned here yesterday afternoon, I would like to ask you to look at the other side of the question.

To our great satisfaction, numerous instructive cases of very specific cures were presented here yesterday.[17] Let me make a suggestion—if only so that you choose *not* to implement it, though it is very tempting to do so—about a very simple way of making these cures much less frequent. (Of course, it is possible for me to talk about this only in a circle of people with experience in Anthroposophy.) You would simply need to do everything in your power to make Ritter's therapeutic method a matter of common knowledge and concern.[18] What you are failing to consider with regard to these therapeutic successes of yours is that you are standing there as isolated physicians. Of course some of you may well be aware of individually having to do battle with the great majority of other physicians and that as soon as you succeed in making Ritter's therapy a subject of study for the universities, when many—if not all—physicians begin using this method to cure people and you find yourselves belonging to the majority rather than the opposition, you will experience a considerable reduction in your cure rates. Strange as this may seem, such things do happen in real life. Matters are sometimes completely different from how you imagine them.

As an individual physician you have the greatest interest in curing individual patients, and modern materialistic medicine has even found a legal argument of sorts for focusing exclusively on healing individuals. This legal argument consists in saying that illnesses do not exist; there are only individuals who are ill. If people were as isolated

---

17. The present lecture course, originally intended to consist of fourteen lectures and last for two weeks, was extended to three weeks with six additional lectures. During this time, there were lectures by participants and additional gatherings during which doctors presented cases for discussion, which Steiner attended whenever possible.

18. Marie Ritter (d. 1924, Munich). Rudolf Steiner had visited her as early as December, 1908. She developed therapies using light and color, which Steiner later stated are effective only while the illness remains in the etheric body. See *Anleitung zum praktischen Gebrauch von M. Ritter's photodynamischen Heilmitteln* [Introduction to using M. Ritter's photodynamic remedies], Munich 1913, and *Die neuro-dynamische Therapeutik im Anschluß an Studien und Erfahrungen über die photo-dynamische Wirkung von Fluorescenz- und Luminescenz-Stoffen auf Zellengebiete und Nervenendigungen* [Neurodynamic therapy in connection with studies and empirical findings on the photodynamic effect of fluorescent and luminescent substances on certain cell areas and nerve endings], Leipzig 1905.

with regard to illness as they outwardly appear to be today, there would be some basis for this legal argument. But in fact people are not that isolated. In this context, what Dr. E. presented yesterday was very significant. Certain diseases tend to cover very broad territories, and if you have cured one person, you can never be sure how many others you may have saddled with the illness in another instance. You do not see the single case in the context of the whole process, so the details of such circumstances are very striking. But anyone who has the totality of human health in mind must speak from a different perspective. This is what makes it necessary to avoid a one-sided, merely therapeutic orientation and to fully develop therapy on the basis of pathology. This is precisely what we will attempt here in order to bring some kind of rationality into what is otherwise only an empirical and statistical way of thinking.[19]

Today we will begin with a fact that is generally known but has certainly not been given its due in the context of scientific medical thought, a fact that can provide the basis for assessing the relationship of the human being to the nonhuman natural world. As you know, the human being is a threefold being with a sensory-nervous system, a circulatory (or rhythmic) system, and a metabolic system. By virtue of our metabolism, we human beings stand in a negative relationship to what is going on out in the natural world of plants. Please call to mind the fact that if we consider only the natural world's flora, we will notice that plants tend to concentrate carbon. Carbon becomes the basis of the entire plant kingdom. To the extent that we are surrounded by plants, we are surrounded by organisms or structures whose existence is based on concentrating carbon. Please do not forget that although the principle underlying this formative process also appears in the human organism, it is the very nature of the human organism to constantly negate this process in its nascent state, to destroy it and replace it with its opposite. The beginnings of this process are present within us, in what I have been calling the lower human

---

19. Regarding the nature of disease and epidemics and their relationship to karma, see Steiner's lectures in *Manifestations of Karma*, London: Rudolf Steiner Press, 1995, lectures 3, 4, 5, and 7.

being. There we deposit carbon; out of our own forces, we begin the process of becoming plants but then our upper organization makes us resist this process. We negate the process by counteracting the carbon with oxygen, by processing it into carbonic acid. Thus, the internal process we must develop is the opposite of becoming a plant.

Please pay attention to these processes that counteract outer nature wherever you may find them, for if you do, you will acquire an ever more thorough understanding of the real human being. You do not understand the human being as such if you simply weigh an individual—taking this as a symbol of all other methods of physical examination—but you immediately understand something about human mechanics if you consider that the brain is known to weigh an average of 1,300 grams. But if the brain bore down with its actual weight, if it exerted this amount of pressure on the lower surface of the skull, the entire network of delicate blood vessels would be crushed. The pressure that the brain actually exerts on the underlying surface does not exceed twenty grams. This is due to the fact that the brain, according to Archimedes' well-known hydraulic principle, has a certain buoyancy because it is actually floating in cerebral fluid, so that most of its weight does not come to bear on the base of the skull but is canceled out by buoyancy. Gravity is overcome so that we are subject to buoyancy, the force that counteracts physical weight, rather than to the physical weight of our own organism. Similar conditions prevail in other human processes. In actual fact, we live within what *physis* [or physical reality] sublates in us rather than in what it does to us.[20] Thus, we are also not subject to any of the processes that we perceive as being present in outer nature and culminating in the plant kingdom. Instead, we live by sublating the process of becoming a plant. This is a very important concept to consider if we want to make the connection between the diseased human organism and phytotherapeutic substances.[21]

---

20. *Sublate* – "raise up and neutralize (but at the same time preserve)."
21. *Phytotherapy* – plant, or herbal, therapy.

Now imagine the following fictional situation: We look at all the beautiful flora surrounding us in the world. We are highly delighted, and rightly so. It is different when we cut open a dead sheep and immediately experience another type of flora, which is brought about by factors similar to those calling forth the outer flora. When the odor of decay drifts toward us from inside the sheep, we are certainly much less delighted about the existence of intestinal flora. This is the main point to focus on, because clearly, in this instance, the same causes that give rise to the flora of the nonhuman natural world must be combated in the human being to prevent intestinal flora from coming about. This opens up a very broad field of comparative research into the intestinal structures of different forms of animals, including the mammals and going right up to human beings. I would like to recommend that you younger medical students use as much as possible from this field in your doctoral dissertations. This will prove to be an extremely rich field of research because many very important issues have not yet been investigated. In particular, try to discover why a sheep, when we open its carcass, emits such a terrible stench of decay and why this is not the case even with carrion-eating birds, which actually smell relatively pleasant when we open them up.

These subjects contain a great deal that has not been worked through scientifically at all as of now. Furthermore, there are numerous possibilities in this field for investigating intestinal morphology. Consider the fact that on the whole, bird species differ significantly from mammals and humans. In avian species, you find that the bladder and colon are extremely poorly developed. Materialistic physicians like Dr. Metschnikoff of Paris made very great errors in considering these issues.[22] Colonlike structures and bladderlike bulges develop only in the large flightless birds. This points to the important fact that birds lack the possibility of temporarily storing their excreta within the organism in order to eliminate them deliberately at an opportune moment. Instead, intake and excretion are continually being balanced out.

---

22. Elias Metschnikoff (1845–1916), professor of zoology in Odessa and later director of the Institut Pasteur in Paris.

We are taking a very superficial view of the matter if we imagine that diseases are caused by all the flora—and also fauna, as we shall see—that appear in the intestines or anywhere else in the human organism. Examining the literature on pathology today, in every chapter you come across statements about the discovery that this bacterium is associated with this disease or that bacterium with that disease, and so forth. All of these facts are extremely interesting as far as the botany and zoology of the human intestines are concerned, but none of it has any significance for illness except possibly as a sign that allows us to recognize the disease, because when one or the other form of disease is present, the human organism can be said to offer one or the other interesting little animal or plant a substrate upon which it can develop. It does not mean anything more than this. The growth of microscopic fauna and flora has very little to do with the actual disease—only indirectly, if at all. As you see, the logic that modern medicine develops here is very peculiar. Imagine that you discover a countryside where you find a large number of admirably well-fed, healthy-looking cows. Are you then going to say that everything you see is the way it is because these cows have somehow been flown in and the countryside has been infected with them? This thought probably will not occur to you. Instead, you need to investigate why there are hardworking people in this region, why the soil is especially suited to raising certain types of livestock—in short, you will most likely limit your thinking to all of the possible reasons why the well-cared-for cows are there.

It will not occur to you that what is going on is the result of the countryside having been infected and invaded by well-cared-for cows, but this is no different from the logic that modern medical science develops with regard to microbes and the like. The presence of these interesting creatures tells us only that the habitat suits them, nothing more. We need to focus on studying this habitat. Of course, other things can happen as a direct or indirect result. For example, we might say, "There are well cared-for cows in this area; if we add a few more, maybe a few more people will pull themselves together and start to work hard," and such a situation might indeed arise. Of course, it can happen that a bacterial invasion provokes a well-prepared habitat to succumb to disease processes of its own accord. In reality, however, current bacteriological studies have nothing to do with the study of disease. If people would pay attention to developing sound logic, these pronouncements by official science and their devastating consequences for sound thinking would be impossible.

One issue that needs serious consideration is the fact that a certain connection between the upper and the lower regions of the human being, as described in the past few days, can be the cause of an incorrect interrelationship between these two aspects. The lower human being is predisposed to a process of becoming plantlike, and this needs to be arrested. But the forces active in the lower human being may be unable to stop this vegetative process if they are too weakly counteracted from above. This situation presents an opportunity for the development of an abundance of intestinal flora, which then become a sign that the lower part of the human body is not working in the appropriate way.

The peculiar thing is that in the human being, activities that should be played out on lower levels are dammed up when they cannot run their course in the right place. That is, if the lower body is organized in accordance with certain processes that then cannot be played out there after all, these processes are pushed back. Although this may sound like layperson's terminology to some of you, these expressions are more scientific than much of the content of today's standard pathology texts. These processes, which under normal circumstances are meant to take place in the lower parts of the human being, are pushed back into the upper parts. We need to trace the origin of excretions from the lungs, or from other upper organs such as the pleura, by checking what is going on in normal or abnormal excretory processes in the lower part of the body. It is extremely important to take a good look at what happens when the lower part of the body pushes organic processes back toward the upper body. Much of what can take place in the upper body is nothing other than lower-body processes that have been pushed upward. If the right interaction does not take place between the upper and the lower human being, then these processes are pushed up.

Please consider one additional phenomenon. You are familiar from everyday experience with another circumstance that has simply not undergone the adequate evaluation that is essential for sound science.

The moment you have thoughts about a particular organ—or, to put it better, thoughts that are connected with any particular organ—the organ itself becomes active in a certain way. Once again, this is a promising field for future doctoral dissertations. Simply study the connection between certain thoughts that appear in the human being and salivation, for example, or mucus secretion in the intestines or the secretion of milk, urine, or semen; study how specific thoughts appear, paralleling these organic activities.

What sort of a phenomenon are you encountering here? Certain thoughts appear within your soul life; organic processes take place as parallel phenomena. What does this mean? Everything that appears in your thoughts is contained within the organs in question. If you have a thought and a particular glandular secretion runs parallel to it, you have drawn the activity that underlies your thinking out of that gland. You carry out this activity separately from that gland, leaving the gland to its own fate. As a result, it devotes itself to its own activity—secretion. Secretion is prevented—that is, whatever the gland would otherwise discharge remains united with it—whenever the corresponding thought keeps it united. This is a clearly visible example of how formative activity leaves our organs and enters our thoughts. You might say that if you had not been thinking in that way, your gland would not have secreted anything. You withdrew a force from the gland and transferred it to your soul life, and then the gland began secreting.

There you have in the human organism itself the most obvious proof of a statement I made in a previous lecture, that what we experience on the level of soul and spirit is actually nothing other than disjunct formative forces of the sort that shape what we encounter in the rest of the natural order. In the rest of nature, the formative forces that we withdraw from our intestinal flora are still present in the development of external flora, which parallels that of our intestinal flora. If you look around outside at mountain and meadow flora, you must acknowledge that the forces inherent in them are the same forces that you use in developing your thoughts when you imagine something or have feelings. Your intestinal flora are different from the flora outside because the latter do not need to have thoughts taken away from them. The thoughts remain as intrinsic to the plants as their stalks,

leaves, and flowers. This example will give you an idea of the relationship between what governs flowers or leaves and what goes on within
you when you develop an intestinal flora but do not allow it to retain
its formative forces. You take these forces away because if you did not,
you would not be a thinking human being. Your intestinal flora has
had these forces taken away from it, but the outer flora retain them.

This is no less the case with regard to fauna. Without insight into
these issues, it is impossible to understand the connection between
the human being and a phytotherapeutic substance. Similarly, without an awareness of the fact that we human beings are depriving our
own intestinal fauna of the forces that bestow form in the external
animal kingdom, it is equally impossible to conceive of the appropriate therapeutic use of animal serums. As you can see, a rational and
systematic approach to these questions is possible only when we really
take a look at the connection between human beings and their environment.

But next I would like to draw your attention to another matter
that is extremely significant. I don't know whether many of you
remember, it was some time ago, when those ridiculous prohibitions
against spitting in public went into effect everywhere in the attempt
to combat tuberculosis. Such prohibitions are ridiculous for the simple reason that, as everyone should know, even ordinary diffuse sunlight kills tubercle bacilli in a very short time. If you examine sputum
after a period of time, even after a very short time, there are no more
tubercle bacilli in it. Sunlight kills them immediately. Even if the
supposition of ordinary medicine were correct, prohibiting spitting
would still be highly ridiculous. At most, such prohibitions make
sense in terms of ordinary cleanliness, but not in terms of public
hygiene in the broadest sense.

If we once again begin to assess the facts correctly, this example is very
significant because it reminds us that the bacillus belonging to the
fauna or flora of tuberculosis cannot survive in sunlight. The bacillus
cannot survive there; it is not adapted to sunlight. But where can it survive? In the interior of the human body. And why can it survive precisely there? (Not that it does the actual damage, but we do have to look
at what is active in the diseased body.) Here we encounter a situation

we have tended to disregard. We are constantly surrounded by light, and light—as you probably recall from studying science—is extremely significant in the development of nonhuman organisms and especially for all the flora outside the human being. We are surrounded by this light. But something very significant happens to this light, which is purely etheric, at the boundary between ourselves and the outer world—it is, and must be, transformed.

You see, just as the process of becoming plantlike is arrested by human beings, interrupted and counteracted by the formation of carbonic acid, what is active in the light is also broken off. Thus, if we look for light within the human being, it must be different, a metamorphosis of light. As soon as we cross the boundary into the interior of the human being, we find metamorphosed light. This means that we human beings not only transform ordinary, tangible natural processes within ourselves; we also transform intangibles. We transform light; we turn it into something else. If judged correctly, the fact that the tubercle bacillus does well within the human being but immediately perishes in the presence of sunlight is simply evidence that this bacillus is in its element in the product of the transformation of light that appears inside the human being. Therefore, if the bacillus thrives too well there, something must be wrong with this transformed light.

Taking this finding as your starting point, you can realize that one of the causes of tuberculosis must be the fact that within the human being (who would otherwise not take in an excess of the ever-present tubercle bacilli) something that should not happen is happening to this transformed light, this metamorphosis of light. Tubercle bacilli are always present, although not in sufficient quantities, but they are superabundant in a person who contracts tuberculosis. Tubercle bacilli would not be present to such an extent if something abnormal were not taking place with regard to the process of transforming sunlight.

I can present these ideas only as points of view, of course, but you will be overwhelmed by the empirical confirmation that you will encounter. If a sufficient number of dissertations and treatises are written on this subject, it will not be difficult to discover that what happens when an individual becomes a suitable breeding ground for tubercle bacilli is due either to that person's reduced ability to take in

sunlight or to a lifestyle that does not allow him or her to get enough
sunlight, so that the appropriate balance does not exist between the
sunlight entering the person and the light-metamorphosing process.
As a result, the person in question has to draw down reserves of internal metamorphosed light.

Please take into account the fact that simply being human means that
we always have an internal store of metamorphosed light. Our organization needs it. Whenever the interchange between the human being
and external sunlight does not take place in the right way, metamorphosed light is withdrawn as needed and in a way similar to the withdrawal of fat in weight loss. Human beings in this situation face the
dilemma of either allowing the upper part of the body to become ill or
withdrawing what the upper part needs from the lower—that is, making
the lower part of the body sick by withdrawing its metamorphosed light.

As you see, the organization of the human being requires more than
transformed tangible substances that come from outside. Observing
the human being correctly shows us that intangible or etheric substances are also present within the human being, but in metamorphosed form. This points out how the foundations we are now
developing make it possible to develop a correct view of the healing
effect of sunlight. For example, on the one hand, an individual may be
directly exposed to sunlight in order to regulate the disturbance in his
or her internal interchange with environmental sunlight. On the other
hand, this person may be prescribed substances to take internally that
will balance out the irregularity that arises when metamorphosed light
is withdrawn. The withdrawal of metamorphosed light must be immo-
bilized by what comes from the remedies. Here you have an example of
being able to see into the organization of the human being.

After some time, anyone who is at all capable of looking at the world
begins—strangely enough—to rage in some way against all this
microscopy, all these investigations on a minute level, because microscopy actually leads not toward but away from a healthy view of life and
life's disturbances. (Excuse me for putting this somewhat undiplo-
matically. Although it would seem possible to contradict what I am
saying, it is meant completely objectively, without any sympathy or
antipathy.) All of the processes that actually concern us in a healthy

or sick human being can be studied much better on a macroscopic than on a microscopic level. We must simply look for opportunities to investigate these processes in the macrocosm.

Note that because their urinary bladders and colons are poorly developed, avian species are subject to a process that continually balances intake and excretion. Birds can eliminate while flying. They have no opportunity to retain or store the remains of their food; if they were able to do so, they would immediately develop a fatal illness. By being human, physically human, we have advanced beyond the developmental level of birds. This is in line with the modern view of the matter, but it would be more accurate to say that we have descended below the level of birds. Birds do not need to become involved in mighty battles against their intestinal flora, because they do not have any. In contrast, this is necessary for higher animals and human beings. But with regard to one of our somewhat higher capacities—for example, the transformation of the etheric factor that I have just discussed, the metamorphosis of light—we are on the same level as birds. We have a physical colon and a physical bladder, but with regard to our etheric body, we are birds as far as these organs are concerned. On the dynamic level, they are not present in the cosmos. We are dependent on immediately transforming the light we receive and eliminating the by-products. If any disturbance occurs in this process, it does not correspond to a specific organ and therefore cannot simply be tolerated without damaging our health. Thus, when we observe a bird with its little brain, we must be clear that this is a macrocosmic image of our more subtle organization. If you choose to study human beings with regard to the more delicate organization that imprints itself on our coarser organization (which has descended below the avian level), you must make a macrocosmic study of the processes of the avian world.

At this point, I would simply like to state parenthetically that the outlook for human life would be very dismal if our etheric organism had the same idiosyncrasy as our physical organism in comparison to the avian species, because the etheric body cannot be so shut off from the outer world. If we had etheric organs of smell, the process of storing metamorphosed light, for example, would have terrible consequences for our life with our fellow human beings. It would be similar to what we experience when we cut open a dead sheep and have to endure its innards. As things stand, however, with regard to our etheric component, we encounter each other in a way that can be compared to the not-at-all unpleasant smell (relatively speaking, that is; everything is relative) that is evident on cutting open even a carrion-eating bird or an animal such as a horse, which is not a true ruminant but whose organization tends in that direction.

Thus, the important point here is to investigate the correspondences between what happens in the outer flora and fauna and what happens, but must be counteracted, in the intestinal fauna and flora within the human organism. And if we want to establish the connection between any therapeutic substance and a particular organ, we must move on from the general characterizations we have developed today to more specific characterizations, which will appear in the lectures to follow.

Taking the need to counteract our internal intestinal fauna and flora as our starting point, let us now proceed to our circulation, where the struggle against becoming plantlike takes place, and then move on to the actual sensory-neural aspect of the human being. This is much more significant for our life as a whole than we generally believe. Having raised science to such a high level of abstraction, we have lost all possibility of considering the human being as a being of nerves and senses in any appropriate way. We have been unable to consider the fact that this being of nerves and senses—which permits the light and the warmth associated with it to enter the human being as a whole—is intimately related to the life within us, since the intangible factors that enter along with the light must be transformed within the organs; their role in the forming of organs is as important as anything that exists in the tangible realm. We have failed to consider that this being of nerves and senses is particularly significant for our human organization as a whole. As we descend deeper into the lower part of the human being, we move from the forces that build up the intestinal flora to those that build up the intestinal fauna, but when we ascend, we move from the realm where the internal flora is counteracted into the realm where the human tendency to mineralize or become sclerotic must constantly be combated. The increased boniness of the head is enough to permit you to study how the organization of the human being tends to become increasingly mineral-like as it develops upward. This tendency to mineralize, however, is extremely significant for the entire organization of the human being.

Here we encounter an issue that bears frequent repetition; I have even spoken of it in public lectures. If we divide the human being into three systems as a being with a head, torso, and limbs, we really should not imagine that these three systems are adjacent to each other and separated by external spatial boundaries. Of course, qualitatively speaking, the human being is entirely a head being. What constitutes the head extends over the entire human being and merely predominates in the head. It is the same with the other systems, the circulatory system and the meta-bolic/limb system. Each of them always encompasses the entire human being. As a matter of course, what is essential for the head being is present as a potential everywhere in the human being, and this potential for mineralization must be combated throughout the body. This consti-tutes a field of study that modern individuals cannot understand at all if they consult old texts that are the products of atavistic clairvoyance. Very few people gain anything sensible from reading what Paracelsus has to say about salt processes. But the salt process belongs to the field that I have just characterized. Similarly, the sulfur process belongs to the field that I characterized earlier [that is, the process of becoming plantlike].

So we are dealing with an inherent human tendency toward mineral-ization. In a certain sense, just as it is possible for what underlies the activities of fauna and flora to become independent, it is also possible for the mineralizing tendency in the entire human being to become independent. And how should this mineralizing tendency be counter-acted? The only way to do so is by splitting it up, by constantly driving little wedges into it, as it were. At this point you will have to begin to make the transition from animal serum therapy and phytotherapy to mineral therapy. You will not be able to do without mineral therapy because the clue to providing the necessary support in the human battle against mineralization or sclerotization can be found only in connec-tions between minerals and the internal human element that wants to become mineral. You will not accomplish anything—and this will have to be thoroughly discussed in another lecture—by simply introducing a mineral in its outer state into the human organism. What emerges here points to a homeopathic principle of some sort, to the need to expose the mineral-derived forces that counteract the workings of the outer mineral kingdom. It has been pointed out—and quite correctly—that we simply need to take a look at the minimal mineral content of some spring waters that have therapeutic effects to see that a homeopathic process is evident in these springs. This process shows that as soon as the mineral's cohesion is released from the forces we can grasp outwardly, completely different forces emerge. These forces must first be released in a special way through potentization. But as I said, these topics will be discussed in a separate lecture.

There is something else that I would still like to tell you today, and I ask that the younger people among you especially take it to heart. If you perform actual comparative studies of the transformation of the entire intestinal system as it evolves from fish through amphibians and reptiles—especially amphibians and reptiles—to birds on the one hand and to mammals and, ultimately, humans on the other hand, you will find that remarkable transformations occur. Some examples are the appearance in lower mammals of an appendix, or what develops into the appendix in humans; the beginnings of an appendix in some birds, which may be thought of as something of a deviation of the avian organization from its usual path; and the manner in which the colon evolves as we move from the fish species, which have no such organ, up through the so-called more highly evolved orders to those with actual colons and then to those with appendices (some species have several of them) and on to the human being with a full-fledged appendix. You will find a remarkable interaction taking place in all this.

A comparative study would need to heavily emphasize this interaction. You could simply inquire in a superficial way—and you know how frequently this is done—about the purpose of an organ like the human appendix, which is closed off toward the outside. This question is frequently asked, but when people ask such questions, they usually do not consider the fact that the human being manifests as a duality and that anything taking on form down below is always parallel to an organ that appears up above. Certain organs cannot appear in the upper body unless their parallel organs, or counterparts, are able to develop in the lower body. The more the forebrain develops in the course of animal evolution, eventually assuming the form it has in the human being, the more the intestines develop in the direction that leads to storing the remains of food. There is an intimate connection between the formation of intestines and the formation of the brain; if the colon and the appendix had not appeared in the course of the evolution of animals, physical human beings who can think would also ultimately not have been able to appear, because humans have brains at the expense—at the very pronounced expense—of their intestinal organs.

The intestinal organs are the faithful obverse of the structures in the brain. To make it possible for you to be relieved, on the one hand, of physical activity for the sake of thinking, you must burden your organism on the other hand with everything that gives rise to the need for a fully developed colon and bladder. This means that the highest activity of soul and spirit in the human physical world, to the extent that it is bound to the full development of the brain, is also bound to the corresponding development of the intestines. This is an extremely significant connection, a connection that sheds a great deal of light on all of natural creation. If you ask yourself why human beings have an appendix, the answer—paradoxical as it may sound—is so that they can think in a way that befits human beings. What develops in the appendix has its counterpart in the human brain. Everything on the one level corresponds to something on the other.

This is knowledge that we will have to achieve again through a new type of cognition. Today, of course, we have little to gain from simply parroting the physicians of times gone by, who still had some grounding in atavistic clairvoyance. But we must indeed acquire this understanding again, and a purely materialistic study of medicine that does not look for such connections at all is a real obstacle to doing so. As far as today's science and medicine are concerned, the brain is an internal organ, and so are the contents of the lower body. No one notices that this error is just like saying that positive and negative electricity are the same. It is all the more important to observe these things, because just as tension develops between positive and negative electricity and seeks to balance itself out, there is also constant tension in the human being between the upper and lower parts of the body. The primary goal of all our searching in the field of medicine should be to master this tension, which is expressed in the forces concentrated in two organs, the pineal gland and the pituitary gland, or hypophysis. All of the forces of the upper body are expressed in the pineal gland, and a state of tension exists between them and the forces of the pituitary, or *hypophysis cerebri*, which are lower forces. This relationship is a true state of tension. If we were always to derive an idea of this state of tension from a person's overall state of health, it would be a very good basis for further healing. We will continue talking about this subject tomorrow. You will see that I will incorporate all of your questions, but as I said before, I must first create the basis for doing so.

LECTURE 5

DORNACH, MARCH 25, 1920

IN the course of these lectures, as we draw ever closer to that special field where pathology is meant to pervade therapy, bridging the gap between the two, we will have to mention all sorts of topics that can serve only as therapeutic ideals and cannot necessarily be fully implemented. Nevertheless, if we have an overview of what should be considered in treating patients, the details we discover about an illness will yield something of use to us, and at least we will know how to evaluate the inevitably fragmentary conclusions.

Above all, we need to examine the importance of understanding the whole person before us, even when treating the most specialized case. Also this understanding of the human being as a whole should always include the most important events of the patient's life. Members of the medical professions sometimes confide in me and discuss some aspect of a case. After listening to a few words, I have often asked how old the patient was and been astonished to find that the medical professional was unaware of the patient's age and unable to give me any precise information. As we will see in the next few days, it is most important to inform yourself about the patient's age with some degree of accuracy, because therapy is dependent on the age of the patient to a great extent. The day before yesterday, certain therapies were presented as having been extremely helpful in some cases but not in others.[23]

---

23. This took place in a lecture by one of the participants in this course.

In view of such statements, the very obvious question is, what is the connection between this inefficacy and the age of the patient in question? It is essential to record all the details with regard to how the age of the patient influences the working of therapeutic substances.

Moving on, it is essential to observe carefully how your patient's body has developed. Is this person short and compact or tall and lanky? The answer is significant because it tells us about the forces of that person's etheric body, as we call it. (I have given this a great deal of thought and have concluded that the use of such terms as etheric body and so forth, which are simply part and parcel of the reality of the human being, is unavoidable, and you would probably not want me to avoid them. We could substitute ones that are more popular among non-anthroposophists, and we may be able to do this at the end of our discussion. But for now, for the sake of better understanding, we will continue to use such terms when necessary.) The intensity of the working of the etheric body, then, can be assessed on the basis of your patient's growth patterns. As I said, it is not always possible to take everything into account because the information may simply be unavailable, but it is good to know about all this. Whenever possible, it is especially important to inquire about whether the person in question grew quickly or slowly during adolescence. Did he or she remain small for a long time or have a growth spurt at a relatively early age and lag behind later? All of these questions point to what we might call the behavior of the etheric body, the functional manifestations of the individual in relationship to the physical body, which must be taken into account when we hope to recognize a connection between the patient and particular remedies.

In addition, we must also understand the relationship of the physical and etheric bodies to the higher members of the human constitution, to what we call the astral body (the soul element) and the I (the spiritual element). We need to learn this from our patients. And you should not hesitate to ask, for example, whether they dream a lot or only a little. Frequent dreaming is extremely significant for a patient's entire constitution because it shows that the astral body and the I have a tendency to develop activity of their own and therefore do not want to become involved with the physical body too strongly or in too much detail. As a result, the formative forces of the human soul do not flow into that person's organ systems.

Furthermore, even if you are uncomfortable in asking this question, you should also inquire whether the person is active and hardworking or tends to be sluggish. In a personality with a sluggish tendency, the inner mobility of the astral body and the I is strong. This may sound paradoxical, but this type of mobility does not become conscious; it remains unconscious. And because it is unconscious, the person is not hardworking, even with regard to consciousness, but is sluggish overall. This is because what I call the opposite of sluggishness is the individual's organic capacity for using the higher members to intervene in the lower human being—that is, for leading activity over into the physical and etheric bodies from the astral body and the I. This capacity is very limited in a sluggish person. From the perspective of spiritual science, a sluggish person is a sleeping person.

After that, you should find out whether your patient is nearsighted or farsighted. A nearsighted person is somewhat reserved with regard to how the I and astral body relate to the physical body. Nearsightedness is one of the most important signs that you are dealing with a person whose spirit and soul are reluctant to intervene in the physical body.

This next indication is extremely important in treating patients and may become practicable someday. I believe it could acquire practical significance once the individual medical professions have developed a better sense of cooperation. It is extremely important for dentists to take advantage of everything they know about the teeth, the digestive system, and so on by providing each patient with some sort of checklist after each visit, noting their findings with regard to the development of the patient's teeth, whether there was an early tendency to dental caries, whether the teeth remained in good condition until a later age, and the like. As we will see in the next few days, the condition of the teeth is extremely significant for assessing a person's overall constitution. Making this characteristic signature of the patient's state of health available to the attending physician in the form of a report of dental findings could provide a very significant clue. Of course the patients in question would have to give their consent, but in an atmosphere of cooperation this should be possible.

Next, it is extremely important to become aware of the patient's physical likes and dislikes. You would have to find out, for example, what foods the person in question craves. It is especially significant to determine whether the person you are treating has a craving for salt, for example, or for something else. If your patient has a particular craving for salty foods, you are dealing with a person with an overly strong connection of the I and the astral body to the physical and etheric bodies. In this person, the spirit and soul have an overly strong affinity for the physical body.

Dizzy spells brought on by outer mechanical processes, such as rapid turning motions, are also indicative of a strong affinity of this sort. We should ascertain whether mechanical body movements tend to make the patient dizzy.

Additionally, as is fairly generally known, we should always find out about any disturbances in secretion, in the patient's overall glandular functioning. When disturbances in secretion are evident, a disturbance is also always present in the ability of the I and astral body to maintain their grip on the etheric and physical bodies.

I have given you some details about what we would need to know when we meet a patient. I have highlighted details, but you will see where these subjects are pointing insofar as they relate to the constitution of the body itself. As we continue, we will also discuss the need to learn about lifestyle issues—whether or not it is possible for the patient to breathe good air, and so forth. We can consider this further when we discuss individual issues. In this way, you will first gain an insight of sorts into the type of person you have to treat. Only when you have acquired such insight will you be in a position, in any specific instance, to know how a particular remedy should be formulated.

Next, I will mention in general terms an indication that has emerged from some of the lectures of the past few days, namely, the inner relationship of the human being to the entire nonhuman outer world. Spiritual science often states—although abstractly, to begin with—that in the course of evolution, humankind has discharged the other kingdoms from within itself and that everything external to human beings therefore bears a certain relationship to their own nature and constitution. In contrast to this abstract manifestation of the connection, we will repeatedly have to point to very specific associations when it comes to the treatment of organs. Above all, however, the basis of the healing relationship between the human being and nonhuman external nature must first be clear to us.

You know that there is a great deal of debate on this subject and that methods of healing, which we will also discuss in greater detail as we proceed, are engaged in fierce struggles with each other. One struggle in particular is well known—the struggle between physicians who favor homeopathy and those who think allopathically. It might interest you to know how spiritual science is meant to intervene in this quarrel.

For today, I will first speak in general terms about this topic and go into the details later. The way in which spiritual science should intervene in this question is actually rather strange. It becomes apparent to spiritual science that there really are no allopaths because even a substance prescribed as an allopathic medication undergoes a process of potentization within the organism, and healing occurs only through this process. Thus, all allopathic physicians find their procedures supported by the body's homeopathic tendency, which brings about a transformation allopaths neglect—namely, breaking down the cohesion of the remedy's individual particles.

Admittedly, it does make a considerable difference whether or not we relieve the organism of this potentization process, for the simple reason that healing processes within the organism are probably connected to the state remedies gradually achieve through potentization. Initially, however, a remedy confronts the body as a foreign entity, as matter that would otherwise belong to the outer world and has no therapeutic relationship to the body. We subject the organism to a great deal of work and disruption if we burden it with all the forces that come to expression when we administer a medication in the allopathic state. We will speak later specifically about cases where it is impossible to relieve the body of this potentizing function.

Homeopathy is a method of healing that has been learned by listening very carefully to nature, at least to some extent, although fanaticism has also brought about significant leaps, as we shall see. The important point, however, is to discover ways of relating specific details about the human being to the nonhuman environment. We cannot, as I said yesterday in a different context, simply parrot the physicians of antiquity, although it can be useful to immerse ourselves in ancient medical literature if we understand it. Instead, for example, we must use all the methods of modern science to explore this interaction between the human being and the nonhuman environment. First of all, we must realize that chemical investigations of substances—that is, delving into what individual substances reveal in the laboratory—will not get us very far. I have already pointed out that microscopy—and such chemical investigations are also a form of microscopy—ought to be replaced with macroscopic observation, with what is revealed by observing the cosmos itself.

Today I will present significant principles that will point out correspondences between a form of "threefolding" in the nonhuman world and the threefold human being. In this connection, we must look first at the dissolving process. You see, solubility was the last property that was of special importance in the evolution of our planet Earth. What precipitated out as the Earth's solid portion can be traced back, to a considerable extent, to a cosmic dissolving process that was overcome and killed off, precipitating the solid parts. It is superficial to think only of the mechanical deposition of sediments and to base geognosy and geology entirely on that process.[24] What was primarily involved in the Earth-forming process, in incorporating solid components into the body of the Earth, consisted of special instances of crystallizing or precipitating out of solution. We can say that to the extent the dissolving process is something that happens in outer, nonhuman nature, it is something that human beings have excluded from themselves. External dissolving processes involve activities that human beings have excluded from themselves. The important point here is to investigate the nature of the connection between these processes in the external, nonhuman cosmos and inner processes in the human organism.

---

24. *Geognosy* is the study of the Earth, its structure and strata, and includes geology, which studies the Earth's crust.

I mentioned earlier that people tend to crave salt when the connection between the spirit and soul and the physical and etheric bodies is overly strong. This is of fundamental importance. These people want to reverse the process of salt precipitation in their own organism, that is, they want to cancel out this Earth-forming process, essentially making salt revert to an earlier stage, before its solidification in Earth's evolution. It is especially important to look at such phenomena because they allow us to investigate the connections between the human organism and outer, nonhuman nature, to realize that there is an organic need in the nature of the human being to reverse or oppose certain activities that take place in the outer world. As you know, I mentioned yesterday that we even struggle against gravity through the development of the buoyancy that supports the human brain. In general, human beings have a tendency to oppose the forces of nature.

The first question is, what is the meaning of our opposition to the Earth-forming process? Essentially, it means nothing less than freeing the lower part of the human being from the spirit and soul, driving the soul and spirit out of the lower region of the human body, perhaps into the upper part, at least initially. All cases of salt craving show us that in some way the lower part of the human being wants to free itself of the overly strong effects of the spirit and soul within it and to allow them to flow out into the upper part of the body.

Let us assume that we encounter recognizable disturbances in the lower part of the body. We will later learn about the means of recognizing them and the individual diseases they lead to. But what will we be able to do about them?

At this point I would like to interject an observation that may be important for those tending toward a certain one-sidedness in their use of therapeutic substances. Some physicians have an aversion of sorts to mineral remedies. This aversion is not justified, because we will see that pure phytotherapeutic substances can be effective only within very definite limits and that mineral remedies are very significant, especially in more serious cases. Please do not be offended if I take mineral remedies as my point of departure for these very basic observations. More specifically, I will talk about how the effects of these mineral remedies are incorporated into organic life.

Studying the oyster may be a revelation to you with regard to certain methods of treatment that apply to the lower parts of the human body in their relationship to the upper areas. Shell formation in the oyster is an extremely interesting subject because, you see, the oyster produces its calcium carbonate shell from the inside out. If you study the oyster from a spiritual-scientific perspective—and it is indeed necessary for spiritual science to assist us somewhat in this investigation—you will realize that although the oyster occupies a very low position in the evolution of animals, its standing in the cosmos as a whole is quite elevated because it secretes what human beings carry within them in the form of thinking. In a certain way, the forces that shape the oyster's shell, working from the inside out, show how the oyster extrudes a substance that would make it very intelligent if it were linked to its organic growth, a substance that would shape the oyster into a very highly evolved animal being. Instead, this factor is channeled to the outside. You can positively see the work of calcium carbonate, *Calcarea carbonica*, in the development of an oyster shell. This work guides excessive activity of spirit and soul out of the organism.

If you find evidence of excessive activity of soul and spirit in the lower part of the body—and this does indeed appear in certain forms of illness that we will describe further—you will need to turn to the remedies we owe to oyster shells or similar substances that work from the inside out through the mysterious forces of calcium carbonate. Thus, an essential component of our therapeutic repertoire will depend on our understanding of the specific healing forces present in this outward-directed impulse. You see, everything that is linked to *Calcarea carbonica* and related remedies can be studied rationally only by looking at it in such a context.

The inherent forces of phosphorus, for example, are like the polar opposite of the forces of calcium carbonate. In their real meaning, the terms I will now use are truly no less scientific than what so frequently passes as science today. If the typical behavior of everything of a saltlike nature is to give itself up to the environment, the reason is that everything saltlike comes about because the substances in question are laid bare, freed from the workings of light and other intangibles within them. You might say that in the process of coming about, any saltlike substance repels the intangible factor as being inwardly incompatible with it.

The exact opposite is the case with phosphorus. Ancient atavistic knowledge, realizing quite correctly that phosphorus contains the intangible factor—the light—within itself, was not totally unjustified in describing phosphorus as a light-bearer. What salt wards off, phosphorus carries within itself. In this way, substances that are the polar opposites of salt are the ones that are appropriate and internalize intangibles—especially light, but also others, such as warmth. This is the basis of the therapeutic efficacy of the inherent properties of phosphorus and of everything that is therapeutically related to it. Phosphorus, which internalizes intangibles, is especially suited to pushing the astral body and the I back into the human body when they are reluctant to approach.

Suppose one of your patients has an illness—later we will mention the specific illnesses that come into question—and you discover that this patient experiences increased dreaming. This means that the astral body prefers to separate from the physical body and become involved in activity of its own. This patient may also have an organic tendency to develop peripheral inflammations, which is another indication that the astral body and the I are not properly embedded in the physical body. In this case, you will be able to apply the force that phosphorus uses to retain its intangibles to make the person's astral body and I become more involved in the physical body. You will be able to use phosphorus for a great variety of illnesses, especially in people with sleep disturbances, because it tends to lead the I and the astral body back into the physical and etheric bodies in the appropriate way.

We have seen that in a certain way, phosphorus-like substances and saltlike substances are polar opposites. Let me emphasize that we need to pay much more attention to the status of these substances in the entire cosmic process than to the specific names that modern chemistry, for example, has applied to individual substances. As time goes on, we will see how the "phosphorus" in substances that work in ways similar to actual phosphorus can also be used therapeutically.

As you see, we have posited the existence of two opposing states in outer nature, salt activity and phosphorus activity. Mercurial activity stands between these two. As you know, the human being is a three-fold being with a sensory-nervous system, a circulatory system, and a metabolic system, with the circulatory system occupying a mediating position between the metabolism and sensory-nervous activity. Similarly, in outer nature the mediating factor is neither salt activity, which yields to the external world, nor the activity that internalizes intangibles strongly, but rather the factor that holds the balance between these two activities by choosing to exist in drop form. Basically, the mercurial principle always tends toward drop formation because of the inner cohesiveness of its forces. The significant aspect of the mercurial principle is not the fact that we call a certain substance "mercury," but rather this cohesion of forces, which holds the balance between the dissolving tendency of salt and the inwardness and retention of intangibles in phosphorus. It is therefore important to study the forces that are most evident in anything of a mercurial nature. Thus you will also find that this mercurial principle is essentially connected to everything that can be counted upon to bring about a balance between the activities to which phosphorus and salt are suited. Especially when we talk about syphilis and similar diseases, we will see that the organic effects of the mercurial principle do not contradict what I have just said.

In discussing the phosphorus, mercury, and salt principles, I have presented you with types that are particularly distinctive in the mineral kingdom. It is true, however, that in speaking of salt, we had to consider the organic process that is intrinsic to and underlies the formation of oyster shell. In a certain sense, this process is also present when phosphorus concentrates intangibles. In the latter case, the process is internalized and is therefore less readily apparent on the outside.

We must now move on from looking at this typical formative process in the outer world to the plantlike element that humankind discharged at some time in the past. As we already saw yesterday from other perspectives, the plant represents the opposite of the activity present within the human organism. In the plant itself, however, we can clearly distinguish three different elements. This triple distinction is especially obvious if you look, on the one hand, at everything that develops earthward in the form of roots and then at everything that shoots upward into seeds, fruits, and flowers. The contrast between the plant and the human being—although not between the plant and the animal, in this case—is visible even in their external alignment. This contrast is extremely important and significant. The plant sinks into the earth with its roots and pushes upward with its flowers—that is, with its reproductive organs. With regard to our own orientation in the cosmos, we human beings are the exact opposite. In complete contrast to plants, we root upward with our heads and push downward with our reproductive organs. It really is not nonsense to picture a plant within the human being, a plant that roots upward and develops its blossom below, in the direction of the reproductive organs. In this way, a particular form of the plant element is incorporated into the human being. Once again, this is an important characteristic for distinguishing between human beings and animals. In an animal, the plant is generally incorporated horizontally, at a right angle to the plant's own direction, while the human being's orientation in the cosmos constitutes a complete 180° turn in comparison to the plant.

This is one of the most instructive lessons we can learn by considering the relationship of the human being to the external world. If our medical students would pay more attention to these macroscopic findings, they would also discover more about the forces at work in cells, for example, than they would through microscopy. There is actually very little to be gained from microscopy, because the most important forces that are at work in cells can also be observed on the macroscopic level, with variations depending on whether the being in question is a plant, an animal, or a human. We can study human cells much better by investigating the interactions among the forces that work vertically upward, those that work vertically downward, and those that hold the balance horizontally. These forces, which can be observed in the macrocosm, work right down into the cellular level. And what is active in cells is essentially nothing other than a copy of this macrocosmic activity.

In studying the Earth's plant kingdom, it is critical to avoid looking at it in the usual manner—that is, by walking around and looking at one plant next to the other, observing the subtle distinctions between them, and inventing a name with two or three parts to establish each plant's place in taxonomy. Instead, you must consider the entire Earth as a single being and the whole plant kingdom as belonging to the organism of the Earth in the same way that the hairs on your head belong to your own organism (although admittedly your individual hairs are all alike, at least in some respects, while plants differ from each other). An individual plant should no more be considered in isolation than a single hair can be considered an independent organism. That plants differ is due only to the fact that the Earth, in its interaction with the rest of the cosmos, develops forces in many different directions. For this reason, plants are structured in different ways, but the life and growth of all plants are based on a single unity within the organization of the Earth.

This makes it especially important to be attentive to certain details. When you study fungi, for example, you will find that the Earth itself is a matrix, or growth medium, for these fungi. When you move on to higher herbaceous plants, you will find that this is still the case, but that supra-earthly factors, such as light, exert a certain influence on these leafy plants in the formation of their flowers, leaves, and so on. And when you turn your attention to a tree it is especially interesting to note that its trunk formation, which is what makes it perennial, constitutes a continuation of what the entire Earth otherwise provides for plants that sit directly on the ground. You see, you must imagine that you have the Earth with the plants sprouting up out of it, and in this case we can look for forces within the Earth that underlay plant growth and interact with what is streaming in from the cosmos. Please don't be too shocked by what I am going to say next, because it really is true. When a tree grows, it is as if the ground rises up over what used to flow directly from the Earth into the tree. This force shoots into the trunk, and all trunks are basically outgrowths of the Earth. That we do not look at it like this is simply due to the truly distorted modern materialistic view that the Earth consists only of mineral matter. This view totally fails to acknowledge the impossibility of the idea of a mineral Earth. In addition to precipitating minerals, the Earth also contains forces that shoot upward into the plant kingdom. These are the forces that rise up to become the trunk. And what then grows out of the trunk is comparable to what grows directly out of the ground in the case of lower and herbaceous plant forms. I would say that the Earth itself is the trunk or stem of lower and herbaceous plants and that the plants whose flowers and seed capsules cling to a stem have created an extra stem for themselves. As you can see, it makes a difference whether I take a flower from a tree or from a herbaceous plant.

From this same perspective, then, please consider the development of parasitic plants, specifically mistletoe. In this case, a process that otherwise remains organically connected to the plant, namely the attachment of flowering and seed-bearing organs to the stem, is more like an outer excretion or an independent process. The development of mistletoe must be seen as enhancing the usual formation of flowers and seed and separating this process in a certain way from the forces of the Earth. In the development of mistletoe, the plant's nonearthly aspect is emancipated, so to speak. In general, the aspect of the plant that strives upward from the Earth and interacts with supra-earthly factors gradually separates from the Earth as flowers and seeds form; in mistletoe, this results in an exceptionally strongly individualized emancipation.

If you relate this phenomenon to the usual structures you perceive in plants, you will have to say that the situation is considerably different from that of a plant that tends more toward root formation, devoting a greater proportion of its growth primarily to its roots while its flowers remain small or atrophied. Such plants are more inclined toward earthly factors. In contrast, plants that emancipate themselves from these earthly factors are ones that emphasize the formation of seeds and flowers, and especially those that assume the role of parasites within the plant kingdom. Every plant has a tendency to promote one of its organs to prominence. Just look at how the pineapple plant emphasizes its stem, for example. Or take any other plant. You can say that each of the main plant organs—root, stem, leaf, flower, fruit—becomes the primary organ in some form of plant. Take a plant such as *Equisetum*, for example. All of its efforts are subsumed in stem formation. Other plants emphasize leaf development, while still others concentrate on flower growth and allow their stems and leaves to atrophy.

As it turns out, there is a certain parallel between these different tendencies in plant growth and the three types of mineral activity in nonhuman nature that I mentioned earlier today. If we look at what appears particularly strongly in the plant that tends to emancipate itself—that is, at the process that culminates in the inner workings of parasites—we find a tendency to internalize intangibles. If the appropriate organs predominate in the plant, the intangible factors that stream toward the Earth from the cosmos are conserved in them just as they are in phosphoric substances. We could also say that in a certain way, flowers, seeds, and everything that tends in the direction of mistletoe and the like are phosphoric. Conversely, if we study the rooting process that a plant develops if it considers the Earth its matrix, we find that it is intimately related to the formation of salts. In this way, we encounter these two polar opposites in the plant kingdom. And in the mediating activity in plants, which is always present between the flowering and fruiting element that pushes upward and the rooting element that holds fast down below, you have the mercurial process that brings about a balance. If you take into account the reversal of the plant in the human being, you will realize that any inner predisposition to flower and fruit formation must relate very strongly to organs that are either located in or governed by the lower human body and that the same is true of phosphoric substances. In the next few days, we will see that this view is absolutely correct. In contrast, any plant part that strives to become rootlike will have a particular relationship to all the organs of the upper body.

Of course, you must keep in mind that we cannot simply divide the human being into three parts according to an external plan. For example, the digestive system, which belongs to the lowest region, certainly attempts to continue right up into the head. It is erroneous to think that the gray matter of the brain is providing the material basis for thinking, because this is not the case. Gray matter is essentially there to nourish the brain. It is actually an outpost of the digestive system that serves to nourish the brain, while the brain's white matter is what is significant as the material basis of thinking. This is why you will find an aspect of the anatomical constitution of gray matter that has far more extensive connections to one of the body's overall activities than to the function ordinarily ascribed to it. So you see, when we speak of digestion we cannot refer exclusively to the abdomen or the lower part of the body. And it is certainly true that when we look at the rootlike element, we find that it relates not only to the upper part of the human being but also to the rest of the body.

Everything in the plant that brings about the balance between the flowering and fruiting element and the root element—that is, everything that comes to expression in the leafy parts of ordinary herbaceous plants—will prove to be especially important, even in extract form, for everything that relates to circulatory disturbances—that is, for the rhythmical balance between the upper and lower areas of the body. Earlier in this lecture, we looked at the minerals that internalize intangibles, the minerals that ward off intangibles, and the intermediate types. As you can see now, we find parallels in the overall configuration of the plant. Here you have the very first rational means of establishing an interaction between the human organism and the plant itself, based on the emphasis the plant places on developing one or the other of its organs. Later on, we will consider specialized manifestations of this interaction.

Up to this point, we have been able to point out that such interrelationships exist between plants or minerals and the human being. Recently, something very promising has been added to the picture with regard to the interrelationship that is supposed to exist between humans and animals. However, even disregarding the fact that the development of animal serotherapy took place under rather strange circumstances, principled objections must be raised to the usual form of this therapy. You see, Behring actually proceeded in a very strange way while developing serotherapy.[25]

---

25. Emil Adolf von Behring (1854–1917), a German bacteriologist at the Koch Institute of Hygiene and at the Institute for Infectious Disease in Berlin, professor at the University of Halle, and later director of the Institute of Hygiene in Marburg. See the extensive note at end of this lecture.

If you follow the speeches that were given and the publications that appeared more peripherally (which discussed only what the serum was meant to help) you are given the impression that serotherapy has the potential to reform the entire medical system. However, if you carefully examination the basic studies an astonishing fact is revealed (and this is not an exaggeration, as one or another of you will probably recognize).

The researchers were attempting to develop a treatment by studying guinea pigs so that they could then apply it to human beings. It yielded a "strangely high" percentage of unfavorable results in guinea pigs. In fact, out of the large number of guinea pigs treated with the serum, the result was favorable in only one case—in one single guinea pig, thus masking its healing process—at the very moment when people were beginning to drum up support for serotherapy in a big way! I would simply like to present this as a fact, of which I believe some of you are already aware. The extraordinary sloppiness evidenced in this incident deserves to be considered more carefully in the context of the history of science.

But there is a principle that I want to introduce to conclude today's lecture and that I will elaborate upon tomorrow, or at some time during the next few days: Today you have seen that the natural, outer processes that directly affect the human being are not those that exist on the immediate surface. Instead, they must be brought up from the depths. In a certain sense, processes that human beings have eliminated from within themselves—the processes of phosphorus and salt and the plant's flowering, fruiting, rooting, and leaf-forming—are closely related to the human being, but in such a way that the human being lives in their inverse and has an innate tendency to negate anything expressed in nonhuman nature, turning it into its opposite.

The same is not true of animals. They have already gone halfway through this process, so human beings are not the opposite of animals in the same sense. Humans stand at a right angle to animals, as it were, but are removed 180° from plants. This must certainly be considered when raising the issue of using animal remedies such as serums or the like.

A Note on the Critiques of Emil Adolf von Behring

"On the Development of Diphtheria Immunity and Tetanus Immunity in Animals" (*German Medical Weekly*, no. 4, Dec. 4, 1890), an article on Behring and Kitasato, begins with the words, "In our long-term studies of diphtheria (Behring) and tetanus (Kitasato) we have also drawn closer to the issues of therapy and immunization, and in infectious disease we have been able to both cure infected animals and pretreat healthy ones in such a way that they no longer contracted diphtheria or tetanus after treatment.[26]

"The way in which immunization and cure are effected will be discussed here only to the extent that this is needed in order to prove the following statement correct.... Details will follow in the magazine *Hygiene*."

The remainder of this article speaks only of experiments with tetanus. In the same weekly (no. 50), Behring describes attempts to bring about immunity to diphtheria. He says of the treatment, "I must emphasize that I have no remedy for diphtheria in human beings—I am merely looking for one." This must be contrasted with the sentence from the first article, quoted previously. At the end of the second article, he tells us that serum injections have been successful in treating animals with tetanus. The essay concludes: "The *possibility* of curing even illnesses that take an acute form can thus no longer be questioned."

The promised article in *Hygiene* finally appeared in 1892; no prior article has been discovered. It documents two series of experiments involving a total of sixty animals, fifty-nine of whom were either immunized or given the serum *at the same time as*, or days before, being infected with diphtheria. The procedure used on humans (infection on day 1, one day of illness on day 2, serum injection on day 3) was copied in the case of only *one* animal, which was cured. In the other "cured" animals, either the illness had not yet developed (Series II experiments, Dec. 1891–Jan. 1892) or, in most cases where the serum was injected before infection, death resulted (Series I experiments, September-December 1891.)

From a volume of critical essays on the question of diphtheria serum ("Physicians Speak Out About and Against Behring and His Therapeutic Serum," Dr. Carl Gerster, ed., A. Zimmers Verlag, 1895), it appears that such publicity was not well received in medical circles at that time.

---

26. Shibasaburo Kitasato (1852–1931), Japanese bacteriologist who studied under Robert Koch (1843–1910) in Berlin. He isolated the bacilli of tetanus, symptomatic anthrax, and dysentery, and prepared a diphtheria antitoxin. He also discovered the etiological agent of bubonic plague.

LECTURE 6

DORNACH, MARCH 26, 1920

I have some concern about what I am going to present today. If I had three months to explain these ideas, you would find it difficult to take them as mere fantasies. The material that follows involves specialized aspects of healing, but during this hour today I can present these ideas only briefly in an attempt to make them fully comprehensible to you. Consequently, many statements will seem purely arbitrary. Nevertheless, through my manner of presenting them, I will attempt to demonstrate that all of these thoughts are at least as well founded as those assumptions upon which modern science is built.

I would like to begin today by showing you the process of plant development, as such, in its cosmic context. I have already drawn your attention to the fact that the inverse of this process is active in the human being on the functional level. This process of plant development needs to be described, at least sketchily, if we are to discover the plant world's direct connection to the human being. If you look at plants, you will find that their overall developmental process incorporates two distinctly opposite tendencies. One works toward the Earth. I pointed out yesterday that the Earth is mounded up, as it were, in the trunks or stems of woody plants, so that a tree's flowers and leaves are rooted in the trunk in the same way that merely herbaceous plants or still lower plants are rooted in the ground.

This points to the plant's Earth-directed tendency on the one hand. But on the other hand the plant strives upward, away from the Earth. It does so not only through a mechanical force that counteracts

Earth's gravity but also in all of its developmental processes, even the internal ones. The processes taking place in the flower become differentiated from those taking place in the root. Flower processes become much more dependent than root processes on forces from outside the Earth. The dependence of flower formation on forces that do not truly belong to the Earth is the first thing we must look at. Because of the reversal of the plant process in the human being on the functional level, a reversal I pointed to in earlier lectures, we will find that the forces used by the plant to initiate flower and seed formation are also present in the human abdomen in elimination, secretion, and the organic basis of sexuality. Therefore, when we find this connection between the human being and the plant, even the details point to both extratelluric and earthly processes in the plant.

I must not omit to make you aware of the fact that what I am presenting here has not been taken from ancient medical works but is based on present-day spiritual-scientific research. Some of my terminology, however, harkens back to this ancient literature because modern medical literature has not yet developed a terminology of its own in this field. But you would be very mistaken if you were to believe that anything presented here is derived exclusively from ancient writings.

If you follow the process of plant growth as it moves upward, away from the earthly element, the first thing to become aware of is the spiral path of development of both leaves and flowers. The plant's formative forces trace a spiral of sorts around the stem. This spiral path cannot be deduced from inner forces of tension within the plant but must be attributed to extratelluric influences and especially to the effects of the apparent path of the Sun. I say "apparent" advisedly, because the Earth's motion in relationship to the Sun must be considered only relative, hence I say, "the apparent path of the Sun." In certain respects, the clues to the movement of the stars that are found in the path of a plant's developmental processes are much better than Galileo's mathematical clues, because the plant is a faithful replica of what the stars are doing.

We would go completely astray, however, if we believed that the only developmental path that is active in the plant is the Sun-dependent one that moves upward from the Earth. In fact, the workings of the stars are combined with the movements of our planetary system that are brought about by the Sun. The Sun force would take possession of plants completely and make them continue into infinity if it, in turn, were not counteracted by the forces of the so-called outer planets and their spirals. In actuality, the planets move in spirals rather than in ellipses.

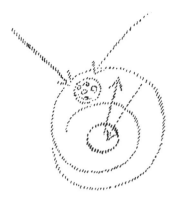

By now, the entire Copernican view of the universe should be reexamined and replaced with another one. We must count Mars, Jupiter, and Saturn as belonging to the so-called outer planets. Uranus and Neptune belong to our solar system only from a purely astronomical point of view; they actually entered the solar system as foreign bodies and were received as "guests," so we are right to disregard them. In any case, the forces of the outer planets cause the upward-directed force to retreat. They bring about the development of flowers and fruit by restraining what would otherwise be expressed only in the spiral of the leaves. If you study plant growth above the leaves, you must attribute its origin to the forces that come about as the result of the Sun working together with Mars, Jupiter, and Saturn.

Not only do these two elements work together, however, but they are also counteracted by what comes from the Moon, in particular, and also from the so-called inner planets, Mercury and Venus. Mercury, Venus, and the Moon engender the downward, Earth-directed tendency in the plant; their most characteristic expression lies in the development of roots. Everything that appears earthly is actually simultaneously influenced by the Moon and the inner planets. You might say that the plant is an expression of our entire solar system. Until we know how this solar system manifests in plants on the one hand and in human beings on the other, we cannot truly grasp the connection between the plant world and the human organism.

All you need to do is look at the fact that when you burn plants that tend to be rooty—that is, plants that are less involved in the process of flower and seed formation than those that tend toward flower formation—or the roots of any plant, the ash has many more constituents than it does when you burn flowers, mistletoe, or woody plants. This difference is simply due to the fact that the forces of the inner planets, the forces of Moon, Mercury, and Venus, have more effect on plants that tend strongly toward root formation. In their ashes, you will find iron, manganese, silica—in short, constituents that are direct remedies and function as such whenever anything derived from these plants is administered. In contrast, you find fewer constituents in the ash that results from burning the opposite type of plants. What is thus expressed in the combustion process is first and foremost a real outer documentation of the fact that the plant belongs not only to what can be found on Earth but also to the entire cosmos.

Look at the process of plant growth more thoroughly. If we are dealing with annual plants, the process breaks off at a certain season and draws to a close in seed formation. Thus we must attribute seed formation primarily to supra-earthly factors. The process is broken off, handed over to the earthly element; something that achieved a certain higher level in the old year must continue at a lower level in the new year. You can see a peculiar process in the totality of plant growth. Imagine that this is the Earth's surface, and here you have the entire plant growing out of the Earth toward the supra-earthly influences.

What is shaped by these influences is returned to the Earth and the cycle begins again. If you consider plant growth as a totality, each year the heavenly forces sink down into the Earth to unite with the Earth's forces and repeat the cycle. Each year, the heavenly forces submerge the flowering, fruiting element into the root element to bring about the cycles to which all plant growth is subject.

This picture points out that when we consider the Earth's flora, we are actually concerned with the interaction between the Earth as a whole and factors beyond Earth. This interaction extends not only to plant structure but also to a plant's internal chemical activity and its entire system of organs. Just as earthly mechanics are overcome in the human form, extratelluric factors also overcome the earthly chemical activity in the plant. But once it has been overcome to a certain extent, it must be reincorporated into the earthly element to produce earthly chemical activity. At this point, you are not far from the realization that earthly chemical activity is outwardly evident in ash and everything ash stands for; that is, earthly chemical activity can be expressed by what falls out of the realm of the living. Non-living substances, however, are subject to gravity, while the upward growth of the plant constantly overcomes gravity and other earth-bound forces, so that we can speak of gravity and light as polar opposites. Light is what constantly overcomes gravity. And in a certain way, the plant is enmeshed in this struggle between heaviness and light, between what longs to become ash and what longs to become fire. Here we are pointed toward the polar opposites of ash formation and what manifests in fire, to the contrast between the tangible and the intangible. Here we have the plant world in its cosmic context.

You will also find, according to our discussions of previous days, that it is impossible to understand the human being without imagining human orientation as polar. I described how, in a plant, what grows from below upward grows in the human being from above downward, and, as a result, in the human being the flowering and fruiting process works downward in sexual and excretory processes while the rooting process works upward. The difference is that this is a process of function in the human being and a process of matter in the plant. From this you can see that we discover something in the human being that is the opposite of what we find in the plant. In the human being, however, we encounter not only the opposite process but also the bearer of that process. At the human being's functional level, you have an element that roots upward and the growing, plantlike element that moves downward; on the other hand, these elements are surrounded by the material aspect, which also tends to move upward from below. In this way a process that would have to be artificially induced in the plant—removing something from the upper sphere and submerging it in the lower—takes place continuously in the human being. The processes whose tendency is to work from above downward and those that work from below upward are always working together. Human illness or health is determined by this interplay. You see, we do not understand complicated human processes at all if we fail to consider what I have just described—that on the one hand a carrier is present that works upward from the Earth, while, on the other hand, a force inserts itself into this carrier and works downward from above.

How human illness and well-being are determined by this interplay of forces can easily be seen when, in some desperation, we confront a very important fact, namely, that the human organism requires quite different therapy depending on whether its upper parts or the parts below the heart come into consideration. The human being must be seen according to different principles in these two instances. This fact is expressed in phenomena such as the often mystifying relationship between craniotabes and ordinary rickets.[27] Those who view the human being as a unity consider these two conditions to be very closely related, though it must be understood that they are governed by different principles, since they originate in opposite parts of the human being. In a significant way, this difference extends even to the healing process. Physicians who report some success in treating rickets with phosphorus will probably not have the slightest success if they apply this treatment to craniotabes, which would need the opposite type of treatment, possibly with some sort of calcium carbonate or the like. I would like to say, however, that this example is only an expression of a very general state of affairs that is somewhat uncomfortable

---

27. *Craniotabes* refers to a progressive decrease in calcification, or emaciation, of the skull.

to mention but is nonetheless very true, namely, that whenever we are dealing with medical treatment of human beings, if any statement can be made, its exact opposite can also be the right solution in certain cases. This, you see, is the fatal aspect of the question. It is completely possible for someone to cite a totally correct course of treatment for one or the other illness, yet it may be no treatment at all for symptoms that appear to be exactly the same, for which the exact opposite course would have to be implemented. As a result, one theory of healing in medicine can always be forced to give way to another if we are not aware that one method of therapy treats only one part of the human being and that another part will require a different therapeutic method. This is what we have to realize.

It is important to take a good look at what we encounter as existing separately in the plant and as one aspect of the human organization. Yesterday I drew your attention to the three formative impulses inherent in the outer, nonhuman natural world—the saltlike and mercurial formative impulses and the impulse consisting of certain substances such as phosphorus or sulfur inasmuch as they are carriers of intangibles and store up the forces of these intangible factors within themselves.

With regard to what I said yesterday, what are the differences among these three formative impulses intrinsic to the nonhuman natural world? All processes that are saltlike or—to put it better—lead to the formation of salts guide inner processes into the domain of gravity. Those who read ancient medical texts would do well to consider the following discussion whenever there is talk of substances becoming saltlike. Through this process, the force of the substance in question becomes subject to gravity, whereas through the opposite process, the light process, intangibles are withdrawn from the force of gravity. If we think of light as representing all other intangibles, we must also imagine the all-pervasive struggle between light and gravity in the nonhuman natural world, the struggle between a force that aspires to become supra-earthly and one that makes earthly substances tend to draw toward the center. What we first see here is the contrast between gravity and light and the constant, alternating search for balance between them. This is expressed by the mercurial principle, which consists of nothing other than the constant search for balance between light and gravity.

The point is to incorporate the differences that exist among the salt-like, phosphoric, and mercurial principles into the context of the entire cosmos—into gravity, into light, and into the contrast between them, the search for balance. You see, in a strange way the entire activity of the human heart finds its place within this contrast. The most disastrous thing about our modern scientific view—aside from the pump theory it applies to the heart, which is totally untenable, as I have already explained—is that it thinks every activity has to runs its course entirely within the confines of the skin of the being in question. Today we imagine the heart's connections as being more or less limited to what is pulsing through the body, but this is not the case. Through having organs, the human being is incorporated into the entire cosmic process, and the human heart not only is an organ within the human organism but also belongs to this cosmic process. What is played out in the plant in the interaction of influences coming from the inner or outer planets is also played out within the human being, coming to expression in the movements of the heart. The heart's movements are not only an expression of what is going on within but also an imprint of circumstances external to the human being. If you consider the human heart, the entire cosmic process is essentially reflected in it. Human beings are individualized only in that they are beings of soul and spirit. On the other levels, they are incorporated into the entire cosmic process by virtue of the fact—to use one example—that the beating human heart is an expression not of something happening within the individual but of the struggle between light and gravity that is played out in the entire cosmos.

I have often attempted to describe human integration with the cosmos to lay audiences in a crudely illustrative way by making use of the following calculation. If you assume that a human being takes approximately eighteen breaths a minute, you will find that the number of breaths in a twenty-four-hour day comes to 25,920. If you take a single day in the life of a human being, consider that there are 365 days in a year, and assume that the maximum human life span averages 71 years—although people can live to be much older—you come up with almost exactly the same number of days in a human lifetime as there are breaths in a twenty-four hour day—25,915. And if you look at the Sun's course through the entire zodiac—that is, a platonic year, the length of time that the Sun's rising point at the vernal equinox takes to move once around the zodiac—it also takes 25,920 years. This number is a remarkable example of how the human being is connected to the entire cosmos, because the platonic year of the Sun's course through the zodiac turns out to have as many years as there are days in a human lifetime.

This circumstance can be illustrated quite concretely, but it leads us into extraordinary depths in the existence of the cosmos. You simply need to keep in mind something else that we have to emphasize in Anthroposophy—that the I and the astral body withdraw from the physical and etheric bodies when a human being sleeps and move back in when the person wakes up. Simply imagine this as a sort of exhalation and inhalation of the soul and spirit by the physical body, and you have 25,915 or 25,920 (leap years account for the discrepancy) of the type of breaths that are completed during a human lifetime, which must constitute a day on some other level. And, in turn, there must be something in the cosmos that relates an apparent revolution of the Sun to this same number.

Here you have a rhythm in the cosmos that is expressed first on the grand scale, then in an individual human lifetime, and then in the respiratory processes of a single day. It will no longer seem astonishing to you that the prehistoric world of atavistic clairvoyance spoke of the days and nights of Brahma, of the inhalation and exhalation of the cosmos, because people back then had discovered that this cosmic inhalation and exhalation has a microcosmic image in the daily process of human life.

It is through such very concretely based observations, and not through sympathies or antipathies of any sort, that we actually achieve a real reverence for ancient wisdom. I can assure you that I myself would be no admirer of ancient wisdom if I had not convinced myself in countless instances that we are now rediscovering ancient truths that had totally disappeared in the interim. Anyone who truly strives for insight does not learn to revere ancient wisdom because of some general attraction to it. This reverence develops directly out of an understanding of very concrete relationships.

If we want to find the light-like element, we must look at everything that lies beyond the Sun in our solar system, at Mars, Jupiter, and Saturn. And since everything that happens on the Earth is in some sense a result of forces that exist outside the Earth, we must look for the effects of cosmic events in the earthly element. Consequently, we do not look for reasons for the configuration or the solid state of earthly substances in as abstract and fantastical a way as modern molecular physics or molecular and atomic chemistry do. Atomic chemistry looks into subjects we cannot really look into, namely, the innermost constitution of solid bodies. It comes up with all kinds of fine notions about atoms and molecules and then talks about its "astronomical understanding" of what is going on inside a solid structure. (This may not be so much the case today, but it is how scientists were talking very proudly a few decades ago.) Today these inner workings are being photographed, as I said in my public lecture the day before yesterday.[28] In spiritualist circles, however, photographs of spirits are also being taken. And since today's scientists are not inclined to believe in spirit photography, they should allow others who understand these matters to refuse to believe in their photographs of atoms, which are subject to the same factors as spirit photography.

The forces we are concerned with in plants are not the same as the forces that are bound to atoms and molecules. The forces in plants work into earthly substance from outside the Earth. In an earthly substance, it is not those demonic little atoms and molecules that cause its configuration, but rather the cosmic forces that are working in a particular way. Let us say that a constellation outside the Earth consists of Saturn being in a position to work on a certain location on Earth in an especially beneficial way and that its effect is most advantageous when other lines of influence—the effects of the Sun, Mars,

---

28. "Anthroposophy and the Modern Sciences," a lecture given on March 24, 1920, published in volume 5 of *Geisteswissenschaft und die Lebensforderungen der Gegenwart* [Spiritual science and the demands of modern life], Dornach 1950.

and so forth—are as far away from its own as possible and do not lie in or near its path. In this instance, Saturn is working alone in a certain respect. If, for other reasons, our Earth is then especially receptive or favorably disposed to these Saturn forces at the location in question, the Saturn forces, which in this case are influenced very little by other extratelluric forces, bring about a particular structure in earthly matter that is different from what is produced when Mars, for example, works under the same conditions. Earthly substances are nothing other than the products of the interaction of stellar forces. In the example I have chosen here, where Saturn works on certain parts of the Earth for longer periods of time and under favorable circumstances, its effects become visible in the product. We are dealing here with the coming about of lead.

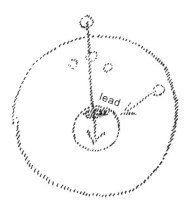

This is the reason why certain earthly substances, especially metals, must be linked to certain constellations in the extratelluric cosmos. Here again, there is an inevitable parallelism between what modern spiritual-scientific research has to offer and what was formerly offered by ancient wisdom, which can be understood today only if it is discovered anew. These ancient writings are almost unreadable for modern individuals who think in terms of chemistry or physics. This can be illustrated by an example recorded by a very intelligent Scandinavian scholar in his history of alchemy. He described a process that, as he very correctly stated, is nonsense according to modern chemical concepts because it does not lead to any discovery.[29] The process in question was a lead process, but this worthy gentleman failed to realize that the explanation applied to the process of seed formation.[30] Instead, he believed that it applied to a process taking place in the laboratory, and on that level it is indeed nonsense. Because the terminology needs to be transferred to an entirely different level, we must think of meanings other than the usual when we read certain expressions; because he did not realize this, for him it was nonsense. And he was both right and wrong.

We cannot avoid bringing earthly substances into connection with the forces that work on the Earth from its surroundings. Especially the study of metals, if carried out in ways that I will describe in these lectures, brings us to very specific connections, such that we must attribute lead first and foremost to the undisturbed effects of Saturn, tin to the undisturbed effects of Jupiter, iron to Mars, copper to Venus, and what chemistry now calls mercury to the planet of the same name. This is why the ancients gave the name Mercury to both the planet and the metal. We must also recognize the relationship of everything that is like silver in character—I very deliberately said *like* silver—to the undisturbed effects of the Moon. It is really amusing to read in modern scientific literature that silver's relationship to the Moon was suggested by the Moon's silvery sheen and that people thought only in terms of this outer characteristic. Anyone who knows how carefully the ancient studies of individual metals were conducted, in their own way, will not succumb to this sort of error.

You will see that there is also ample opportunity for other substances to develop, because the ones that I listed—lead, tin, iron, copper, mercury, and silver—are only the most outstanding examples. The fact that other planetary influences competed with those just mentioned—for example, the lines of influence of Mars and Saturn could have intersected—made it possible for other substances to arise. This

---

29. Theodor Svedberg (1884–1971), Swedish chemist who received the Nobel prize for chemistry in 1926. Presumably this comment refers to his book *Matter* (1912), which appeared in German translation in 1914.
30. The word "lead" is missing in the German typescript of this lecture and was inserted because of its correspondence to the process of seed formation.

is how the less representative metals came about. In any case, we must see the Earth's metals as resulting from the influence of extratelluric forces. At this point, however, what is expressed in the workings of metals merges with what we see in plant development, because if you take the active principles in lead, tin, or iron, these same principles must also be inherent in all aspects of the development of flowers and seeds, insofar as these processes take place outside the earthly element and above the surface of the Earth. Similarly, all aspects of plant root formation must be connected to everything that is coppery, mercurial, or silvery in character.

While the mercurial principle exists as a certain balance on the one hand, on the other you will naturally have to look for a different balance. Mercury is the balance between earthly and supra-earthly factors. In reality, however, our entire universe is pervaded with spirit, and here another polarity sets in. If you imagine the earthly element here and there the supra-earthly element, you have the contrast between light and gravity in the earthly and supra-earthly factors, but this gives you only the possibility of looking at a balance between these two factors.

There is also another state of balance between the all-pervading element that does not distinguish between earthly and extratelluric and the elements it pervades—that is, between spirit and matter, regardless of whether matter is construed as tangible or intangible. At every point in the material element, even in the cosmos, the balance must be maintained between matter and the spirit. The nearest cosmic body that maintains this balance is the Sun itself. The Sun holds the balance between the spiritual and the material in the cosmos. For this reason the Sun, you might say, is a cosmic body that both maintains order in the solar system and brings order into the forces pervading our material system. Just as we can establish the connection of individual planets to the metals, as I described earlier, we can also establish that there is a connection between the Sun and gold. In this instance, too, the ancients valued gold for its connection to the balance between spirit and matter rather than for its ahrimanic value.

It is important to always keep in mind that in the natural world, things that we separate both in our thoughts and in anything we accomplish on Earth are always united in some way. In our thoughts,

we separate what is subject to gravity (and therefore tends toward salt formation) both from the bearers of light, which tend toward the effects of light, and from what forms the basis of the balance between the two. There is no such separation, however, in the natural world. In nature, these ways of working are united with one another and interpenetrate, forming very intricate structural systems. These intricate edifices are present in the gleam of gold, because through gold, in a certain way, the spiritual element in its pure form looks into the outer world. This makes us aware of something I would like to note parenthetically, because you may be able to work very fruitfully toward putting the impulses that can still be gained from ancient medical literature to good use in modern literature. If you write dissertations such as those I mentioned yesterday, ancient literature will offer many a stimulus if you understand it correctly.

It is extremely important to note that this ancient literature sees three principles—the saltlike, mercurial, and phosphoric (or sulfurlike) principles—coming together in some sort of connection in every substance. We must also note that the ancients were very concerned with separating these three principles out of any substance. They held the view that lead comes about as we have indicated here, but that lead, just like gold or copper, contains all three principles, the saltlike, the mercurial, and the phosphoric. The important point here is that we can use these principles to treat the human being if we extricate them from their combinations in some way. In ancient chemistry, the greatest care was devoted to this process, which was found to be most difficult in the case of gold. This is the reason for the Latin saying *Facilius est aurum facere quam destruere* ("It is easier to make gold than to destroy it"). This is really one of the examples that makes us revere ancient knowledge, because people thought that the three essential principles of nature—the saltlike, the mercurial, and the phosphoric—were so strongly connected to each other in gold that it would be more difficult to extract them from that substance than from any other.

It is absolutely true that if we ourselves were to proceed today exactly as the ancients did in the process of extricating these three principles of nature, it would not be easy for us to accomplish it. But if we totally disregard ancient knowledge, as should happen in these lectures (after all, we are shedding only occasional light on the ancient literature), and investigate what can still be researched today, we discover that in order to extract these three necessary principles from natural substances, the substances in question must undergo a certain process of combustion. Through this combustion process, for example, the fire-bearing, light-bearing principle is driven off first. For certain purposes, we would then have to continue, extracting the mercurial principle from these natural substances so that in the end everything remaining tends in the direction of the salty principle and can be extracted with an acidic substance, yielding a truly saltlike remedy, whether from plants or from minerals. I will go into more detail later. Thus, we must either look for a light-bearing substance in nature from which to derive the extratelluric element; attempt to extract this extratelluric element from earthly substances, leaving behind the truly saltlike components, if those are what we need; or try to extract a substance that represents the balance between these two poles.

At this point we can take either one of two routes, which are different in character even though both lead to the same goal, at least to a certain extent. It is also possible to take both routes. We can take the perspective of ancient physicians, who were always intent on extracting what they viewed as phosphorus, salt, or mercury from familiar substances and then making use of it. For them, the distinct and specific effects of remedies resulted from differences between them that were due to their having been derived from lead or from copper; that is, they took the origin of the substance into account. As far as they were concerned, when they produced a salt from lead, it was different in character from a salt produced from copper. Even when they said "salt," they meant that the particular salt was one of a variety of salts. Simply by being a salt, it was earthly, but by being a salt derived from one of a variety of metals, it was extratelluric and had a connection to the varied aspects of the human being that we will be able to characterize first thing tomorrow. This is one of the routes that medicine can take in producing saltlike remedies.

We can also take the route that was chosen after the ancient route was obscured but at a time when people still had the distinct feeling that the human being was more than just a test tube. In this case, we simply attempt to take what is present and to make the underlying forces in existing substances useful through potentization. This is the method inherent in Hahnemann's school of thought in particular.[31] It represents a new ascent away from the entire school of medical thinking that developed after the old ways had been obscured, when people no longer knew anything about any supra-earthly connections or the like.

This is the reason for the desperation of the modern medical profession—that modern medicine no longer looks at the extratelluric element that underlies the earthly and always attempts to make do with exclusively earthly substances and forces. The homeopathic system attempts to transcend this limitation, as do physical or naturopathic methods of therapy, which resort to direct applications of mercury, light, or air because they no longer have access to insight into the right way of using phosphorus, the light bearer, or the carriers of air. Of course, this constitutes a third route.

But a true and favorable route will open up again only when spiritual science allows us to penetrate once more the connection between the mineral element and the supra-earthly, between the plant kingdom and the supra-earthly, and between the animal kingdom and the supra-earthly. By the time we get to the animal kingdom—as I pointed out yesterday—we are already questionably close to the human being. The ancients drew the line here, at a boundary that we must seek to reestablish on the basis of more recent research. They said that plants lie within the realm of the solar system, as do minerals, but that when we get to the animal world, we leave the solar system and are much less free to experiment with the things we find there in ways that were permissible as long as we remained within the planetary realm of extratelluric activity. The forces leading to the development of animals and especially of humans are much farther away and much more spread out in the cosmos than the forces in minerals and plants. The ancients drew the zodiac as a boundary so that people would not look for therapeutic forces beyond what was

31. See note 8, p. 9.

present in plants or minerals, or would at least be aware that they were entering a questionable zone.

Today, however, this zone has been entered along a route that I began to characterize yesterday. We will discuss this in more detail when we come to specialized aspects of pathology and serotherapy. Such routes usually lead to detailed measures, and as a consequence they call forth very strong illusions that completely mask the dangers lurking behind them.

7

YESTERDAY I drew your attention to several considerations that we must take as our basis for understanding how human beings adapt to earthly and cosmic circumstances. These aspects, which were more spatial in character, must be combined with temporal aspects, because we must never forget that the human being must be seen as a totality. As a whole, each human being is in some respects a child, an adult, and an elderly person and is organized in such a way that these three essential developmental stages are actually present simultaneously. What we accomplish along these lines today will then have to be brought together with the supersensible aspect; only then will we be able to move on to more detailed considerations. Above all, I would like to make you aware that just as pedagogy is forced to pay attention to the difference between the various stages of childhood—from birth to the second dentition, from the second dentition to puberty, and so on—any aspect of medicine must also consider the entire human being from birth to death. As I said earlier, I will use our customary anthroposophical expressions to begin with. Toward the end I will explore possible ways of translating these expressions for outsiders. This translation process will be easier once we have progressed a little further in our studies.

First and foremost, we will need to realize in looking at childhood, for example, that the inherent functions of the I and the astral body, as we call these things, are in the process of just being integrated into the human being at this age. During childhood, these functions are first integrated into the organic aspect in such a way as to then be able to work with the child's flexible and elastic organic substance. At this particular stage, and especially during the ages from seven to about fourteen, fifteen, or sixteen—which is the time when the etheric body must have consolidated its position in relationship to the physical body so that puberty can begin—it is not surprising to note the appearance of disturbances having to do with integrating the higher aspect of the human being into the lower. In many cases, it is possible that the elasticity of the physical body and that of the etheric body do not coincide.

It is essentially the task of the astral body to bring about a balance between these physical and etheric elasticities. If they do not work together, the astral body is often obliged to strengthen its forces, and if these forces remain inadequate, the disease symptoms that then appear will require outside intervention. This is why it is common to find disease symptoms in childhood that are discharged on the physical level, as in [Sydenham's] chorea, for instance.[32] All illnesses leading to such syndromes, in which nervous or psychological disturbances occur in addition to what is happening on the organic level, are related to the somewhat unaccustomed work the astral body is being called upon to perform to balance the elasticity of the physical and etheric bodies.

If chorea-like symptoms appear during pregnancy, the cause will be only too obvious. Pregnancy, of course, disrupts the harmony between the elasticity of the physical and etheric bodies, so once again you must expect the astral body to behave as it does in childhood. Therefore, in such illnesses, which occur in children and sometimes also as concomitant symptoms during pregnancy, we will have to seek remedies that increase the astral body's overall effectiveness so that its functions fall into line with its task of balancing the elasticity of the physical and etheric bodies. These are questions that will be discussed in the next few days.

In contrast—and this is why I emphasized the importance of taking the patients' ages into account—you will find that diseases tending

---

32. Sydenham's chorea typically occurs in children and adolescents (also called St. Vitus's dance). Along with Sydenham's (contracted by infection), the best-known form of chorea is Huntington's (a hereditary disease), which generally occurs in adults.

toward polyarthritis or other related symptoms appear most frequently from the mid-teens to late twenties. During this time, the astral body itself must establish the right relationship to the physical and etheric bodies. If it is insufficiently prepared—for example, if the right things have not been done in childhood to prepare it—it will be unable to bring about the right relationship. As a consequence, disease symptoms will appear either at this age or in the next stage of life.

This is the important point—to include the time factor in our study of illnesses. If I may be permitted to express myself somewhat one-sidedly, we must not assume that nature has arranged the human organism in a way that makes it as easy and comfortable as possible for us to simply read off the cure. We tend to mistakenly assume that it should be as easy as possible to discover how to cure a patient.

In a certain respect, the law of similars, the principle of "like cures like," is correct. It may happen, however, that the primary syndrome occurs in one stage of life, but the remedy can induce similar symptoms only during a different stage. For example, certain medications may provoke a disease process, a specific complex of symptoms, in a person who has not yet reached the age of twenty, but those same medications may become true remedies in a later stage of the person's life. This is what must be considered when we hear the frequently emphasized statement "like cures like."

If we want to look at the overall state of health of an individual, whether healthy or sick, it is essential to know that in a certain sense the human being lives through two polar opposite stages of life and is exposed to different influences in youth—specifically the influences of Saturn, Jupiter, and Mars, the planets beyond the Sun—than at a later age, when the individual is more influenced by the inner planets, Venus, Mercury, and Moon, if I need to name them in accordance with what we said yesterday. The Moon influence, however, appears earliest and most obviously.

This example points out once again that we must always combine the spatial factor with the temporal in studying the human being. Only if we do so will we be able to see in the right light certain phenomena that appear during a person's lifetime. Later, when we focus on details, we will also constantly touch on how we must proceed in order to see these relationships that are so necessary for understanding the human being in the right light.

You see, what works on the human being commences before birth and even before conception. In researching these issues, I have often wondered why so many disease processes in conventional medical literature are described as being of unknown origin, "etiology unknown." This stems from a total disregard for the fact that the extratelluric complex of forces we pointed to yesterday is already present as an individual approaches conception—not only birth, but also conception—and that all the forces that work on an individual in this way later produce the opposite effects. This means that certain processes present before conception produce countereffects after conception, or especially after birth. Sometimes all we can observe is what begins to take effect in a person's life after birth, a countereffect of sorts to what was present before conception in the overall context of natural existence.

What I have just said relates especially strongly to everything having to do with ossification and sclerosis. These are processes that have counterparts in the time before conception. As entirely normal, organic, formative processes, they counter the process of expansion or dispersion that is active in the human being prior to conception. It is extremely important to look at this fact. We will not be able to control the sclerotic process if we cannot relate it in this way to a supra-human and extratelluric process that precedes conception, even if this extratelluric principle later appears within the human being, either after birth or beginning with conception.

All of these necessary forces can also overstep a certain boundary— the midpoint of their oscillation, so to speak. In some respects, processes such as sclerosis or ossification oscillate around a midpoint, and it is possible for them to overshoot the mark and become too strong. They then appear in a very different form. Initially, they appear as predispositions, which reveal a great deal about the essential nature of an individual. If a normal process of ossification or sclerosis, or one that becomes abnormal only in its own domain in the course of a person's lifetime, swings to the other side, so that it takes place not in its own domain but in some other organ system, then the pathological counterimage of a preconceptional process appears. This is what we encounter in the various types of carcinoma.

It is possible to look at these questions only if we really try to understand the human being's entire development and existence. Without that understanding—that is, if we cannot relate it to anything that must work within the individual in some way but has become distorted and has shifted its activity to a different domain—a condition such as carcinoma will always remain a relatively unknown factor in human life.

Another condition, namely, the phenomenon of infantile hydrocephaly, must also be considered in a similar way. Actually, hydrocephaly must exist, and we are all predisposed to it. If it did not exist, the human brain and nervous system would never be able to develop in the right way, because they must be derived from the fluid element that is present within the human being. In childhood, therefore, a struggle is always apparent between hydrocephaly and the process that takes place in the human organization in order to combat it. We should actually never speak of hydrocephaly alone but should also include its opposite, the loss of too much water in the brain. The latter, a disease that tends to be overlooked, is simply the necessary opposite of hydrocephaly. As little children, we alternate between the two extremes of hydrocephaly and, later, its opposite.

It can happen—and we will consider the treatment more closely later—that we may overlook an important factor in this connection. We may disregard the fact that there is an appropriate the moment for hydrocephaly to disappear more or less completely and try to eliminate the hydrocephalic tendency too early, whether through education, diet, or treatment in childhood or in infancy. It is quite possible to make hydrocephaly disappear too early, and if we do so, we will definitely encounter the harm that can be done by failing to consider the person's entire life span. Once again, let me point out that this subject would support an entire army of medical theses if we were simply willing to look for the connection between the hydrocephalic process in childhood and syphilis or the predisposition to syphilis in later life. There is nothing to be gained by tracking down microorganisms in this instance. There is truly something to be gained only when we are capable of encompassing factors such as I have just laid out. It would do a great deal to prevent syphilis if we made the effort to safeguard people in earliest childhood against what can later appear as syphilitic symptoms, which vary considerably, as we shall hear later.

In the course of diagnosis, it is always necessary to remember such connections and to go back to the actual cause as revealed by the course of an individual's development. In this context, the following point is tremendously significant. It can be said that a shift occurs in the entire organic process, both the process in the upper part of the human being that moves down toward the heart and the process in the lower human being that moves upward toward the heart from the lower part of the abdomen. The human being's entire formative process pushes toward the heart, the actual damming-up organ, from both sides. However, this push takes place during different stages of life. If we tackle the symptoms, if we learn how to look at all the symptoms that appear especially at a younger age and may ultimately lead to pneumonia or pleurisy in childhood, if we add up everything that plays into these processes, then we discover that this is a displaced process, a process that has shifted. It is the same as the process that comes to expression as hydrocephaly at an even earlier age. It is simply hydrocephaly that has been displaced to a lower level in the human organization, where it develops into a predisposition to pneumonia, pleuritic symptoms, or related childhood symptoms.

All of these childhood symptoms have counterpart processes in later life; that is, they return later, but as their polar opposites. Many people would be able to understand all of the processes played out in endocarditis, for example (even acute endocarditis), if they merely investigated the course of disease symptoms earlier in life connected with pneumonia or pleurisy. This should help us to ensure that pneumonia and pleuritic symptoms are not suppressed prematurely or too quickly in children. Parents and teachers naturally want to get rid of such symptoms as quickly as possible, but in these disease states in particular it is really very important to allow them their own destiny. As a physician, you should intervene only to divert conditions that would otherwise cause damage. Aside from this, you should allow the disease process to run its course to the very end. It is never more important than with the symptoms related to childhood pneumonia or pleurisy—and certain others as well—to implement some kind of physical (or, as it is now called, "naturopathic") treatment. In other words, try to allow the disease process as much as possible to run its normal course without speeding it up or cutting it off prematurely. This is important, because such a disease process, if cut off too soon, leads relatively quickly to a predisposition to cardiac disease and related syndromes, and it leads especially to a predisposition to such conditions as polyarthritis. Consequently, it is particularly important to avoid disrupting the disease process in this realm. For many people, simply by not intervening in the intentions of pleurisy and pneumonia, we could eliminate predispositions to all kinds of illnesses that later manifest as cardiac irregularities. The cohesiveness of a person's entire course of development is evident here.

At this point we might also remind ourselves of the need to look at the milder cases of illness that are more easily cured, and not just at the more extreme cases of truly serious illnesses. In fact, at times we may be unable to tell whether we have brought about a cure; or we may simply need to tell a patient not to insist on treatment, since the condition will get better by itself. It can be very important to not do too much curing. There is nothing wrong with being cured, of course, but we must also consider the many individuals who, to their own way of thinking, have experienced all sorts of illness—those who have survived so many different medications and methods of treatment that when they are older (and they are always sick) it is difficult to find anything that reassures them. It would be better to help people understand that in most cases they are not as sick as they think they are. This approach, of course, also has its negative aspects, but it is certainly proper to mention it in this context.

Now, however, you must see all of these matters in view of the fact that the human being is complicated and consists of various members: a physical organization; an etheric organization, which has a great deal of work to do between the ages of seven and fourteen in order to penetrate into the physical organism, only to be driven out again during conditions such as pregnancy; an astral body, which begins to work its way in effectively only after the age of fourteen; and the I, which finds its way in even later, but in the meantime must not be thought of as outside the body. In the waking state, the I is never outside the organism. The integration of the I into the organism enhances the cooperative work that takes place there. In any disturbance in the organism, we are always dealing with the fact that the I is experiencing certain difficulties in asserting itself within the other members in the right way.

It must be said that modern medicine (though it is unaware of this) has the capacity to show how the I struggles to come to terms with the other three human organizations; it illustrates in an extremely instructive way the struggle of the I with the other three bodies. We simply fail to recognize these illustrations for what they are, because we live in an age whose philosophy of life is materialistic. Each time you chart a real fever curve, however, you see a precise imprint of the struggle I just characterized. To gain insight into this relationship, there is nothing more illustrative than tracing the fever curves of various disease states. Admittedly, this exercise may be much less important for therapy than it is for pathology, but we do need to understand something about these matters, at least in a general way. You see, understanding a condition like pneumonia or typhoid fever depends on coming to an understanding about the course of the fever as plotted on the chart below.

When you study the two main types of fever curves in pneumonia and compare the fever curves of crisis and lysis, you can see how differently the I—whose intervention in the organism has been disturbed—handles its response in these two instances. In pneumonia, for example, the fever curve (which I am sketching only schematically) shows first the struggle and then the rebound of the I when the patient's temperature takes a critical dive below normal.

The previous exertions of the I enable it later to effect the rebound. In the other, more lytic course of the illness, it is less possible for the I to incorporate the reactions into its own forces, which is why the other, more irregular drop in temperature is the more dangerous course. If you consider the fever curve in typhoid fever, however, you will be able to see especially closely into the entire work of the I as it confronts the other three organizations. There you have a graphic image of how the I actually struggles.

This example shows that the merger of science and medicine makes it necessary to consider these different human organizations. All the confusion in medical science is due entirely to the fact that science has become materialistic and has restricted itself to observing only the processes of the physical body, whose processes, however, are never independent. Above all, they do not all have equal value in their own way. You see, any given process in the physical body may depend on the fact that the etheric body, or perhaps the astral body or the I, is working in it. These are all physical processes, but they become specialized and the character they assume may vary greatly depending upon which one of the higher members is at work in that part of the physical organization.

Taking all of what I said yesterday about human dependence on supra-earthly and earthly principles and combining it with what I added today about the human being's temporal course of development, you will realize something that will be helpful with regard to how to conduct the type of investigation that I am discussing. You will realize that forces are constantly being exerted upon the human being. Initially, these are either extratelluric forces or telluric forces, which work in the opposite direction. In other words, they are either forces that come from Saturn, Jupiter, and Mars or ones that come from Venus, Mercury, and the Moon, the latter having been transformed into telluric influences. With regard to the relationship between the Earth and the Moon, it is very easy to deceive ourselves about what is going on. It is easy to think that the Moon is up there and exerts its influence from above. But this is incomplete thinking. The Moon is more than just the Earth's companion, revolving around it. The same force that is inherent in the Moon and works on the Earth from above is also present within the Earth itself. The Earth has its own moonlike nature, which works out of the Earth from the inside [see drawing].

On the physical plane, all the processes that manifest in ebb and flood tides and in many other phenomena—menstruation, for example—are lunar effects rather than actual telluric effects, but they do not result from the direct influence of the Moon, as more recent theories would have it, but rather from the Earth's own moonlike nature. That is why there is an outward correspondence but generally no direct temporal connection between these things. Similarly, when we talk about one of the inner planets, we must also look for its counterimage within the Earth and then its more physical effects. We must imagine that it is working back onto the physical plane from the terrestrial element.

What comes about more on the level of soul and spirit must be attributed directly to the planets outside the Earth. In the case of the Moon, it works as follows: The Moon casts certain formative forces onto the Earth, which come to expression by stimulating creative imagination in human beings. The Moon has a great influence on the soul's imaginative creativity. Although they are not adequately taken into account in this materialistic age, such influences are definitely present and will have to be studied at some point. On the level of soul and spirit, the Moon has a strong effect on human creative imagination. The counterimage, the Moon's effect on the organic level, affects the human organization from the opposite direction, working out of the Earth's moonlike nature. This influence is what needs to be taken into account. It also applies to the inner planets that are farther away than the Moon.

As we have seen, telluric localized forces—that is, terrestrial forces—and extratelluric localized forces work on the human being in many different ways. We can study these forces only when we see the result of their cooperative interaction in the entire human being—never in any single part of the human being and least of all in the single cell. Please take note of this—especially not in the single cell. For what is a cell? A cell is something that stubbornly asserts itself in its own growth and its own life in opposition to what the human being really is. If, on the one hand, you see the entire form of the human being as it is built up by telluric and extratelluric influences, and on the other hand you consider the cell, you see the cell as a ghostly intrusion into the plans of these initial influences, which it destroys because it wants to develop a life of its own. In the human organism, we are constantly struggling against cellular life. The most crassly absurd view has come about because of cellular pathology and cellular physiology, which take cells as the basis of all life and see the human organism as composed of cells. Actually, the human body is an entirety, an entity that is connected to the cosmos, and as such it always has to combat the stubborn independence of its cells. Essentially, the cell, rather than building up our organism, constantly disturbs it. But of course, now that the basic views of cellular pathology and physiology have infiltrated how we look at everything else, it is not surprising that people come up with the most topsy-turvy ideas about the human body and everything related to it.

In a certain way, therefore, we encounter two opposing sets of forces in the human developmental process and the cellular process. Our organs lie between these two sets of forces, and whether an organ develops into a liver or a heart or some other organ depends on which set of forces preponderates. Each organ represents an ongoing balancing act between the two sets of forces I have described. Some of our organs tend at times more toward the cellular aspect, which is then combated by the cosmic aspect, but there are also organs—we will describe them in detail later—in which the cosmic aspect predominates and the cellular moves into the background. From this perspective, it is especially interesting to consider the organs that are located between the genitourinary tract and the heart. This system of organs demonstrates the greatest similarity to the real intentions of the cells. If you examine the entire human being and consider all the individual organs, you will find the greatest similarity between organs and cell life in this particular part of the body.

This leads us to ask, what is actually going on with the cells? Let us exaggerate a little and say that a cell develops a life of its own. The cell develops a life of its own, but this life is continually being counteracted by another influence from outside, by an outer factor that takes the life away from the cell or from the cell's formative forces. It sucks the life out of the cell, leaving it with a droplike shape. It needs to become common knowledge that everything on Earth that assumes a drop shape, regardless of whether it is inside or outside the human being, is the result of two forces, one that wants to manifest life and another that sucks the life out of the first.

If we look into ancient medicine's ideas of the mercurial principle, it is interesting to note that the physicians of antiquity saw it as the principle whose life was taken away, leaving it in the form of a drop. In the mercurial principle, they saw something that wanted to become a cell, an independent living drop, but was prevented from doing so by the planetary influences of Mercury and thus became a droplet of mercury, the mere corpse of a cell. There you have the intermediate state between the salt and the phosphoric principles, and at the same time you can glimpse the admittedly very complicated route we must take to discover how planetary influences are played out in what we encounter on Earth. Each drop of mercury would be a living being if the planet Mercury were not there. And everything in us that tends most strongly toward the cellular aspect—that is, the part of the human being that I just mentioned as lying between the organs of elimination and the heart—is most dependent on being exposed to the planetary influence of Mercury in the right way. If I may put it like this, it is important that these organs preserve their tendency to maintain the cellular aspect and also that this tendency not be allowed to go so far as to be totally overwhelmed by life. In other words, it is important that these organs continue to be exposed to the Mercury principle that paralyzes life or kills it off. The activity of these organs would immediately become rampant if they did not remain in this intermediate state.

If we continue to pursue this topic even further, we arrive at the connection that exists between these organs and metallic mercury, which represents the Mercury principle. You see, the route we are taking here is a fully rational one. Since it will become increasingly necessary to use outer, sense-perceptible facts to confirm what supersensible perception can discover about humankind's present and future states, you would do well to study, both clinically and in the medical literature, how individual minerals and metals, whether of mineral, plant, or animal origin, actually work on the human organism.

In this connection, we can begin by studying particularly characteristic features. I told you today that a certain preconceptional tendency needs to work to counteract ossification or sclerosis. Ossifying and sclerotic processes, however, have a polar opposite. To make this opposite proliferate, all you need to do is induce lead poisoning in an individual. Of course experiments cannot go so far as to actually induce lead poisoning in order to study arteriosclerosis, so the important thing is to keep this in mind as we follow the symptoms that appear when nature does the experimenting for us. In this way, we can discover the inner relationship between lead itself and the factors within the human being that come from the same forces that are active in lead. Following the process that is active in lead and the processes of ossification and sclerosis in the human being is fully in line with our studies.

Similarly, it would be possible to study the interrelationship between the processes inherent in tin and the interaction I described earlier between hydrocephaly and its opposite. We would find that the same forces that are active in tin are also active in this whole childhood syndrome whose purpose is to bring about the right degree of hardness in the head and the soft tissues.

As we have seen, at a later age this process moves on toward the lungs. We do not need to go very far here; all that is needed is to compile and correctly interpret data that have been noted in the medical literature for centuries. Here we arrive at the intimate relationship between the forces in iron and the process connected to all the symptoms that accompany pneumonia and pleurisy. Once again, we will be able to trace this relationship into the usual process that takes place due to the presence of iron in the blood, where it is more or less normal.[33] If you follow the same process that is played out in the interaction between iron and blood further, into the respiratory system and everything related to it, you will then see how effective iron is in the interaction between hydrocephaly and its opposite, which has shifted into the lungs. You can see how these things interact. Only such interactions and their relationship to what is outside the human being make it possible for us to discover the therapeutic effects of potential remedies.

If we truly valued looking at the human being in this way, observers would undoubtedly develop an intuition of sorts that would be an especially important factor in any diagnosis. In this context, it is important to see many different aspects in connection to each other. With each diagnosis, we should look at the individual's current situation in the world, how this person's life has been until now, and how he or she promises to live in the time to come. What do I mean when I say, "promises to live in the time to come"? In a certain way, what a person will experience in the future, especially on the organic level, is definitely present in the form of a potential already present within the individual.

If we look for the connection between all I have now said about the effects of lead, tin, and iron on the human organism and the effects that can emanate from other metals, we find that in some sense the effects we have already discussed are the polar opposites of those of copper, mercury, and silver. What I have just said is not intended to promote any specific remedies, but I do need to point out the existence of very specific interactions between the configuration of forces in these metals and in other substances and the formative forces of the human organism itself. Thus, certain forces such as those associated with copper will counteract in some way those associated with iron. This will show us which other forces we must use when forces of a certain type, such as those of iron, are present and working too strongly. For example, we will find that very specific pathological symptoms in the human organism show that the iron forces must be too strong.

---

33. See lecture 3, pp. 49 ff.

Then it is important to administer copper or a similar remedy, which could also be derived from the plant kingdom.

Today's many-sided overview may have asked a bit much of you. I simply hope that if you look at some of what I presented today, you will be able to see how these questions need to be worked out further in order to yield very fruitful results for transforming medical education and our entire system of medicine.

LECTURE 8

DORNACH, MARCH 28, 1920

W HAT we refer to by saying "ether body," "astral body," and so on—terms we must use to abbreviate or simplify our ideas—can definitely be traced to how they are imprinted in a certain sense in physical processes. It's just that today we are not inclined to correctly associate what is expressed through physical processes with the spiritual foundation of existence. We absolutely must make these associations, however, in order to spiritualize our methods of thinking and observation in the field of medicine. For example, we must investigate how the interplay between what we call the etheric and physical bodies takes place. You know that this interplay takes place within the human being, and we spoke yesterday of one aspect of it, an irregularity that can develop with regard to how the astral body affects it.

This same interplay also takes place outside, however, in nature external to the human being. If you follow this thought through to the end, you will have a thorough insight into the human being's connection to nonhuman nature. When you look out into nature, you are surrounded by all the individual species of plants (let's focus on plants for today), and you become aware of this flora through various senses. If you do this, you can get at least an inkling of the interaction that takes place first of all between this flora and the Earth's entire atmosphere, and second between the plants and the planetary or astral realm that lies outside this earthly sphere. We might say that when we consider the Earth's flora, if this is the Earth's surface, the plants point us in the direction of the atmosphere and the astral or starry realm [see drawing]. They point to the extratelluric principle. Even without going into the esoteric aspects, we can sense the living interaction taking place out there between the phenomenon of plants bursting into flowers and fruits and influences coming from the great expanses of the universe.

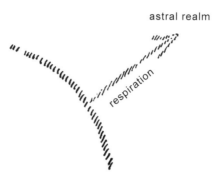

Next, let us turn away from all this and direct our thoughts inward, into ourselves. (This view requires a little help from intuition, but as I have already said, absolutely nothing works in medicine without intuition.) If we redirect our thoughts away from the outer world and into ourselves, we discover a certain relationship to what is outside. Since we must realize that in the plant world, the etheric aspect is intimately connected to the physical, we must also sense that there is a certain relationship between the etheric-physical connection in the plant world and their connection within the human being.

It is important to acknowledge what it is that enables us to speak outwardly and concretely about this relationship between the etheric and the physical. Initially, we can say quite abstractly that because it opens upward, the etheric factor is closer to the astral than to the physical. We will also have to realize that the etheric does have some kind of connection to the physical. We will have to examine this dual relationship of the etheric to the physical on the one hand and the astral on the other, and we will have to look for some way of being guided into this relationship. I would now like to show you as concretely as possible how this can happen.

Let us imagine that you are walking down an avenue that is lined with flowering linden trees. As you walk along, try to be very aware of passing through their scent, and be aware, too, that a process is taking place between that aroma and the nervelike network spreading throughout your organs of smell. If you pay attention to this process, you become aware of the inner factor that is capable of perceiving smell; this factor is shooting upward to meet the linden scent. You must realize that in the process taking place here an inner element comes forth to meet an outer one, and that these two elements some- how bring a process to completion because of the inner relationship between them. Your actual perception of the scent internalizes an external element dispersed by the scent of the flowering trees, an ele- ment that is undoubtedly based on how the plants interact with their entire extra-earthly environment and open themselves up to it. Because you perceive, a force present within you must be working from the etheric body into the astral body, because otherwise you would be unable to perceive, and the whole process would take place only on the level of life functions. In perceiving smell, the very process itself is evidence of the astral body's involvement. But while this rela- tionship to the outer world is being disclosed, you also realize that the development of the sweetish scent given off by the linden blossoms is somehow related to or is the opposite pole of what is going on in your organs of smell. In fact, in the linden blossoms' pervasive scent, we rec- ognize the interaction of the etheric element in the plant with the sur- rounding element, the astral element that pervades universal space. As the perceptive process is played out, we participate in the aspect of the plant world that is related to the extratelluric astral element.

Now let us choose any taste, just to have an example that relates to the previous one. A similar process occurs when we taste the flavor of licorice or sweet grapes, but in this case the process takes place in our organs of taste as opposed to our organs of smell. You know how closely related our organs of taste and smell are, so you will immedi- ately have some idea of how closely the processes of tasting and smell- ing are related with regard to the whole course of natural events. You must also be clear, however, that tasting is a much more organic and inward process than smelling. Smelling takes place closer to the sur- face and participates in processes of the nonhuman outer world that dissipate or are dispersed in space. This is not the case with tasting.

Through tasting, you discover certain properties that necessarily lie within substances and that must therefore be bound up with the substantial element itself. Through tasting more than through smelling, you discover the internal character of substances—in this case of plant substances. And you simply need a bit of help from your intuition to realize that everything that has to do with solidification in plants, with organic solidification, is revealed or disclosed by tasting what is in the plant. However, the plant kingdom resists becoming solid, as is demonstrated by the substances that cause plants to become aromatic. You will not be able to doubt that the process of tasting is related to the etheric's connection to the physical.

Now, take smelling and tasting together. Surrounded by plant odors and taste, you are in the midst of the etheric's dual connection to the astral and the physical. You go right into the etheric, or rather into its imprint, when you pay attention to smelling and tasting. The seat of smelling and tasting in the human being is a revelation within the physical world of the etheric's connections to the astral and the physical. In some respects we remain on the surface of the human being when we investigate the processes of smelling and tasting. But you see, the important point today is that in our efforts to fructify real science, we finally go beyond the abstract and the mystical and move on to concretely grasp the spirit. What good does it do if people talk on and on about grasping the divine element in the human being if they understand this divine element as an abstract divinity at best? This way of looking at things becomes fruitful only when we are able to delve into concrete phenomena, if we consider the internalization of outer processes in this concrete sense. For example, while we are engaged in smelling and tasting, we must consider both the outer, living etheric element that is related to the human being and its internalization. We need to see what is perhaps the crudest of our upper sensory processes as a direct internalization of outer processes. It is so very important for our times to move beyond the merely abstract and mystical.

You will also realize now that everything in nature is in a constant state of transition to another form. Each process in nature tends to move on to another, to metamorphose into a different one. If you take what we have just said about smelling lying closer to the surface [see drawing below] and tasting taking place deeper within the human being and relate it to plants, you find that these processes take place in the etheric element inasmuch as it opens up toward the astral or solidifies into the physical. That is, it either moves outward, dispersing and becoming aromatic, or (in the case of tasting) it refrains from becoming aromatic, internalizing the outer tendency toward solidification. In a certain respect, the outer and the inner merge when we focus on smelling and tasting.

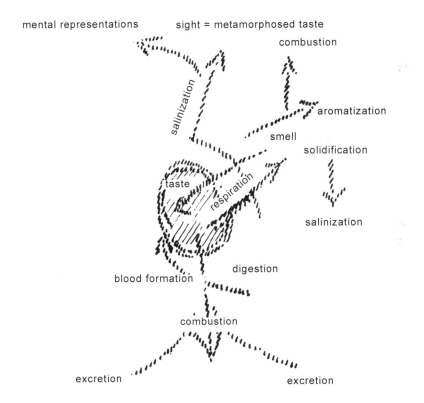

In nature, however, any given process always leads into a different one. Let us consider the aromatic aspect of the plant—that is, everything that allows the plant to avoid becoming solid by giving off its plant essence, extending its spirituality—pardon the lay expression—into the atmosphere, so that the atmosphere contains something of the plant's essence in the form of fragrance. Ghostly replicas of plants are present in what we smell out in the world. Consider what is actually happening in the external world when a plant gives off its ghostly fragrance, when it does not allow itself to become a totally solid plant, when its flowers emit a substance that wants to become a flower but refrains from doing so and persists in a dispersed state. This is nothing other than a restrained combustion process. If you imagine the metamorphosed extension of the process of becoming aromatic, you will have to think of it as a restrained combustion process. You see combustion and the plants' aromatic process and recognize them as two metamorphoses of a common entity. I might say that becoming aromatic *is* the process of combustion on a different level.

Let us look at the aspect of the plant that causes flavor and therefore lies deeper within the plant. Rather than sending its vegetative formative force out into the environment in ghost-like form, the plant holds it together and uses it to develop internal forms. Because you participate in this internal formative process when you taste, you arrive at a process that parallels the plant's solidification on a lower level. On this other level, however, it is a metamorphosis in the direction of becoming saltlike inasmuch as plants do this, because we are still talking about the plant world here [see drawing, p. 121].

Consider this strange metamorphosis in the plant. On the one hand, you see the upward-directed process of becoming aromatic, which is a restrained combustion in some respects. It can lead to the beginnings of combustion, because the activities involved in flowering are simply combustion processes that are incorporated into the plant. Down below, on the other hand, you have solidification, the process of becoming saltlike. What you taste in a plant is a restrained salt formation. But when salts are actually incorporated into the plant, when you find salts within the plant itself, these plant salts have gone beyond the process of plant formation. The plant has imprinted its own ghostly replica on its fundamental nature. Here we recognize the rationale behind a remedy. In a certain sense, we begin to see light dawning within the plant world because we are able to see into what is going on there. I must repeatedly emphasize the importance of this concrete way of seeing.

In order to move on, you must simply recall that wherever possible, and purely for higher opportunistic reasons, I will be linking what we are discussing to the common parlance of today so that you will be in a position to bridge the gap between external science and what spiritual science has to offer. I could also characterize what I am going to explain in the next few sentences in more spiritual-scientific terms, but my intention is to forge a link to modern, conventional scientific ideas that are already available. The physiologists of today speak of matters that are accessible to them but not necessarily to spiritual scientists, who do not need to study anatomy in the same way. Nonetheless, let us make the connection with conventional scientific ideas. We do not have to perpetuate the analytical anatomical inaccuracies of others, but we do need to deal with the presence of these other scientists and their results. They will stop only when natural science has been fructified by spiritual science to some extent. So let us try it!

Spiritual science will clarify the intimate relationship between the process in the eye and the processes in smelling and tasting (especially tasting)—between the extension of the taste buds into the rest of the material organ of taste and the spreading of the optic nerve in the eye. This is such a close connection that it is almost impossible to avoid looking for analogies in the tasting process when we characterize the inner aspects of the process of seeing. Of course, the extension of the taste buds into the material organ of tasting is not linked to anything as elaborate as the structure of the eye, which is interposed in front of the extension of the optic nerve, thus making seeing something completely different. But the visual process that begins behind the elaborate structure of the physical eye is inwardly very closely related to the process of tasting. I might say that, in seeing, we carry out metamorphosed tasting—metamorphosed in the sense that whatever happens as a result of the eye's elaborate structure is interposed in front of organ processes similar to those that take place during tasting.

With regard to each different sense, of course, we must distinguish between what our organism presents to the outer world and what the outer world brings to meet our organism. We must look, for example, at the internal but outward-directed activity that results from blood streaming into the eye—that is, from the organism as a whole working into the eye. This activity is even more pronounced in certain animals whose eyes include (in addition to the structures in the human eye) structures such as the pecten and the xiphoid cartilage,[34] blood organs that allow the I to be driven into the eyeball to a greater extent, while in humans the I withdraws, leaving the eyeball inwardly free. The entire organization, the whole organism, works via the blood through the eye into the sensory process, and in the visual process, the act of tasting is metamorphosed in such a way that we can call seeing a metamorphosis of tasting. For this reason we should place seeing, as a metamorphosis of tasting, above tasting and smelling [see drawing, p. 121]. Thus, both the process of tasting and that of seeing consist of an outer factor working together with an inner one. The process must simply metamorphose upward, as it were—the visual process is a metamorphosis of the tasting process.

There must also be a corresponding lower metamorphosis of this tasting process deeper inside the body. In the visual process, we ascend toward the outer world. The eye is enclosed only in its bony socket; we meet the outer world there because the eye is a surface organ and the activity of seeing is organized with reference to an outer factor. In the opposite direction, we must now think our way deeper into the body, into the lower metamorphosis of the tasting process. Here we arrive at sight's opposite pole or counterpart in the organism. This is a topic that will shed a tremendous amount of light on our subsequent considerations.

What do we find when we trace the downward metamorphosis of the tasting process? This is where digestion comes about, and you will arrive at a true inner understanding of digestion only if you conceive of sight as a metamorphosed extension of tasting in one direction and of digestion as its extension in the other direction. You must be able to grasp digestion as the complete and polar opposite of externalized seeing, because externalized seeing leads you to recognize digestion's counterpart in the outer world, the outer factor whose organic internalization is digestion. Similarly, you also become aware of how the digestive process must be thought of as related to the tasting process.

----

34. *Pecten*, resembling a comb, is a folded, vascular, pigmented membrane that projects into the vitreous humor of the eye of a bird or reptile; *xiphoid cartilage* (or process) is the posterior and lowest division of the human sternum, remaining somewhat cartilaginous throughout life.

You simply cannot understand the subtle, localized digestive activities in the human organism if you do not conceive of good digestion as being based on the ability to "taste" with the entire digestive tract and bad digestion on the inability to do so.

The process we have considered here separates into two, tasting and smelling. The activity of tasting relates more to the interaction of the etheric and the physical, that of smelling to the etheric's connection to the astral. What we recognized as tasting's continuation in the organism is subjected to the same division when we look first at digestion, which leads to fecal elimination via the intestines, and then at excretion via the kidneys, which leads to urination. There are exact correspondences [between elimination via the bowels and urination] in the lower human being and [tasting and smelling in] the upper human being. The results of separating tasting from smelling and ordinary digestion from everything involved in the more subtle workings of the kidneys are like counterparts in a polarity.

At this point it becomes possible to see events in the organism enclosed within the skin as the internalization of something external. In everything that has an upward continuation, we approach and open up to what is outside. We must now pursue this matter further in order to recognize our mental activity that is bound to the body (and I mean this not in the materialistic sense but in another sense that will be familiar to you from my lectures) as a metamorphosis of seeing, again transposed inward. We must think of the organs that form the basis for thinking or conceptualization [see drawing, p. 121]—that is, the structures in the interior of the human head—as organs of sight that have metamorphosed in a specific direction. Please consider the fact that most ideas are simply extensions of visual representations that live in your thinking. You need only compare this condition to the inner life of a person who is congenitally blind. Thinking is the inner extension of seeing.

We come to realize that this also sheds light on the strange interaction that takes place between the anatomy of the head and brain and the activity of thinking. Strangely enough, for example, if we tackle our thought processes—and this, by the way, would be a very nice chapter for a medical dissertation—and investigate the connection between associative thinking and the brain's organization, we discover structures in the brain that resemble transformations of the olfactory nerve. We might say that, seen from within, dispersed, analytical thinking is very similar to its counterpart in seeing. But from this same inner, organic perspective, summarizing what we have seen and relating ideas to each other are activities very similar to smelling. In a very remarkable way, this similarity is even expressed in the brain's anatomical structure. In any case, pursuing this [sequence of senses] in one direction leads us to the thinking, or conceptualizing, process.

Where do we arrive if we again look for the inner activity? From the perspective of seeing, ideation is seeing's inner reflection, the attempt to reverse the seeing process and guide it back to the organism. Its polar opposite, therefore, will attempt to lead the existing process outward rather than inward. This is digestion, which becomes the counterimage of conceptual activity because it leads to excretion [see drawing, p. 121]. Here, from a different, more intimate standpoint, you can see another example of what I showed you a few days ago by means of comparative anatomy—that the very structure of the human being and specifically the appearance of intestinal flora suggest a close relationship between the human being's so-called spiritual capacities and the regulated or unregulated human process of excretion. This is the same thing viewed from a different perspective. Just as we see the activity of thinking as an inner extension of the process of seeing, we also see elimination as an outer extension of the digestive process.

Getting back to our earlier observations that becoming aromatic is a restrained combustion process and solidification a restrained salt-forming process in plants, we will have shed light on what is happening here on the inside. We must simply be clear that a reversal is taking place. Up above is a reversal of seeing in an inward direction; down below is a reversal in the direction of externalization. Thus, in the upper region, we acknowledge the relationship of these processes to salt formation, and in the lower region we recognize their relationship to the development of fire, to combustion [see drawing, page 121]. You help the lower body when something associated with aroma and the restrained combustion process in plants is guided into the lower part of the body. Similarly, you aid the processes of the upper region if the agent responsible for restraining, or internalizing, the salt process in plants is introduced into the upper part of the human being. This then must be implemented in detail.

Here you see how everything outside can be reflected on the inside. And the deeper we go within the human being, the more we must look for internalized outer factors. In the activities taking place in the digestive organs and particularly in the kidneys, we must look for something that is very, very closely related to the aromatic/combustion process but is simply its other pole. And in the activities that begin in the lungs and move upward through the larynx and the head, we must look for something that is inwardly related to everything that tends toward salt formation in both plants and human beings. You might say—no, you actually *can* say—that if you know how the different plant species accumulate salts, you need only look for correspondences in the human organization. We have looked for this correspondence on the grand scale today, and we will look for detailed correspondences in the lectures to come.

These descriptions, then, encompass all the basic principles of phytotherapy. Its basis becomes apparent. I might say that the entire process that takes place in the interaction between inner and outer becomes apparent. You have also seen several specialized aspects. Now, consider the odors that tend more toward tastes, such that you discover the plant's true smell only by chewing it. That is, you actually perceive a synthesis of taste and smell, as is the case with lemon balm or ground ivy [*Glechoma hederacea*]. You find that a substance inherent in these plants tends toward salt formation; the processes of salt formation and aromatization are working together. This suggests that the organs related to plants such as lemon balm must lie closer to the outside, near the chest, while the organs related to strongly fragrant plants, such as the linden or the rose, must lie deep within the abdomen or at least closer to the abdomen.

From the perspective of the relevant organs, you find another process introduced into the upper body, among the organs that belong to smelling or tasting. In a somewhat more profound sense, this is an important life process for the human being—respiration, which interposes itself here [see drawing, p. 121]. We can also look for its polar

opposite, which must be an activity that separates from the digestive
process, inasmuch as digestion leads to excretion and is the polar opposite of the organic activity of conceptualization. Something must separate off that is located close to the organs of digestion, just as respiration
is located near the organs of smelling or tasting. The process in question is everything that is involved in the formation of lymph and blood,
or to put it more precisely, everything that is pushed inward by the
digestive system and thus has its seat in the lymph glands and so forth,
in all the organs that play a part in blood formation.

Here you see two polar processes, one separated off from digestion,
the other, respiration, separated off from the more externally located
sensory activities. Respiration is located behind the sensory processes
(mental representations are nourishment for the soul, and the respiratory process is inserted in between); the blood and lymph-forming
process is inserted in front of digestion inasmuch as digestion leads to
elimination. Strangely enough, we are moving from the process itself
into the entire human being, while it is customary today to consider
the human being only from the point of view of the organs in question. Here we are attempting to understand the entire human being
from the perspective of the relevant process and of the connection
between the human being and the nonhuman outer world, and in fact
we have discovered connections that provide us with a direct image of
all the etheric activity in the human being. This is what we have been
studying for the past hour today. These two processes, respiration and
blood formation, meet up again in the human heart. You see, we
encounter the entire outer world, including the external aspect of the
human being, as a duality that is held back in the human heart, where
it attempts to achieve a balance of sorts.

Thus we can arrive at a remarkable image that contrasts the *synthe-
sizing* process in the human heart—with its inwardness and its activity
of gathering the substances and forces that enter the body from outside and move toward the perimeter of the body—and the *analyzing*
process in the outer world, where everything that gathers in the heart
is dispersed throughout. Here we come to a very important idea; it can
be expressed in this way: We look out into the world and see the
periphery and wonder what is working into us from out there. How

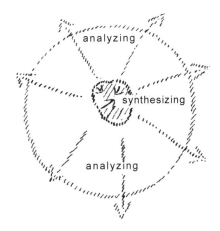

do we find a correspondence within ourselves—something related and similar in character to the contents of the outer world? By looking into our own heart! The reversed heavens are there, the polar opposite, as it were, of the heavens. In the outer world you have the periphery, the point expanded into infinity, and in the human heart you have the circle gathered together with the entire world within it. To use a crude image, we can simply imagine a human being standing on a mountaintop and looking out into the great expanse of the universe. Then we imagine a tiny dwarf inside the human heart and try to visualize what that little dwarf sees as the reversal and synthesis of the image of the whole universe. This may be a mere symbolic representation, an imagination of sorts, but if we take it in the right way, it is also a legitimate guiding image that can function as a regulatory principle and can stimulate us to correctly sum up the details we have recognized. By now I have laid most of the foundations both for our more specialized studies and for detailed answers to the many different questions that have been raised.

LECTURE 9

YESTERDAY we discussed how the human organism draws close to outer, nonhuman nature. In the interaction that takes place in two senses, smell and taste, we can see how our human organization establishes a closer connection to what is happening outside in the natural world. We are studying this connection because spiritual science recognizes the need to closely link processes in the human organization to therapeutic procedures.

Healing is always a matter of understanding which factors are inherent in what we administer to the body—whether by chemical, physiological, or physical means—and which ones are inherent in what the organism is capable of accomplishing when it is healthy but not when it is diseased.

In our thinking, we must be able to unite the external process and the process taking place within the human organism. Now these two processes come closest to each other in the perception of smell and taste, while with regard to the other senses, they are further apart. For example, seeing and digestion are quite far apart if what we mean by "digestion" includes only what happens to food from the time it is chewed in the mouth to the time it is processed by the intestinal glands. This is the whole of my meaning of the term *digestion*. I would have to consider everything else as an aspect of evacuation, either internal evacuation (or the absorption of substances) or external evacuation, which I would refer to as elimination. I would count all postglandular processes as belonging to elimination.

Now let us consider seeing. Here we encounter forms in the outer world that contain within themselves an element that lies closer to the surface in the processes of smelling and tasting. In the process of smelling, this element leaves the realm of nonhuman nature in order to become perceptible to human beings. In other instances, where this element is enclosed in the substances of the nonhuman natural world, we look at it. When we look at visible forms and so on, we are encountering the formative principle outside us, the same principle that is also disclosed (but only on the level of substance) in the process of smelling. I would like to suggest that if we trace the being that reveals itself in smell out into the plant or mineral kingdom, we will find that the same principle that becomes evident in smell is revealed in formative processes that take place in the external world of nature.

The exact opposite process is digestion. It "takes possession" of what is revealed in taste, concealing it within the organism again. It is extremely significant to point out that until now we have had to describe outer, nonhuman nature as lying more in the unconscious. For you see, the connections that we were able to note from the perspective of the entire universe are present within the human being. The human being is associated with the Saturn-like element, the Jupiter-like element, and so on, but this association is extremely well concealed in the depths of the human organization. If it is not too offensive to modern ways of thinking, we might say that in the human being, the astronomical factor is the least conscious of all the factors. Of all the processes in the organism, it ends up furthest in the background.

We also have organs that "open up" the human organism on the inside in a certain way. These organs bring the human body more into connection with what develops close to our Earth's surface, with meteorology in the broadest sense. If we do not restrict ourselves to looking only at therapeutic substances but also trace the course of therapeutic processes, we must look at the connections that exist between the human being and meteorological processes in general.

At this point, we can distinguish between the human organs that relate more closely to the astronomical factor and those that relate more closely to the meteorological factor. Admittedly, a more refined method of observation must be implemented here. How this distinction must be made will initially shock you somewhat, but as time goes on you will recognize it as the best possible foundation for healing. If we look at the organs in the human organism that open themselves up to the meteorological factor—in the same way that deeper-lying organs relate to the astronomical factor—the primary organs that we have to consider are the liver and everything that is vesicular in character, everything the bladder represents. (In the context of pathology, the bladder is extremely important. As strange as it may sound at first, the bladder is one of the most important organs to consider in studying pathology.) In this context we can also look at the lungs, which are open to the outside in that they make breathing possible. In a certain respect, we must also consider the heart as one of the organs through which the organism as a whole opens itself up to the outside, toward meteorology. You will understand this immediately if you take some things I said in previous lectures in the right way. These organs are all associated with specific meteorological impulses. What this means can be studied only by investigating the human being's entire relationship to the surrounding world, and especially the relationship of human activity to the surrounding world.

Above all, I would like to suggest that you make a concerted effort to trace any cardiac damage you encounter to disruptions of human activity. You should conduct studies of how the cardiac function of people who tend their fields as farmers and have little respite from this work differs from that of people whose professions require them to spend a great deal of time driving cars or even riding trains. It would be extraordinarily interesting to set up more thorough research studies on this subject. You would find that the tendency to cardiac disease is essentially dependent on whether or not people sit still when they are being transported by some outer vehicle, as is the case with a car or a train. Passive submission to being moved "deforms" all the processes that are held back in the heart.

Everything that plays into the human world in this way is related to how human beings maintain bodily warmth. Here you see how cardiac function relates to the impulse of warmth in the outer world to which we are connected. You can see that if an individual engenders enough warmth through his or her own activity, this adequate measure of self-engendered warmth in that person's vital processes is also the measure of the health of the person's heart. With cardiac patients, we would always have to make sure to induce thoroughly enlivened self-movement. I am convinced that in fifteen years or so, people will think more calmly about these issues than they do today and will begin to comment about how remarkable it is that people's cardiac activity has become healthy again through eurythmy, because doing eurythmy essentially regulates ensouled self-movement in accordance with certain laws. Perhaps there is nothing wrong with saying that from this perspective we should point out the healing exercises that can be derived from eurythmy when we are dealing with cardiac irregularities.

Next we come to a condition that is more likely to be expressed through reduced bladder activity in the human organism. What I am about to say in this connection may seem somewhat amateurish, but it is not. I can confidently say that it is more scientific than anything that is called scientific today. Essentially, the bladder is a suction device. It functions as a cavity within the human organism, a cavity that creates suction. It is dependent on the fact that the human organism is hollowed out at this particular location. The effect of the bladder on the rest of the organism is just like the effect of a bubble of gas in water. A gas bubble in water is a sphere of dilute matter surrounded by denser matter, and the effect that emanates from this diluted sphere is similar to that of the entire bladder on the human organism. With regard to all the bladder's intended functions, we create disturbances if we have little opportunity to complete internal movements in the right way. One example of this is failing to pay careful attention to the act of eating, disrupting the entire digestive process by gulping down our food instead of chewing. Another is not maintaining the right balance between rest and movement during the digestive process, and so on. Everything that disrupts inner mobility from within also disrupts what we might call the life of the bladder.

People will still accept it if you prescribe ensouled movement of some sort for suspected cardiac irregularities, but they will not be very receptive if you want to regulate their inner movements, which are dependent on habit. You will manage to accomplish this, however, if you implement a meteorological treatment for someone who deprives the body of necessary rest by gulping down food or disturbing the digestive process in some other way. This means bringing the person in question into an atmosphere that is richer in oxygen so that he or she must breathe more and is unconsciously forced to expend more care on the respiratory process. Regulating respiration in this way carries over into the regulation of other organic processes, so you will find that if you either artificially or, better yet, naturally bring an individual who suffers from irregularities in bladder function into a different, more oxygen-rich atmosphere, a certain balance will be effected simply through this change in lifestyle.

It is especially important to take note of the liver, the third organ that is connected to outer meteorology in the widest sense. Although seemingly contained within the human organism, it is nonetheless associated with the outer world to a great extent. You can notice this in the fact that liver health is always dependent on the composition of the local water. In order to properly consider the liver health of the people living in a particular place, we would always have to study the composition of the local water. Tasting promotes liver development, but when it occurs in excess it promotes liver degeneration. In human beings, liver degeneration is the same as excessive indulgence. Finding food pleasant or unpleasant, sympathetic or unsympathetic, ought to be restricted to the tongue and palate, and extending this sympathy and antipathy into the interior leads to liver degeneration. We need to pay attention to this and try to persuade people with any type of liver damage (which is often very difficult to notice) to investigate taste and to discover something essential in taste. Conducting a thorough study of the inner relationship of liver function to the composition of the water in any particular locality will prove very difficult since the dependencies are extremely subtle. For example, we would expect liver disorders in localities where the water contains a lot of calcium to be different from those in areas where the water contains less calcium. We will do well to notice this and to bear in mind that liver function is always supported by eliminating calcium from water as much as possible. Of course, then we must find ways and means of accomplishing this.

The life of the lungs is intimately connected to everything a region offers simply because of its geological configuration, whether we are dealing with one such as this where the soil contains a great deal of lime, or an ancient mountainous region where the soil contains a great deal of silica. Human pulmonary function always differs greatly because of such things, since the lungs are essentially dependent on the composition of the solid ground in the locality. One of the first tasks of a physician who establishes a practice in any area should be to thoroughly study the local geology. Studying local geology and examining the local people's lungs are actually the same. We will have to realize that the least favorable situation is when a person's lungs are totally unable to adapt to the local environment.

Now you must not misunderstand what I am saying in this connection. In pointing out the lungs' dependency on the environment, I am not referring to respiration. I mean the internal structure of the lungs themselves. Of course, respiration in turn is dependent on good or poor functioning, which is determined by the lungs' internal structure. But with regard to this dependency, I am referring to the actual internal structure of the lungs. Whether a tendency toward incrustation or excessive mucus or the like is present essentially depends on the environment. But then the lungs are also very sensitive to physical labor and will certainly be damaged if a person has to do physical work to the point of excessive fatigue.

These are connections that can lead us to recognize the dependent relationships of internal organs, such as the lungs, liver, bladder, and heart, which open up to the outside, toward the meteorological factor. Whenever diseases of these organs are present, we will have to attempt to achieve therapeutic results through physical or naturopathic means. In a certain way, such results are permanent. If we have noticed that someone with a tendency to some sort of lung weakness is quite unadapted to a particular locale, convincing that person to move to a different, more suitable area is often the best thing we can do. Similarly, with regard to the organs located above the lungs, a radical change in domicile and lifestyle is often the greatest possible boon. Such changes do relatively little for the organs that lie below the heart, but they accomplish a great deal for the lungs and all the organs above the lungs.

Of course we must be clear that everything in the organism interacts, and when something goes wrong we must look for a possible hidden interaction. For example, if we discover cardiac or vascular degeneration, we must ask whether there is any tendency toward pulmonary degeneration that would require us to deal with the illness from that perspective.

This at least gives an indication of the human being's relationship to meteorological factors. But behind and masked by meteorological factors in the outer world lie astronomical factors. Like the meteorological factors, they are also present within the human being. Internal meteorological factors encompass only the lungs, liver, bladder, and heart, just as external meteorological factors encompass only the qualities of solid ground, air, water, and warmth. The formative forces of the plant and mineral kingdoms lie behind everything encompassed by ascertainable meteorological factors, both within the human being and in the outer world. These formative forces are very close to the extratelluric, astronomical factor, and their counterpart within the human being is always hidden behind the meteorological process, that is, deeper in the interior than the four above-mentioned organ systems. Because the connection between what is outwardly present in plant and stone and what lies hidden behind the human lungs, liver, and so forth is not so readily apparent, studying therapeutic processes that have their origin in this realm is naturally considerably more difficult. We can, however, discover a rational way to do this if we realize that in some respects the human being always has an inner, organic tendency to do the opposite of whatever is happening externally.

Let us take silicic acid processes as a concrete example. First of all, it is quite evident that silicic acid processes are taking place wherever silicates—quartz and similar rocks—are formed. These processes have their counterpart in the human organism, but they also underlie certain other activities that unfortunately tend to be disregarded today. These other activities take place in cultivated ground and in the interaction between cultivated soil or the Earth as a whole—which is, after all, siliceous—and the roots and similar organs that plants sink into the ground.

Everything we can derive from plant ashes is also intimately related to the external silica process. This external silica process, however, has its counterpart inside the human being and specifically in the organs lying above the activity of the heart and tending in the direction of lung activity—if I can put it in this way—or rather of the inner organic activity that shapes the lungs and lies closer to the head. Here, in everything that lies above the activity of the heart, we have the polar counterpart of silica formation in the external world. To a great extent, this inner organic process is essentially a potentization of external silica formation, as I have indicated in previous lectures. A particular symptom complex that has its seat in the area above the heart's activity may lead to all kinds of other disturbances in the organism. Extensive pulmonary discharge is crude evidence of an illness of this sort, but so is meningitis or pseudo-meningitis. Because everything is reciprocal in the organism, these lung disorders also influence cardiovascular disorders. Such disturbances may tend toward inflammatory conditions in the brain; however, this tendency may be suppressed and appear instead in the form of inflammation of the digestive organs or related organs. In this case the problem is knowing where the actual starting point lies. But we can talk more about this later.

In all such cases it will be important to introduce a substance into the organism that dilutes or potentizes the external effects of silica to the greatest possible extent. If you consider this connection in the right way, it proves to be extremely characteristic and important. It also shows you that when something goes wrong that can be directly observed in the upper parts of the body, we need to transform nature's important silica processes by breaking the silica apart, dividing it and grinding it up. If lower parts of the body, such as the heart itself, are damaged as a result of reciprocal effects, then under certain circumstances the process that is induced by plants containing a great deal of silicic acid could be used, either directly or in some metamorphosed form, to evoke a healing process. All plants that contain silica compounds should be carefully studied with regard to the extent of their effects on all activities that are played out below the level of the heart in the human organism, although of course these effects in turn work back on the rest of the organism.

In the external natural world, the complete opposite of silica formation is carbonic acid formation. Carbonic acid formation is the polar
opposite of silicic acid formation. This is why it is so necessary to trace
the process of carbonic acid formation with respect to everything in
the organism that contrasts with what I characterized earlier, that is,
everything that has to do with digestion in the broadest sense or even
has its source or starting point in the digestive system. Any carbonic
acid compounds, especially if they are used in a natural, plant-derived
form, will allow us to cope remarkably well with these forms of illness.

It is very important, however, to take one particular connection into
account. The sense of smell directs us only outward, into the rest of
the visible world, while the sense of taste directs us inward, toward
what lies hidden within the organism. If you trace substances according to what they offer by way of smell and taste, if you study digestion
with this in mind, you will realize that at the beginning of the digestive
process, substances mingle and flow into one another. As these substances continue to move through our digestive organs, however, we
must separate again what has been mingled. This applies not so much
to the material aspects as to the respective processes. To separate what
mingles when we ingest food is in fact one of the organism's main
functions. First of all it has to separate everything that is meant to be
excreted via the bowels on the one hand and via the urine on the other.

Medical intuition will be unusually important in treating the system
of organs we are now approaching, namely, the renal system and its
wonderful workings and the extraordinary branching that is evident
there, even on the level of processes. We will say more about this later.
At the moment, the important point, as was demonstrated in previous
lectures, is that everything eliminated via the bowels has a connection
to activities taking place in the head. These two belong together. Similarly, everything eliminated via the urine is connected to processes taking place in and around the heart, in the cardiovascular system. In all
elimination via the bowels, we are essentially dealing with a human
copy of the silica-forming process, while in all aspects of urine formation we are dealing with a copy of the carbonic acid process. These connections permit us to conclude that there is a link between what takes
place in the healthy individual and what is taking place in someone

who is sick. We are pointed toward connections that exist on the level
of processes, but these connections cannot be considered in a one-
sided manner. We will see that we must master all of these phenomena
in order to correctly assess the law of similars that Dr. Scheidegger presented to us in such an illuminating way yesterday.[35]

Although it conceals something extremely important, the law of
similars needs to be built up out of all the elements we acquire by
studying connections such as those we are establishing here. Once
again, the human being's connection to metals lies behind everything
I have just explained to you. We speak about the siliceous quality as
what gives form to the human being in contrast to the dissolving
capacity of carbonic acid within the human being, and the process of
life itself is inherent in this constant tendency to acquire form and
redissolve. If we look first at the siliceous quality that gives form to
human beings, we must not forget that the particular areas within the
human organization that resemble this siliceous quality, for reasons I
have already explained in part on previous days, have a relationship to
the metallic qualities of lead, tin, and iron. Thus we can say that when
we look at the area above the heart, we must look at what works within
the human being on the basis of silicic acid on the one hand and on
the basis of the qualities of lead, tin, and iron on the other. The iron
quality has more to do with the lungs' formative process, the tin quality with the head's general formative principle, and the lead quality
with the formative force that is localized in the bones, because bone
structure and bone growth essentially originate from the upper part of
the human being, not the lower part.

It is important to learn to weigh how these things work together,
how salts of silicic acid, for example, can be used, always testing the
respective metal for its similarity to these three representative types.
And at the same time we must be clear that the lower region of the
human being is related to copper, mercury, and silver, and that we

---

35. In a lecture to participants in this course. Edwin Scheidegger was a leading physician
and the builder of the Merian Iselin Hospital in Basel. The "law of similars" was a basic
element of Paracelsus's doctrine of healing and was later put into practice in homeopathy
by Samuel Hahnemann (1755–1843), who postulated that medicine produces symptoms in healthy people that are similar to those that it relieves in sick people.

must consider the extent to which we can apply these metals themselves or related metals by combining them somehow with processes
that form carbonic acid. In this way, we unite three things: the metallic
quality as defined by the extratelluric element working within the
earthly element; a quality that is otherwise stony, which takes shape
under the influence of the principle that forms carbonic acid; and
what takes shape under the influence of the principle that forms silicic
acid. We gradually draw closer to the possibility of discovering concrete external substances that we must introduce into the human
organism in order to bring about healing in one or the other case.

As we do this, we will always have to note that very high dilutions
can be effective if the substance in question has little effect on the
lower senses of smell and taste and therefore does not put its essential
nature on display so outwardly, whereas we will need lower dilutions
of substances that blatantly present their inner nature to our senses of
smell and taste. If we understand their healing aspects clearly, substances with strong smells and tastes are often extremely good remedies in their natural state, especially if their therapeutic effect is not
canceled out by a conventional diet.

Admittedly, in order to delve still further into these questions, we
must at least be aware that each human sense possesses the power to
distinguish differences and that human subjects are the best reagents,
the best means of discovering reactions. Of course, this will be difficult
in the case of substances with no pronounced smell or taste. But let me
make you aware of a type of self-education that is especially important
for physicians. It consists of developing all the subtle sensing capacities
that can possibly be developed, the ones that lead us to have sensations
even with respect to the external natural process of silica formation or
the like. It must be meaningful that quartz, although it always produces very regular formations on its own, is a mineral whose related
substances tend toward all kinds of possible crystalline shapes. Enormous variety exists in the crystallization of silicates. Anyone who has
a sense for such things also senses that the dispersing element predominates in all their different formative possibilities. A dispersing element
must preexist if the degree of formative capacity that the silicates possess is to be present in outer nature. This suggests that silicates must

be broken apart before they are used. We need to develop the ability to sense this, because this sensing ability leads to a means of evaluating remedies.

It is also necessary for each of us to become a good reactive medium in terms of acquiring the sensory abilities to discover that smells are sevenfold, just like sensations of color. If we acquire the ability to distinguish sweetish smells, pungent smells, and so on, we will discover that the sense of smell is differentiated into seven nuances, as is the sense of taste. The interesting point here is that by mastering the "spectrum" or "scale" of scents, we also acquire a means of learning how to find our way among all the phenomena of combustible substances; we delve into the nature of combustible substances, as it were. Tomorrow we will see how this is done. And if we acquire specific sensory possibilities with regard to taste, so that we can easily distinguish between sweet tastes and the tastes of salts and the five other nuances, then we acquire a certain inner relationship to the salt-forming principle in nature. Having acquired this relationship, we reach the point of being able to sense, in the impressions we receive from nature, that one thing is useful for one aspect of the human organism, another for another aspect. Although we need a firm foundation in careful, precise scientific studies of the effects of various substances, it is still very important for us to unfailingly unite the results of these studies with our own subjective powers of perception and gain a certain inner feeling of kinship with nature by doing so. Tomorrow I would like to take up again what we have discussed today and then continue to move closer to the specifics.

LECTURE 10

DORNACH, MARCH 30, 1920

ESSENTIALLY, what we are trying to do here is more concerned with discovering a method of enriching the study of medicine than with getting lost in the dissection of details, which are never more than of relative importance. The methodical study of the human being's connection to external, nonhuman nature should indeed be suitable for equipping all individuals to begin making their own observations about nature. Today, therefore, let us begin by presenting a few topics that will constitute our path to many discoveries in a certain field.

True spiritual-scientific research, by providing counterbalances, can unearth many discoveries that can then be verified in terms of Dr. Stein's lecture yesterday.[36] On the other hand, if we go into these particular subjects, we find that they are leitmotivs for many other topics. Today I would like to point out a few examples that can be significant. Let us remain within the realm of plants for the moment. You will note, for example, the characteristic effects of anise (*Pimpinella anisum*) on the human organism. We find that its typical effect is to promote secretion; it is a diuretic and promotes both lactation and perspiration. What could this capacity be related to? In the case of this particular plant, we will find that its efficacy is connected to its very finely dispersed content of iron or iron salts. We can clearly perceive how anise works: it takes a process that is otherwise played out in the

---

36. Walter Johannes Stein (1891–1957), history teacher at the Stuttgart Independent Waldorf School from 1919 to 1932, and later active in England.

blood because of the blood's iron content, removes it from the blood, and temporarily pushes it into a region below that of the blood.

Because certain plants have strong effects on the middle region between the inner and the outer realms, between the body's surface and the heart, it is especially easy for us to study how their effects extend into different areas. In these plants we can find a recurring theme for what can be discovered through a rational study of therapeutic substances. For example, let us observe a plant that is one of nature's great teachers in this connection, namely chicory (*Cichorium intybus*). If we are only willing to investigate this plant, we can study numerous different aspects of the human organism. We find that, on the one hand, *Cichorium intybus* is a remedy for digestive weakness, for symptoms in the organs that are in direct contact with the human outer world.[37] On the other hand, it also works on the blood itself and prevents it from failing to perform its necessary functions and allowing disturbances to appear within the blood serum. One final very significant point about *Cichorium intybus* is that its therapeutic effect extends to very peripheral processes. Under certain circumstances, it even has an effect on the organs of the head and especially on those of the throat and chest, the pulmonary organs. It is interesting to study *Cichorium intybus* simply because it has such strong effects on so many different parts of the human being. We can see these effects fanning out, so to speak. If we wonder about the basis of its effectiveness against digestive weakness, we discover that it is due to the bitter extract that causes chicory's strong taste. Such bitter extracts, which remain strongly plantlike in character, are very strongly related to substances within the human being that have not yet been thoroughly processed by the individual and still retain something of the appearance they had in the outer world.

We must realize that the outer world's substances undergo very little processing within us in the parts of the body leading to the stomach. After passing through the stomach, they are processed further; they are substantially changed by the time they reach the bloodstream via the

---

37. This refers, presumably, not only to the skin but to the digestive tract and other organs that are exposed to what a person takes in from the outside world.

intestines and are most strongly transformed on the periphery, in the skeletal, nervous, and muscular systems. Plant extracts have a very strong relationship to outer substances that are still unprocessed.

But *Cichorium intybus* also contains alkaline salts, potassium. We must look to potassium as the constituent that affects the blood. Here we see a separation of forces. The forces inherent in chicory extract are related to the digestive organs and move in that direction, while the forces inherent in the alkaline salts are related to and move toward blood-related organs or the blood itself. In addition, a considerable amount of silicic acid is present. Silicic acid works via the blood into the peripheral organs, through the nervous and muscular systems and into the skeletal system itself. Thus *Cichorium intybus* is a substance that really tells us, "Here I am, allowing myself to be split into three so that I can influence all three members of the human organism." This is an example of the experiments nature performs for us, which are much more meaningful than experiments we set up, because nature's intentions are much richer than ours can possibly be when we ask nature questions with our experiments.

Horsetail, *Equisetum arvense*, is also very interesting in this connection. Here, too, we see powerful effects on digestive weakness combined with strong peripheral effects. We simply need to ask what the basis is for these strong peripheral effects of *Equisetum arvense*, and the answer is its silicic acid content. Simply through a comparative study of these two constituents, we find that any plant extract, anything that is still plantlike, retains a relationship to the digestive tract, while silicic acid, the plant constituent that tends toward the mineral kingdom, absolutely insists on moving from the center of the human being toward the periphery, where it works therapeutically. If you make a real study of medical botany, you will discover multiple examples, very many more examples than I have given you here.

A magnificent plant whose effect is very simple but tremendously instructive is *Fragaria vesca*, the woodland strawberry. Its effect is frequently not noticed because in people who eat its berries, the therapeutic effect is obscured. It would be possible, however, to conduct experiments with people who normally do not eat strawberries and are therefore still receptive and sensitive to effects that are otherwise masked. Then the wonderful significance of this woodland strawberry would become evident. On the one hand, it is especially capable of normalizing the process of blood formation. It does everything to promote the formation of blood, and for this reason it can even be used to treat diarrhea in people who have not been desensitized to strawberries by eating them. In diarrhea, forces appear in the wrong place, in the abdomen. *Fragaria vesca* puts them back where they belong, closer to the blood system itself.

Here we have on the one hand a significant blood-building force and on the other hand silicic acid (which the woodland strawberry also contains), tending toward the peripheral parts of the organism. Just consider what a wonderful plant this strawberry is. Because of its silicic acid, it tends to foster the development of certain forces on the organism's periphery. Ordinarily, the danger is that if too much silicic acid is led to the periphery, the forces become excessive and not enough nutrients are sent to the periphery because the blood has not been enriched enough to support the process induced by silicic acid. The woodland strawberry is a magnificent specimen in that it simultaneously prepares the blood, which must follow and support this process. In a wonderful form, it expresses what we must do to assist the process that we induce through silicic acid compounds in the peripheral parts of the human organism. If we are simply intuitive enough to seek nature out in the right places, it supplies us with wonderful insights at hand of individual specimens. Once again, many more such insights are possible.

I would now like to make you aware of another example seen from the same perspective. Study the rather comprehensive effect of a plant such as *Lavandula* (lavender), for example. You will find that *Lavandula* has a strong therapeutic force that counteracts any undesirable soul weaknesses, such as fainting, neurasthenia, or paralysis. *Lavandula* works in the direction of the periphery of the human organism in such a way that the astral body is driven out and loses its power over the physical body.

In the case of such plants and any such substances that we can recognize as counteracting negative neurological conditions, we must always ask whether any other contrasting conditions, such as scanty menstruation, are present, and you will always find that the substance works in both directions. One plant that has an especially strong effect is lemon balm, *Melissa officinalis*, which can be a strong emmenagogue in addition to being very effective in cases of dizziness and fainting.

I have mentioned these examples in order to demonstrate how we can trace the similarity between an outer plant process and one taking place within the human being. We will have to realize that the plant is related to only one aspect of the human being. I would like to ask those of you who might prefer to resort exclusively and fanatically to phytotherapy—a real tendency today—to consider the following fact. Human beings contain all the kingdoms of nature. Our formative processes and developmental stages are related not only to our own human kingdom but also to all the other natural kingdoms. In a certain regard, we removed all the other natural kingdoms from within ourselves and placed them outside, and in specific instances we again take in aspects of the kingdoms we have externalized. We really do take them back into ourselves, and this internalization is very important.

The last factor to be externalized is the first one we must take back into ourselves for purposes of healing. If we disregard the animal kingdom—we will shed more light on this topic later, but let's disregard it for now—the last kingdom we externalized, later than the plant kingdom, was the mineral kingdom. As a result, we must acknowledge the one-sidedness of looking only for the human being's relationships to the plant kingdom. Nonetheless, the plant kingdom remains instructive because plants induce healing not only through their plant essence but also through the minerals they contain. That is why the plant kingdom remains instructive. We must simply realize that the plant reprocesses a portion of what is present in the mineral kingdom and that this reprocessed substance is not a remedy to the same extent as an unprocessed one. Thus the silicic acid that has been overcome by a plant and incorporated into its vegetative processes is not as strong a remedy as the silicic acid we encounter in minerals. In the case of the latter, the organism must make a much greater effort to assimilate and integrate it than if it were simply dealing with silicic acid from the plant kingdom. This is something that must be repeatedly emphasized: We must develop stronger forces when we encounter stronger forces. In a very positive sense, the forces we encounter when we have to assimilate and overcome minerals are much stronger than those we encounter when we have to assimilate only plants.

Before I make this next statement, please let me emphasize that I am stating it only parenthetically, I do not want to propagandize for, or go on record as supporting, any particular kind of diet. I simply wish to clarify the matter. You see, what I just said about stronger forces is also the basis of the difference between vegetarian and meat diets. If we nourish ourselves exclusively with plants, we human beings must take over the entire process that animals take away from us by having brought plant substance one stage further. We might say that the process plants take to a certain point is taken further by animals, so that the relevant animal formative process stops here [see drawing, "red"], while the plant process stops here ["white"].

People who eat meat do not engage in the process that animals do; they allow animals to relieve them of this effort. Thus, they fail to develop the forces that they would develop in themselves if they consumed only plant foods and had to do this portion of the work themselves. This means that a vegetarian has to muster up quite different forces from the abdomen than a meat eater. Nonetheless, the forces that would have to be used to overcome plant substance and raise it to the animal level are still present in the meat eater. They rebound on the organism and work within it. Essentially, they have a very fatiguing and disruptive effect on the human being. It must be strongly emphasized that a vegetarian diet offers noticeable relief from fatigue.

People become capable of more work if they become accustomed to summoning up forces out of themselves that they do not summon up if they eat meat, in which case these forces disrupt the organism. As I said, however, I am not promoting any particular diet. I know that homeopathic physicians have mentioned to me again and again that we encourage consumptive diseases and the like if we accustom people to not eating meat. This may be the case, but what I have just stated remains the pure fact of the matter. There is nothing more to be said about it; it is simply a fact. I am quite willing to concede that some of the bodies living today cannot tolerate a purely vegetarian diet and absolutely must have meat. This is an issue that must be resolved on a case-by-case basis.

As soon as we begin to emphasize that the therapeutic process also needs to create a relationship to the mineral kingdom and its forces, we encounter another similar issue with regard to the therapeutic process. This is a question that has concerned people for some time, but in my opinion, we can answer it and gain a certain understanding of the subject only when we consider it from the spiritual-scientific point of view. It seems to me that with regard to the therapeutic process, the issue of cooked versus raw food is extremely important. Here again, it is not my intention to champion either one; please do not think that I am agitating for anything in particular! We must, however, objectively investigate the actual phenomena. When human beings eat and assimilate the forces of ordinary food that has been cooked, something has been done externally that the organism itself would have to do if raw foods were consumed. By cooking and preparing food, we are relieved of activity that our bodies would have to perform if we ate raw food.

Now the point is that we human beings are constructed in such a way that while our peripheral parts are connected to all of nature, in the central areas of the body—which include digestion, first and foremost—we separate from nature and become individualized. If we want to visualize this relationship of ours to nature, we can say that our periphery integrates us into the entire universe [see following drawing, "green"] and that we become individualized and separate from nature in the inner processes, which range from digestion through blood formation ["red"], so that the processes that are undergone in this section of the human being no longer correspond totally to outer processes. This is where we assert our uniqueness in contrast to the outer processes, at least to a greater extent than where we are totally harnessed to them. Perhaps the discussion that follows will make this more understandable.

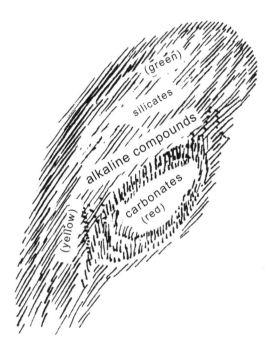

During the past few days, I have talked about how the human being is integrated into the entire cosmos. I said that in the area I have sketched here in green, the formative forces of lead, iron, and tin are working in us, while in the red area the formative forces of copper, mercury, and silver are at work. The balance is brought about by gold, by forces that are localized in the heart in particular. Considering the human being in this way is somewhat like describing a finger as part of the whole organism; we are speaking of the human being as a member of the universe, as incorporated into the entire universe. But, digestion and everything related to it separate and individualize the human being in contrast to the universal processes of the world. And so does the reciprocal process that appears in thinking and seeing.

For this reason, human beings make a selfish demand with respect to everything related to the process of digestion. This selfishness is revealed in the instinct to cook food that is taken directly from nature. If it were ingested directly and without cooking, the average human being, at least, would be much too weak to process it. If we did not cook our food—if I may express myself paradoxically—eating would be a constant therapeutic process. Because of its stronger polar relationship to the environment, eating would be a constant healing process if we did not cook our food. This is why eating raw food is a more therapeutic process, while eating cooked food is simply an activity that nourishes us, at least to a greater extent. I think this is an extremely important statement—that eating raw food is a much stronger healing process than eating cooked food. A raw food diet is much closer to an actual therapy than a diet of cooked food. In addition, I would like to mention that the effect of everything that is cooked is cut short in a certain respect and remains within the area sketched in red [drawing, p. 149], while anything that is introduced into the body in the raw state—fruit and the like—expresses itself much more on the periphery. For example, it causes the blood to send its nourishing energy to the periphery.

You can convince yourselves of this fact if you try putting patients you are treating with *Silicea* on a raw food diet for a while. Such experiments really should be conducted. You will find that this diet significantly enhances the effect of the silicic acid because of its formative influence on what silicic acid wants to accomplish on the periphery, and deformations will heal. I am not talking about crude deformations, but about ones that manifest only on the physiological level and not in any direct anatomical way. What silicic acid attempts to accomplish directly will be supported if you supply it with the appropriate nutrients during treatment.

These are the points I wanted to make from a methodological perspective, both because of the very significant course they take and because I think they are studied far too little. They are studied, of course, but usually only on an empirical basis, without looking for the reasons behind them. This is why what can be noted in this field is usually so unsatisfying.

In all these considerations, of course, the patient's individuality must be seriously taken into account. This is why I mentioned in previous lectures that it is almost impossible to say anything in this field that would not prove true in some specific context. We must understand these things as guidelines, however, even if in some particular case we have to realize that we cannot put a particular patient on a raw foods diet because of the effects that would be induced as a result of the person's entire constitution. We may do it in one case but not in another. Nevertheless, what I have described here remains true. Such considerations are the only means of gaining thorough insight into the totality of the human constitution.

You see, we must clearly distinguish between the peripheral aspect, in which the human being is really more a part of the entire cosmos and which we can influence only by administering minerals (which are far removed from the human being), and this other area I have colored red here. We can influence this second aspect through plant substances, of course, but also by giving the organism substances whose effect is due to their immediately perceptible salty character—namely, the carbonates. Alkaline substances are related to the balance between these two poles [drawing, p. 149, "yellow"]. Here we have carbonates, alkalis, and silicates or silicic acid itself.

These are the insights that point to the human being's relationship to the natural environment. We see the human being as if split into two, with a middle aspect that brings about an oscillation between these two separated parts. Looking at the peripheral human being and the more central, individualized human being in this way, we are led deep into the essence of nature as a whole. The peripheral human being is related to supra-earthly factors, as is demonstrated by the efficacy of minerals—which are dependent on planets and starry constellations—in the peripheral parts of the body. Centrally, as an individual, the human being is related to earthly factors. This relationship to the earthly element comes to expression in the human digestive system and also enables us to become beings capable of thinking and developing our humanity.

We can see this internal human duality as a duality between the supra-earthly or cosmic factors and the earthly factors within the human being. At first we will encounter distinct signs of both supra-earthly and earthly factors in the human organism, and yesterday I pointed out how the peripheral or supra-earthly aspect is reflected not only in the human spiritual organization but also in the human digestive organization that stands in a polar relationship to it, as I have repeatedly pointed out. Everything that has to do with secretion in the sense of digestion and with the secretion in the brain that is the basis of spiritual activity points us toward the peripheral or heavenly human being. This is the fact of the matter, regardless of how strange and paradoxical it may sound. In contrast, everything that is connected to the formation of urine and sweat—whether the processes are fluid or more gaseous ones—points in the direction of the earthly human being, the human being who is becoming individualized. We must see these two divergent poles of human nature as something very significant.

It is unfortunate that in recent times what I am now describing as a duality in human nature has never—at least to my knowledge—been pointed to in any way that was at all useful for therapy. You see, all these questions that we are considering here are meant to bring pathology and therapy together. They should not be two separate fields. This is also the reason for the therapeutic orientation of everything I am putting forward here, so that what we understand in terms of pathology will then enable us to think in terms of therapy. This is why I am formulating these topics in this particular way, although objections are easily possible if insufficient attention is paid to my therapeutic orientation.

You see, those who want to learn about syphilis as an outer phenomenon, for example, will certainly be concerned with finding out to what extent contagion or at least some semblance of contagion is necessary in each case in order for syphilis to appear. Continuing in this vein eventually severs pathology from therapy. Pardon me if I use a somewhat crude comparison, but contagion is no more important in syphilis than the fact that in order to get a lump on the head, the person in question must be hit by a stone or something else that delivers a blow. If this does not happen, no lump will develop. This is true enough, but enumerating the details does not result in a description that is productive for the healing process. The social significance of bricks or the like falling on someone's head may be great, but with regard to studying the organism in order to arrive at a successful treatment, it does not have the slightest significance. We must study the human organism by looking for things that can play a role in therapy. The things I have spoken about, however, do play an important role in the treatment of syphilis. They illumine the therapeutic process. And the subjects we are discussing have been chosen less for the sake of our understanding of pathology than to enable us to bridge the gap between pathology and therapy.

I say this because I want to characterize the particular spirit in which these discussions are undertaken, a spirit that will become more apparent each day. The modern tendency to increasingly emancipate pathology rather than steer it in the direction of therapy diverts our thinking from fruitful subjects, which, if pursued in the right way, are tremendously important for discovering therapeutic procedures. So the question is, what is the meaning of this bodily human duality between the cosmic, peripheral human being, as it were, and the earthly, central human being? Both of these aspects of the human being are systems of forces that are expressed in various ways. Everything peripheral expresses itself as a formative factor. And the ultimate accomplishment of the peripheral factor is everything that is wholly expressed in the human being's periphery and provides the body's human form.

We might even suggest studying how hair relates to silicic acid as an indicator of how the individual's formative processes work in concert with silica's formative processes on the periphery of the human body. You can study the extent to which an individual permits or opposes this influence by examining the power that silicic acid does or does not retain over the formation of the human head. In each case, of course, we must also consider the individual's overall build. But each time you cross a city street today and look at all the bald heads, you can see the extent to which human beings tend to incorporate or reject the formative process of silicic acid. This is a matter of direct perception that can be acquired without any real clairvoyance, simply by being willing to study the efficacy of nature itself. These are primarily formative forces that appear here, not cellular formative forces but forces that shape the totality, forces whose final expression is the human form itself, including the entire configuration of the head and whether it is covered with hair to a greater or lesser extent and so on.

In contrast, the dissolution of form, the destructive or dissolving principle, is inherent in the more centralized aspect that is more closely related to carbon and carbonic acid. We stay alive by continually attempting to destroy and dissolve our own form and recreate it out of the cosmos. As human beings, we live in the constant attempt to break down our form, and this disintegration is constantly balanced out by the cosmos working into us. Formation and breaking down are an inherent duality in the human being; they work together in the human organization.

Imagine you have, on the one hand, the peripheral, cosmic formative forces [see drawing below] working into the human being. They meet up with earthly forces in the heart. I have already explained how the heart brings about a balance. But now assume that these peripheral forces active in the human being, and whose ultimate goal is the heart, deplete themselves and are held back prematurely before they reach the heart where they are meant to be held back [arrows right to left].

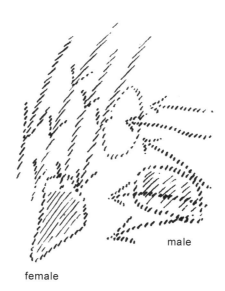

male

female

They are held back prematurely, so that we then have an element in the human being that shows at least to a slight extent how the cosmic, supra-earthly formative process takes place in the human being. Let us also assume that these other forces, which work in the opposite direction—toward the digestion and its transformation as it nears the heart—also deplete themselves before reaching the heart, so that the earthly factor dead-ends here [arrows on the right]. What we see is a backup, a concentration, of everything that works formatively within the human being, spiritually and physically, of everything that is connected to all the excretions in the head and in the intestines. All this activity does not directly counter that of the heart but rather creates a parallel heart activity of sorts. And over here you have a parallel digestion of sorts, in that what emanates from the Earth and its materials as the de-forming element in the human being, as the dissolver of form, accumulates prematurely. This duality in the human being is preserved in organic form, bringing about the female sex organs in one instance and the male sex organs in the other. It is possible to study the female sexual organs by considering their dependence on cosmic, peripheral formative forces. And it is possible to study the male sexual organs, right down to the details of their forms, by seeing them as dependent on telluric, form-dissolving forces.

This is our route to understanding the human organization in a truly scientific way, right down to these points. It is also the route that will show us how plant substances that contain formative forces can work to build up the uterus when its own formative forces are paralyzed. If you study the formative forces in the human organism in this way, you will also learn how to unearth formative forces in the plant and mineral kingdoms. I will look at this subject in detail later, but of course I must first point out the larger connections.

You see, once such things have been recognized, we will finally have a true study of embryology. We have no such thing today because no attention is paid to how strongly the cosmic factor influences the earliest stages of embryological development. In fact, the cosmic factor is just as important as the man's semen in inseminating the female organism. The first stages of human embryological development absolutely must be seen from the perspective of the human being's connection to the cosmos. What is injected by the man's semen appears only later, when the formative forces that the cosmos wants to embed in the female organism, which work in the direction of developing a unified form, are de-formed in such a way that the man's semen can differentiate them into individual organs. The female organization's contribution lies in the overall organization of the human being, while the male organization's contribution lies in the specialization and differentiation of individual organs, in exposing individual organs by de-forming the actual unitary form of the human being. We might say that through the female forces, the human organization strives to become a sphere; through the man's semen, it strives to specialize into heart, kidneys, stomach, and so on.

In the female and male principles, we encounter the Earth/Cosmos polarity directly. This is another point where we begin to have great respect for the ancient wisdom of humanity. We begin to listen with quite different emotions when we are told that Uranus impregnated Gaia, that Cronus impregnated Rhea, and so forth. Approaching these important ancient intuitions with respect does not need to be due merely to some vague mystical feeling. It can be surprising at first when people who are acquiring their first insights into such matters agree with a statement I have often heard, namely that mythology contains more physiology than modern science does. This statement is shocking at first, and understandably so, but there is a tremendous amount of truth in it. The fact is that the further we advance, the more we acknowledge that the modern method, which no longer sees any of these connections, is really not suited to guiding us into understanding the human organization.

I want to mention again that nothing I am saying here comes from studying ancient knowledge. Everything I have to say has been derived solely from the facts themselves, although I occasionally point out how they coincide with ancient wisdom. The content of these lectures, however, is not derived from ancient wisdom. If you follow the processes I characterize here, you simply arrive at ways of looking at things that in turn lead back to some aspect of ancient wisdom. I myself, for example, would never feel called upon to discover anything by studying Paracelsus, but I sometimes do feel a strong need to look up how

Paracelsus presents a subject that I have discovered on my own. Please accept what I have to offer in the spirit in which it was intended. We must, however, acknowledge the fact that when we look deeper into the human organization from the spiritual-scientific point of view, we develop a great respect for ancient wisdom. Of course this is an issue that must be dealt with in a different field of knowledge. We will talk about this tomorrow, after I have given you a chance to digest what I have told you about how the female and the male emerge from two polar tendencies. As we shall see tomorrow, this points us in the direction of more profound connections.

LECTURE 11

DORNACH, MARCH 31, 1920

YESTERDAY we ended up at a very different point from where we started, and today, too, our starting point will be very specific, concrete, and material, but we will then attempt to elaborate on the whole issue. We need to approach our task in concentric circles, as it were, partly because of the very nature of the questions and partly because of the short time allotted to us. We cannot take the scientific route of beginning with axioms and moving on to ever more complicated concerns.

My task today will be to show you the next concentric circles in the way we are looking at things. Our starting point will be *Carbo vegetabilis*. Yesterday we looked at *Cichorium intybus*, woodland strawberry, and the like, and today we will study a material that, although commonly available, is one of the world's most remarkable substances. This is the best way to see that if we are seriously committed to observing nature, we are compelled to look further than modern science tends to look.

It was very interesting to hear Dr. Kolisko point out in last night's lecture that in the future, chemistry will actually have to become a completely different science.[38] The word *physiology* came up repeatedly, indicating that the gap between chemistry and physiology must be bridged. This made me think of many different points that still cannot be fully articulated in public lectures at present, because the prerequisites for understanding them are totally lacking. Certainly, we find carbon in nonhuman nature, or in what appears to be nonhuman

---

38. Eugen Kolisko (1893–1939) was a teacher and school physician at the Stuttgart Independent Waldorf School beginning in 1920, and later became active in England.

nature, as I would prefer to put it. Actually, what aspects of nature truly are external to the human being? None of them, because everything we now encounter as external was removed from humankind and relocated outside in the course of human evolution. Humankind had to pass through evolutionary stages that were possible only because certain processes began to take place externally as opposed to internally, enabling human beings to internalize certain other processes. In this sense, both a contrast and a relationship always exist between certain outer and inner processes.

Now I must say I found a remarkable concordance between what was said yesterday about the need to "physiologize" chemistry—this may not express it very precisely, but you will know what I mean, especially if you heard Dr. Kolisko's lecture—and what Dr. Scheidegger was so kind as to set forth on Sunday in his very interesting presentation, indicating the need to understand the purpose of potentization from a spiritual-scientific perspective.[39] At one point we heard a remarkable statement, one that has concerned me for decades. It is often said that homeopathic physicians, too, are somewhat afraid of becoming mystical, of acquiring a reputation for mysticism.

The reason for my involvement with this question is in very specific views that are absolutely based on realities. Please do not misunderstand what I am going to say here; it is necessary to speak just a bit radically in order to describe matters effectively. You see, in reality, the essence of what we are attempting in the homeopathic therapeutic process lies more in what we do to prepare the substances than in the substances themselves. How we prepare what we encounter in the form of silicic acid or *Carbo vegetabilis*, for instance, is the crucial point. I have studied at length what happens in the effort to prepare homeopathic remedies, which in this case certainly include the Ritter remedies, as Dr. Rascher confirms, although Miss Ritter herself does not admit this.[40]

---

39. Dr. Scheidegger: see note on p. 139, lecture 9.
40. Hanns Rascher (1880–1952), physician in Munich; regarding Marie Ritter, see the note on p. 52, lecture 4.

This raises the question of what actually happens when homeopathic remedies are produced. Everything depends on their preparation, on the entire production process. What are you doing when you produce a high potency of silicic acid? You are working toward a certain point. Everything in nature is based on rhythmic processes. As you proceed along this route, working toward a certain null point, the inherent, immediately apparent effects of the substance in question come to light first. It is as if I have wealth and proceed to spend it. When I reach the null point and continue spending, what I then have is not merely no wealth at all; it goes beyond the point of being wealth and assumes the quality of debt. It is the same when I confront the material qualities of outer substances. If I remain within the effects of these substances, so to speak, I eventually arrive at the null point, where these effects are no longer expressed in tangible form. If I then continue, it is not the case that the effect simply disappears totally; instead, its opposite appears and begins to be incorporated into the surrounding medium.

For this reason, I always saw the opposite effects as being present in the medium, in the ointment or whatever medium was used to incorporate the homeopathic pulverized substance. This medium takes on a different configuration, just as I become a different person in the eyes of society when I make the transition from wealth to debt. Substance makes the transition to its opposite state and then contributes this opposite state, which was formerly within it, to its surroundings. In this sense, I might say that while a substance possesses certain qualities as I reduce it to ever smaller quantities, as I approach a certain null point it acquires a different quality, the ability to radiate its former qualities into its surroundings and to correspondingly stimulate the medium with which I am treating it. This stimulation can consist in directly evoking the opposite effect described here, but it is also possible that this countereffect is evoked only by making the substance fluorescent or phosphorescent during or after exposure to light. Then we have called forth the countereffect in the surrounding medium.

These are the circumstances that must be taken into account. Far from succumbing to mysticism, the issue at hand is to finally observe nature in action for once, to truly study its rhythmic processes as they apply to the qualities of substances. This is a leitmotiv for recognizing where the effects lie. If you potentize a substance, you will eventually reach a null point beyond which the opposite effects are present. But that is not all. On the route that lies beyond the null point, you can then encounter another null point that applies to these opposite effects. By passing this second point, you can achieve even higher effects that work in the direction of the initial ones but are very different in quality. It would be a wonderful task to record the effects that result from potentization and graph them on a curve. We would discover that this graph has to be constructed in a peculiar way. We would have to begin graphing the curve, and then, when we reach the point where certain lower potencies (which are nonetheless effective) cease to have an effect and higher potencies begin to take effect—that is, at the second null point—we would have to continue the graph at a ninety-degree angle, bringing it out into three-dimensional space. These issues, which will be discussed further later on in these lectures, are intimately connected to the human being's entire relationship to external, nonhuman nature.

Considering a substance like *Carbo vegetabilis* strictly from the point of view of what is immediately noticeable, we will say that taken in large doses, it induces a very specific disease picture, a specific symptom complex that, in the view of homeopathic physicians, can be counteracted with a potentization of the same substance. What is apparent to spiritual scientists who look at *Carbo vegetabilis*? They are immediately directed toward nonhuman nature to investigate what is going on in the external world's more mineralized carbon—coal. And there we find that coal is essentially involved in the use of oxygen within the overall processes of the Earth. The Earth's coal or carbon content regulates the oxygen content of the Earth's environment. We come to the direct insight that the Earth as such, if understood as an organism—as indeed it must be—is subject to a breathing process and that its coal or carbon content has to do with this process.

Chemistry of the kind that was asked for yesterday will come about only when we see the existence of coal in connection with human or animal respiration. The interaction between the Earth's coal-forming process and the oxygen process in the Earth's atmosphere is underlaid by a force that, to the spiritual-scientific way of looking at things, is revealed as the tendency to become animal. It is possible to characterize this animalizing tendency only in a somewhat surprising way. We are forced to say that something intrinsic to the external process that confronts us, the interaction between carbonization in the Earth and the processes that take place around the oxygen in the Earth's surroundings, calls forth beings, actual etheric beings, which—in contrast to the animal kingdom—constantly strive to escape from the Earth. We understand the nature of the animal kingdom only when we see it as the Earth's counter response to this process that would de-animalize the Earth. This counter response then comes to light in the animalizing process.

This is why, when we first introduce *Carbo vegetabilis* into the human organism, we are introducing nothing less than the principle that strives to become animal. All the symptoms that appear, from belching to bloating to foul-smelling diarrhea to hemorrhoid formation on the one hand and burning pain of all sorts on the other, stem from the fact that animal nature, which has been externalized by humankind in its process of becoming human, has been taken back into the individual human being. This permits us to say that if human beings are given *Carbo vegetabilis* in large doses, they are challenged to defend themselves against the animalizing process that is invading them. They defend themselves by bringing into play what they owe to having externalized animal nature in the course of their evolution.

The fact that we have expelled animal nature from ourselves is associated with the possibility of creating new light within our organism. You may be astonished, but this is really true. We are creators of light in the upper parts of the body, in contrast to the lower parts, where the organs that allow us to resist becoming completely animal are present so that we can acquire the ability to create light. This is one of the profound differences between human beings and animals. Although the animal kingdom shares other higher spiritual processes with human beings, animals do not have the ability to generate sufficient light within themselves.

At this point, we come to what I might call a truly painful chapter in modern natural science, a chapter that cannot be concealed from you for the simple reason that you cannot circumvent it if your intention is to understand the connection between the human being and the external, nonhuman world. The great obstacles to an objective grasp of how substances in general (and medicinal substances in particular) work in the human organism are the laws of the so-called conservation of energy and of matter. These laws, posited as universal natural laws, are nothing but an absolute contradiction of the process of human development. The entire process of digestion and nutrition is not what the materialistic way of thinking sees it to be. The materialistic viewpoint sees this entire process as the taking in of substances—let's keep carbon as our example—that were initially outside of us, after which the carbon—appropriately processed—is led further into the organism and then absorbed, so that we continually carry within ourselves small particles of what the outer world has given us. As far as this view is concerned, there is no difference between the carbon that is outside us and the carbon we carry around in our bodies. But this is not so. The human organism has the ability to totally destroy external, nonhuman carbon in the lower body, to eliminate this carbon from space and use the countereffect to simply create it anew out of nothing. This is the true fact of the matter: within the human being is a site where substances external to the human being are created, while at the same time the possibility to destroy these substances is present.

Of course, this is not conceded by a modern science that cannot imagine the effects of substances other than in their smallest particles, wandering about like Ahasuerus.[41] It knows nothing of the life, creation, and death of substances nor about how the death and reenlivening of substances takes place within the human organism. The reenlivening of carbon is connected to what we have described from a different point of view as the "formation of light" in the ordinary human being. This internal light-forming process confronts the influx of external light. With regard to the upper part of the body, we are

41. "This is Ahasuerus which reigned, from India even unto Ethiopia, over an hundred and seven and twenty provinces" (Esther 1:1).

organized in such a way that outer light and inner light meet and interact. The most essential aspect of our organization rests on the fact that where these two forms of light are meant to work together, we are in a position to keep them apart rather than allowing them to merge, so that they influence each other but do not mingle. Wherever we confront the outer light, whether through our eyes or through our skin, a dividing wall is erected between the light that originates within us and the light that works in from outside. The light that works in from outside is significant only as a stimulus to the creation of internal light. Thus, in allowing the light from outside to flow in on us, we allow ourselves to be stimulated to create internal light.

Now we must understand this whole process in somewhat greater depth. When we look at our internal involvement in breaking down the material aspect of carbon, we come to the human kidneys and urinary tract and to related upper parts of the body. Thus, we approach the kidney process inside the human being when we consider the activity that is associated with carbon in external, nonhuman nature. At the same time, the path to follow in using something like *Carbo vegetabilis* in the human being is pointed out to us. With regard to less serious illnesses, we realize that *Carbo vegetabilis* allows us to counteract the animalizing process in the human being that leads to nausea.

The symptoms characteristic of *Carbo vegetabilis* are nausea and its extension toward the interior of the human being. The effective counter to this tendency constitutes the counteraction in the human being—that is, everything related to the functioning of the kidney system. If you manage to stimulate this kidney process when you are confronted with the symptom complex that can be artificially induced by administering large doses of *Carbo vegetabilis*—that is, if you manage to enhance or heighten the kidney process by administering higher potencies of *Carbo vegetabilis*—then you are working to counteract this disease process in the human being that resembles the allopathic effects of *Carbo vegetabilis*. In studying the remedy *Carbo vegetabilis*, we must understand how it relates to the entire kidney process with respect to potentization. The kidney process can also have the effect that it asserts its polar opposite in relation to digestion. That is, in cases of digestive disturbances that appear as accompanying symptoms in the disease picture of *Carbo vegetabilis*, the kidney process can assert its counterimage—the polar opposite of digestive disease in the gut— in order to normalize these symptoms.

What is going on in the case of *Carbo vegetabilis* contrasts with the formation of light. What I have now said can be summarized and understood by imagining that this is the Earth [see drawing below], and here is the surrounding air. Above the air, however, we come to something else that we can initially describe as a sort of blanket of warmth around the Earth. If we were to move upward, away from the Earth, we would encounter conditions of warmth that would surprise us because of how they contrast with earthly conditions of warmth. At some distance from the Earth, what is inherent in the forces of warmth plays a role similar to that of the atmosphere itself below this blanket of warmth. The farthest end of this warmth effect (which we will posit as an extratelluric zone of warmth) is opposite to the zone of air. Here everything acts in ways that are opposite to what takes place in our atmosphere. By removing air, eliminating the existence of air, this zone emanates what comes down to us as light.

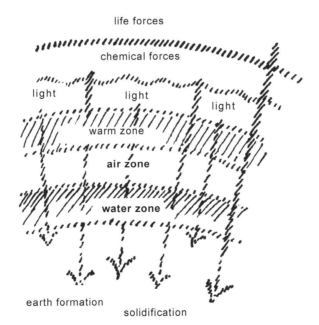

life forces

chemical forces

light   light

light

warm zone

air zone

water zone

earth formation

solidification

It is really nonsense to believe that our earthly light comes from the Sun. This is just a rather disastrous fantasy on the part of physicists and astronomers. Our earthly light comes from this upper zone. This is where light springs up; this is where it is generated. It grows there just as plants grow down here on Earth [referring to drawing].

In this sense, we are justified in saying that the creation of new, original light within human beings is due to the fact that their formative forces have preserved an internal capacity to do something that otherwise takes place only above. That is, they carry within themselves the source of an extratelluric factor. Admittedly, this extratelluric factor also works on human beings from outside, just as it works on the entire plant kingdom, but something inside them also shifts human beings to this upper zone.

Now let us ask what happens if we move one zone closer to the Earth than the air itself. Does the counterpart of this zone bring us a bit deeper into the human being? Well, you see, when we move from the airy element toward the earth element, we arrive at the fluid or watery element. We may well assume that there is a fluid zone beneath the zone of air. This also has its counterpart out in the cosmos, even higher up than the zone of light. Once again, everything in this zone is different, the polar opposite of what is going on in the fluid zone. Something grows up there just as light grows in the preceding zone. Chemical forces grow up there and work into the Earth [see drawing on p. 165]. It is nonsense to look for the driving forces behind earthly chemical effects in the substances themselves; they are not there. They come toward the Earth from this zone.

In this case, too, human beings contain something similar to what is up there in the cosmos. We human beings have an internal "chemicator," if I may put it like that; we incorporate an aspect of the heavenly sphere in which chemical activities originate. What works within the human being in this way is very strongly localized in the liver. Just study the very remarkable activity the liver develops within the human organism—its suction effect with regard to the constitution of the blood, on the one hand, and, on the other, its regulatory function, via the secretion of gall, with regard to the production of blood serum. If you look at the extensive activity of the liver and study it thoroughly, what you find is nothing less than chemistry—real chemistry, because the reality of our external earthly chemistry cannot be found on Earth at all. It must be seen as a mirror image of the external, nonhuman sphere of chemistry that can also be studied in all the wondrous functions of the human liver.

We can now move beyond *Carbo vegetabilis* and its inner properties by combining it with alkalis such as potassium, perhaps in the form of potassium carbonate, and inducing the corresponding effects in the human organism. The effect of all alkaline substances lies deeper in the interior of the organism, in the direction of the liver processes, while all effects related to *Carbo vegetabilis* tend toward the urinary tract. We will be able to perceive an absolutely clear interaction between all alkaline substances and the processes of the liver system. If we were to study the alkaline quality, we would find that it is related to the plant-forming tendency within the human being and to human externalization of the plant kingdom, just as the carbon-like quality relates to the tendency to become animal.

In previous lectures I pointed to the process of oyster shell formation as one that is important if we want to extract and separate effects within the human being from effects occurring in nature. Here we move from the force that results from combining carbon with potassium to the result of combining it with calcium. The interaction between carbon and calcium, however, is not the only factor at work here; it is somewhat moderated by the strong phosphorus effects that are also present in oyster shell and by yet another factor that is due to the surrounding forces of the ocean.

When we observe this process of oyster shell formation, we take another step in understanding the connection between the human being and external nature. If we move downward from water formation [see drawing on p. 165], we come to earth formation, or solidification. We would not be so embarrassed to speak of earth, water, fire, and air if this terminology had not been scorned and fallen into disuse and if it had not been assumed that those so called ignorant people of antiquity were speaking about actual earth and air, and so on. Surely among ourselves we can at least point out such things from time to time. But the formation of solid earth also has its counterpart in the cosmos. And this counterpart, you see, is the formation of life, the origin of vitalization. Actually, this counterpart is what is to be found in the life forces themselves. These, therefore, come from even farther away than the chemical forces and are totally killed off within the solid element in external, nonhuman nature.

I would just like to interject a related issue here because it may be of interest to some of you. Our Earth would be subject to constant proliferation of life, to the constant development of carcinomas, if this proliferation of extratelluric factors were not countered by the mercurial process, by the effects that Mercury exerts on the Earth. It is important to at least think about these issues for once. In oyster shell formation, what generally takes place in the formation of solid earth—which we can also call the formative element in the process of becoming substance—is held back at an earlier stage. Oyster shell is prevented from being completely subsumed by the earth-forming process only because it still has connections to the ocean, to water. It is held back and solidifies at an earlier stage in the earth-forming process. Although earthworms cannot do this because they have no shell, such effects still emanate from them. For this reason, it is quite valid to state that if there were no earthworms, there would be no formative forces in the Earth's interior. Earthworms are significantly involved in ensuring that the earth-forming process continues. Taken as a whole, the world of the earthworms goes beyond the formation of oyster shell but has similar connections to the entire Earth. Instead of going so far as to form actual shells, it gives rise to everything that comes about in cultivated soil and so on.

You will naturally assume that if we look for the process that lies still deeper in the interior of the human being than the chemical process, which is associated with the liver, we will again have to come to different human organs. These organs are none other than the lungs, which must be considered from two different aspects with regard to the human organism. First, they are respiratory organs. But as strange as it may sound, this is the situation only on a superficial level. At the same time, they are also regulatory organs for the earth-forming process deep within the human being. If we move from the outside in, beginning with the digestive process and moving through the processes that form the kidneys and liver, to study the process that forms the lungs in an inner sense (that is, if we disregard them as the basis of respiratory functioning), we find that they are the opposite of the activity expressed in oyster shell formation. In its lung-forming process, the human organization has incorporated a process that lies up here above the zone of chemistry in the external universe [see drawing on p. 165].

All you need to do is study the actual symptom complex that develops in human beings under certain circumstances as a result of calcium carbonate's influence, and you will find that this has very strong connections to all of the lungs' independent life processes. It is difficult, however, to separate these processes from the ones that are influenced solely by respiration. But because the lungs serve the human organization on two fronts, it is especially important to consider that they serve both external and internal functions. You must look for pulmonary degeneration in processes similar to those that appear in oyster shell formation or the like and certainly also in the formation of snail shells, and so on.

Today, in a sense, we have taken a different perspective on a topic we also approached yesterday. It was more possible to complete the circle yesterday than it will be today, but we will manage to achieve closure with regard to today's subject in the next few days. We have reached the point of being able to see kidney, liver, and lung activities as internal human processes that correspond to external activities of air, water, and solid earth. Air activity corresponds to everything that is associated with the renal system in the broadest sense, and especially to all urinary functions. Under certain circumstances, this system, of which the kidney is the part that lies deepest in the interior, can provoke shortness of breath, as can ingesting *Carbo vegetabilis*. Thus we can say that we must look to the renal system for the deeper reasons for such respiratory disturbances as shortness of breath.

And we must look to the liver system for the deeper reasons for balances and imbalances related to water or the fluid element. Thirst is related to the liver system just as the need to breathe—shortness of breath and respiratory regulation—is related to the kidney system. All thirst is related to the liver system. It would be an interesting task to study the interconnections between various human manifestations of thirst and the effects of the liver system. Similarly, the phenomenon of hunger and everything in that area are intimately related to the lungs' inner constitution and internal metabolism.

In actuality, hunger, thirst, and the need to breathe are related on the tangible side to air, water, and earth. Many other things are related to their counterparts out there in the universe. Understandably enough, if we need light stimulation because the internal factor that creates new, original light is exhausted, this light stimulation is best obtained from light itself. As we see, this is a justification for therapeutic methods that use light. It is important to consider, however, that light baths are not always light baths. In reality, light baths are a more intense exposure to the zone of chemistry than we usually have as we go about our life on Earth. Factors accompanying the chemistry that streams in from outside—along with the light, of course—are the effective principle behind most light baths. And directly behind these factors stand—as you can see from the diagram [on p. 165]—the life forces, which are also present as a consequence of allowing intensified light or intensified chemical action to work on a person. It is always a question of moderation and balance, but as long as overly strong effects are avoided, the effects of the chemical and life activities accompanying the light streaming in from the universe can be extremely beneficial.

In conclusion, I would like to comment in passing that it will no longer surprise you that modern science does not succeed in achieving insight into the origin of life itself. Modern science limits its search to regions where, thanks to Mercury's influence, only the counterimage of life—death—is present. To find life itself, we would have to look out there in places where today's scientists do not want to go. They want to avoid having anything to do with extratelluric realms if at all possible. Even when scientists have been unable to avoid considering these realms, they make everything materialistic. Their hypothesis that the seeds of life are carried down to our Earth from other heavenly bodies is a convenient materialistic translation of the working of life forces. Supposedly, these seeds are carried down in a materialistic way by other heavenly bodies, avoiding all the obstacles, and then appear on our Earth. Some people even see meteorites as the vehicles these seeds of life drive down to Earth. So you see, today people can even claim to have successfully explained matters with their materialistic theory. Just as they believe they have explained everything that is observed on a macroscopic level by relegating it to the microscopic level or to the submicroscopic level of molecules and atomic theory, they also believe that they have explained life when they have really only relegated it to someplace else.

LECTURE 12

DORNACH, APRIL 1, 1920

REFLECTING on the connection—which we sometimes encounter in very strange ways—between external phenomena and internal human phenomena is fundamental to the perception of professional healers. Such reflection yields very significant intuitions with regard to the nature of therapeutic substances. To mention a one example, let me remind you of how some good spirit seems to have formulated substances such as Roncegno water or Levico water, developing them in advance in outer, nonhuman nature under specific circumstances expressly in order to prepare a number of forces capable of playing a beneficial role in the human organism.[42] During the next few days, we will characterize such matters thoroughly. If we think about how wonderfully the two forces of copper and of iron offset each other in this water and about how arsenic is also present to provide a broader basis for this interaction, we realize that something is being prepared in the outer world with specific regard to certain conditions in the human being.

It is absolutely possible for such things to have extremely unfavorable effects on some individuals, but even the negative instances demonstrate the general fruitfulness of the overall principle. It is especially important to point this out whenever such things are talked about today, because reflecting on them makes it possible to combat certain

---

42. Roncegno and Levico are mineral waters from the Dolomites (limestone mountains) in northern Italy.

illnesses whose symptoms are only now appearing. Let us not forget that truly unbiased observers are beginning to realize from all sides that very specific circumstances are now spreading over parts of the globe and evoking very specific forms of human illness. We must also not forget another intriguing modern phenomenon, namely, a very peculiar characteristic of even a condition like ordinary influenza in its modern manifestation. It wakens dormant illnesses, illnesses to which the organism is predisposed but that otherwise remain hidden by the organism's counteractive forces. Under certain circumstances, these illnesses might even remain dormant until the death of the person in question, but they are uncovered in some way because the person comes down with the flu.

All of this adds up to a cluster of questions that I will use as the basis of these lectures for the next few days. In order to get off to a productive start, I would like to mention another remarkable concordance whose entire profound significance can become apparent only to spiritual scientists. As you know, oxygen and nitrogen are loosely bound to each other in our atmosphere in a way that cannot be properly explained physically or chemically, as it were. As human beings, as earthly human beings, we are totally enmeshed in the activity that emanates from oxygen and nitrogen. From the very beginning, therefore, we can suspect that the fundamental proportion of oxygen to nitrogen is important.

The important thing that spiritual science shows us is that human sleep disturbances are linked to any change in air composition that tends to alter one way or another the usual proportion of oxygen to nitrogen. This phenomenon leads us to investigate the underlying relationship more exactly. As you know, spiritual science prompts us to say that the human being consists of four members—the physical, etheric, and astral bodies and the I. You also know that the phenomena compel us to say that—on the level of dynamics, at least—the I and astral body leave when a person goes to sleep and they move back in when the person awakes. We must realize that, in the sleeping state, the astral body remains bound to the I and the etheric body to the physical body. Therefore, during the waking state, we see that the astral body and I are related to the etheric and physical bodies more loosely than either the I and the astral body or the etheric body and the physical body. This looser internal relationship within the human being between the upper principles (I and astral body) and the lower (etheric and physical bodies) truly reflects the loose relationship between oxygen and nitrogen in external air. The correspondence is remarkable. Because of how the outer composition of air is fixed, it also provides a gauge for the relative connectedness of the astral body and the etheric body, or of the physical body and the I.

This correspondence also makes us aware of how we must relate to the air's composition. We must pay attention to whether we are in a position to supply people with air of the appropriate composition or whether they must do without. At this point, however, you can delve still deeper into physiology and perceive this correspondence. If you go through all the known substances that fulfil some function in the human organism, you will discover that they are all bound up with other substances in the human organism, generally in the form of compounds and solutions. The only elements that exist in a free state within the human organism are oxygen and nitrogen. Therefore, the constituents of external air play a very specific role in the human organism itself. The interrelationship between oxygen and nitrogen is absolutely central to the material aspect of the human being. Oxygen and nitrogen play a specific part in human bodily functions as the only substances that work in their free state, not allowing their effects to be modified by being bound up with other substances in their sphere within the human organism. This shows you that *what* we can trace extending from external nature into the human organism is not the only important thing; we must also trace the *how*, whether the effects of the substance in question remain free or are linked to those of others. The strange thing is that substances develop specific affinities and relationships to each other within the human organism. If we introduce one substance when another one is already present in the human organism, such an affinity or relationship can appear.

If you pursue this thought further, it leads to a very specific intuition that spiritual science needs to point out. You know that proteins form the basis of plant, animal, and human organisms and that, in the sense of modern chemistry, the chief constituents of protein are the four most important substances in nature: carbon, oxygen, nitrogen, and hydrogen, with the addition of sulfur, which homeopathically pervades what the other four substances do.

We need to come to an idea of how proteins actually function internally. The modern science of chemistry tends to assume that the configuration of such a substance is imposed by its intrinsic forces. The inevitable consequence of this assumption is that substances are described as identical when they are not, or at least not to the extent that we imagine. Whenever any difference at all is acknowledged, equating the two substances is not justified. Seeing plant protein and animal protein as similar, as chemically identical to a certain extent, is only a consequence of this atomistic way of thinking about the structure of protein, and is totally unjustified. If we observe the human organism more precisely, it becomes apparent that plant protein neutralizes animal protein and especially human protein. These two proteins stand in a polar relationship to each other in that the one cancels out the effects of the other on an intimate level. This is the strange phenomenon that we must acknowledge: The functions of animal protein are such that they are diminished or negated, either partly or wholly, by the functions of plant protein. This leads us to ask what the difference is between a substance of this sort as it occurs in the animal or human organism and in the plant organism.

You see, in the past few days I have spoken about the important role played by the organ systems (the kidney-urinary, the liver, and the pulmonary systems) with regard to meteorology, to the supra-earthly factor. To these I added the cardiac system. These four organ systems play a crucial role in the human being's relationship to meteorology, to what is outside. What do they actually signify from a more intimate perspective?

These four organ systems are nothing less than the creators of the structure of human protein. They are what we need to study, not protein's molecular or atomic forces. When we wonder why protein is the way it is, we must understand it as being internally built up as a result of the emanations of these four organ systems. Protein is a consequence of their interactions. This also says something about the internalization of external effects in the human being. What modern chemistry seeks in the structure of substances themselves must be attributed to organ systems. The structure of human protein cannot be imagined to exist out in our earthly surroundings. When it is not under the influence of these four organ systems, this structure cannot persist and absolutely has to change.

It is different with plant protein. Although plant protein at least appears uninfluenced by such organ systems, it is subject to other influences. It is under the influence of oxygen, nitrogen, hydrogen, and carbon and of whatever else is present in the external meteorology of nature as a whole and also to the influence of the sulfur that mediates their functions. In plant protein, these four substances that are dispersed in the atmosphere give rise to what is brought about in the human being by the heart, the lungs, the liver, and so on. In outer, nonhuman nature, these four substances contain the formative forces that are individualized and contained by the four organ systems within the human being.

When we say the names oxygen, hydrogen, and so on, it is important to think of these so-called substances not only in terms of the intrinsic forces modern chemistry speaks of but also in terms of formative effects that always have relationships to one another inasmuch as they contribute to the Earth's repertoire of substances. If we go into detail and associate these substances with the corresponding internal organs, we must equate what oxygen does in the outer world with the renal-urinary system.

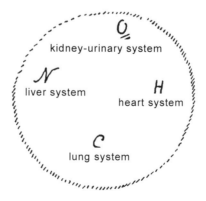

We must equate the formative forces that carbon develops on the outside with the lung system—that is, with the lungs' own formative forces rather than the pulmonary system as a system of respiration. We must equate nitrogen with the liver system and hydrogen with the cardiac system. External hydrogen is the heart of the external world, while nitrogen is the external world's liver, and so on.

It would be desirable for modern humanity to take the initiative to work out these matters instead of merely being persuaded to acknowledge them. You see, if we consider the cardiac system's relationship to the formative forces of hydrogen, we will immediately recognize the importance of hydrogen activity as such for the entire upper region of the human being. Hydrogen's development in the direction of the upper part of the human being is accompanied by the transformation of the more animal aspect down below into something human, something that moves in the direction of concepts, and so on. In a previous lecture, I told you that we encounter an influence that is supra-earthly; and it was identified it as lead. You recall how we described lead, tin, and iron as forces having to do with the upper part of the human being. As yet, there is no great tendency today to acknowledge such connections. There is no great tendency to move outward from the human being, to see lead's effects as particularly related to the phenomenon that the human heart prepares hydrogen, which in turn becomes the vehicle for preparing our thinking apparatus. The unconscious progress of human evolution coerces human beings into acknowledging this fact, although I do not mean this in the sense of propagandizing. Now that science has confirmed that lead, along with helium, is a byproduct of the disintegration of radium, it can no longer be denied that lead plays a role of some sort in external, non-human nature, even if we consider it only with regard to its functions. The lead that has been found in this context, although its so-called atomic weight is not quite right, is nonetheless considered lead. Tin and iron will also be found under similar circumstances. These are substances that are external to the human being but are simultaneously uniquely involved in human nature.

I think we should not simply allow ourselves to be coerced by such phenomena as radiology—which is actually a wonderful hint that if we go out into the nonhuman world, we may discover not crudely material metals, but the metal forces that are working in from above the Earth. This is something that needs to be said today, because the appearance of new, modern types of illness will make us realize that we absolutely must take such matters into account.

At this point we must be particularly interested in the fact that the interaction of external carbon, hydrogen, oxygen, and nitrogen, which is mediated by sulfur, is taken over internally and individualized by the four human organ systems. If you reflect on a matter such as this correctly, you will perceive the depth with which it is possible to see into the human being when considered this way. It will no longer seem miraculous when involuntary human processes (ones that do not initially seem to be immediately subject to our mental functions) are viewed in relation to the whole of external, nonhuman nature. Here again, it is true that each of these four human systems has the tendency to "become" the entire human being. Take the renal system as an example. I might say that the kidney with its functions attempts to become the entire human being, as do the heart, the liver system, and the pulmonary system.

It is important to convince ourselves of the questions that come into consideration here by using our own eyes—or rather our own sensations—to discover how we can observe certain external effects within ourselves. It is almost impossible to avoid pointing out a clear-cut boundary between natural science and spiritual science in this regard. In reality, you see, as you make progress in your meditative life as medical practitioners, as you understand more and more how to achieve harmony with the meditative life so that you feel yourself to be a meditator, you will increasingly acquire concrete self-knowledge of a sort that is truly not to be scorned when we are dealing with positive tasks in life such as healing. As you make progress in meditation, you will notice that you become conscious of things in your own organism that were formerly totally unconscious. By simply taking into account what rises to consciousness, you become aware of something that is still difficult to speak about in lectures to the public or to lay audiences because of a very distinct inclination that emerges in that context. Given the present-day moral constitution of humanity, if we were to talk about such matters—and I am now drawing your attention to one of the elementary ones—and communicate them to wider circles, the following questions would immediately arise: Why don't we take advantage of that? Why should I meditate if I can achieve the same result more easily by simply swallowing some substance or other?

It is more comfortable to take a remedy instead of meditating. In some respects, people who do this destroy themselves morally. Given the present-day moral constitution of humanity, people would be relentless. (You will soon see what I mean.) Instead of meditating, they would prefer to take an external agent that would help them take the first steps toward a result similar to that of meditation. It is really possible for this to happen. You see, if you continue meditating for a certain period of time and are inclined to take such phenomena into account, you will become aware of the radiating effects of iron in the same way that you are aware of having hands that allow you to pick things up and feet that allow you to walk. It really is true that being conscious of the effect of iron appears in the same way as the consciousness that you have arms and legs or a head that you can turn. What appears is the consciousness of feeling yourself as an iron phantom.

I mean that people would come along and say that it is possible to heighten your sensitivity to the iron within you by external means, by means of something you ingest, in order to get the effect of meditation. With regard to certain steps, this is absolutely correct. But then the danger would be that people begin simply experimenting in this way in order to find an easy way to become clairvoyant. These things have often been done. It is different if they are done out of a spirit of sacrifice for humanity, but if they are done out of curiosity, they destroy the moral constitution of the human soul from the ground up. One man who performed a great many such experiments on himself was van Helmont. This was how he discovered much of what you can now read in his writings. In the case of Paracelsus, you have the feeling that his insights arose in him atavistically from within, that he carried them into this world from a super-earthly world, while van Helmont always acquired his strange insights by ingesting some substance or other.[43] This is evident from how he presents his findings, and I believe he also says so quite clearly in certain places. Inner sensitivity to the radiant effects of iron is as close as we can come to the characteristic effect that bears witness to a radiating force that proceeds outward from the upper part of the human being, branching out into all the limbs. We gain a clear perception—and I use this word deliberately—that we are dealing with the iron inside us or rather with its functions and forces.

If I represent this iron radiation schematically, I must also mention at the same time that, as such, it has no ability to work beyond the human organism. We always have the feeling that what is radiating outward is localized within the human organism and remains within it. Some counteracting force, something that arrests these iron-radiating forces, is omnipresent [see Steiner's blackboard drawing on the following page]. We might say that it is as if the iron radiates out toward the periphery and something radiates back toward it in the form of spherical waves. These are the two effects we perceive—the radiating element and its collision with something impenetrable that does not permit it to go beyond the body's surface. We gradually notice that the opposing radiation is the force of protein. This means that iron introduces a functional connection that works against everything emanating from the four organ systems I mentioned earlier. These forces counteract each other. This battle, which is constant in the organism, is the first thing that can be sensed by means of inner perception. If we move on to study human spiritual history, we will clearly note that the medicine of Hippocrates and even that of Galen worked with remnants of inner observations of this sort. Galen himself was no longer able to perceive much, but he recorded all kinds of traditions that came down from earlier times.[44] Anyone who can read Galen in the right way will probably find that a great deal of ancient atavistic medicine, which began to decline in the time of Hippocrates, is still illuminated in Galen's works, which is why they contain so many important views on natural healing processes.

---

43. van Helmont and Paracelsus: see footnote lecture 1, p. 6.
44. Galen: See footnote on p. 5, lecture 1.

1 April 1920.

If we pursue such concerns, we will inevitably come to this polarity in the entire human organism between iron radiations and the influences that block them. It is important to look at these questions because everything that tends to form protein in the way I described always has to do with the blocking effects, while everything metallic that is introduced into the human organism has to do with the radiating effects. Admittedly, there are significant, extraordinarily characteristic exceptions to this rule, but here, too, these very exceptions allow us to look deeply into the strange interaction of the forces that assert themselves within the human organism, but come from all points of the universe.

In order to do so, some things that I have already pointed out, the details of which you can then develop in your own thinking, need to be taken a bit further. For example, I need only mention that the carbon in plants—we can see this in *Carbo vegetabilis*, which we looked at yesterday—lacks an element that animal carbon generally possesses, namely, a certain nitrogen content. This accounts for the very different behavior of animal carbon and plant carbon when they are burned. It also accounts for the tendency of animal carbon to play a part in the production of such substances as bile or mucus or even fat itself. The differences we see here between animal and plant carbon lead us to look at how metals, as opposed to non-metals, work in the human organism. I call this radiation and what arrests radiation.

When we look at this polar interaction, we come to very important matters. You see, in the course of explaining spiritual science, I have often emphasized that human beings go through various periods in life—the period of childhood until the second dentition, the period from the second dentition until puberty, and the third period, which lasts until the early twenties. In reality, these periods of life are connected to processes intrinsic to the human organism. I have often characterized the first period, which concludes with the second dentition, as a process of self-limitation that focuses the entire human organism on separating out and incorporating its solid scaffolding. This process culminates in the emergence of new teeth from this human scaffolding. Obviously, bursting forth into solid form in this way must have to do with the overall development of the human form, especially its development toward the periphery.

It is well worth noting that two substances that are otherwise not given their due in the human organism, namely, fluorine and magnesium, are intimately involved in everything that is taking place here. Fluorine and magnesium are present in dilute form in the human organism and play prominent roles in the process in childhood that leads up to the second dentition. In terms of incorporating solidity into the human organism, what happens here is a constant interaction between the forces of magnesium and the forces of fluorine, with fluorine assuming the role of sculptor in the human being, rounding off and arresting the radiating element, while the magnesium forces ray outward, organizing fiber bundles and the like so that calcium can infiltrate them. To say that a tooth comes about simply because fluorine the sculptor shapes it with regard to its size, cement, and enamel, while magnesium pours in the substance that is to be sculpted, is not nonsense, but is dramatically in line with what happens in nature.

This is why it is so very important to maintain a balance between magnesium intake and fluorine intake in earliest childhood. You will always find that the teeth decay early if this balance is not properly established. We need to begin observing the child's dental development as soon as the first tooth appears to see whether the enamel is underdeveloped or whether the teeth tend to be small. Through appropriate diet, we must make sure to counteract any incipient problem by supplying the appropriate compounds of either fluorine or magnesium. (We will have to speak about these things in more detail, but for now I would like to approach the subject in concentric circles.) This allows us to see into the process of human development, where we discover this interaction between magnesium and fluorine. It is characteristic of the substance fluorine to be markedly external to the human being during the first years of life, because in these early years the human being really belongs to the outer world to a great extent. Fluorine is taken from the world external to the human being, from the external principle that counteracts the radiant effect of metal.

Similarly, if you take the third period of human life, it is very important to bring about the right balance between iron and protein or protein formation. If the right balance is not achieved and no strongly corrective developments emerge to offset the lack of balance between protein and iron, we confront all the outer symptoms of anemia. It is important that we not look at the developing human being only in a crude way, noting phenomena such as tooth decay, for which the groundwork was laid at an earlier age, or looking at anemia only from the modern chemical perspective. We must delve into the entire mystery of the human organism if we want to understand anything of what appears in an individual who is ill.

You all know more or less which metals play a part in building up the human organism internally. With the exception of iron, the metals that I described to you as the most important in a certain connection—lead, tin, copper, mercury, silver, gold, and iron—are not involved. With the exception of iron, as I said, they have no direct effect on the overall functioning of the human organism, but this does not mean that they are any the less active in the human being. If we trace the substance that is most involved in developing what is located near the periphery of the human organism, we find that it is silicon. I have already spoken about this. But the processes going on in the human being are not simply contained within the skin; the human being is also enmeshed in universal processes. Just as the substances

you know of are significant within the human organism, the metals I
have just listed are significant outside the human organism but work
into it. Iron alone plays the role of mediator between what lies within
a human being's skin and what lies outside it.

We can say that the entire system that appears in the pulmonary
human being, which as you know attempts to become a whole human
being, is strongly connected to our entire relationship to the life of
nature in the universe. We must realize that we take only one part of
the human being into account if we consider anatomy alone. This is
not the entire human being, it is simply that aspect that counteracts
the external principle consisting of the effects of lead, tin, copper, and
so on, effects that are external to the human individual. It is never permissible to restrict the human being to what is inside the skin, not
even when we are simply considering the human organization in a natural scientific sense. As we can see, it is not simply a question of effects
that make their way from within outward. We must also take into
account the effects that provide some sort of direction for human
organic processes. What follows will demonstrate that this is a very significant consideration.

You know that certain substances take effect in the human organism
simply because they are bound to alkalis or acids or because they
appear in a neutral form (as is said in science) as salts. But the relationship of bases to acids as polar opposite systems of forces that enter a
neutral state of sorts in salts does not cover this subject in its entirety.
We must also take into account the relationship of the acid-base-salt
trinity to the overall direction of human organ forces. We will find
that all alkalis tend to support processes that begin in the mouth and
continue in digestion, working from front to back. Similarly, all other
processes that run from front to back also have such a role. Bases have
to do with the front-to-back direction, while acids have to do with the
reverse. Only when we look at the contrast between the front and back
of the human being do we arrive at the contrast between bases and
acids. The saltlike principle relates to these two as if it were directed
downward toward the Earth, standing vertically on both. Salt throws
itself into all processes that work from above to what lies below. For
this reason we must absolutely take these three directions into account

in considering how the human being fits into the alkaline, acidic, and salty elements.

These directional forces are another example of how observing the human being bridges the gap between the purely external chemistry of metals and human physiology. Here you also have the entire relationship of the saltlike element to the Earth and the phenomena of bases and acids. Schematically, it could be drawn something like this: If this is the Earth here [see blackboard sketch on p. 181], the saltlike element tends toward the Earth, while bases and acids tend to move around the Earth in circles. This, in turn, suggests that simply by becoming familiar with the directions of functions in the organism, we are then able to intervene in these directions. In this case external remedies such as ointments and salves—everything that works externally—are crucial. At this point we must also study the direction of external effects. Under certain circumstances, the extractive effect of a mustard plaster or the effect of a metal ointment—suitably prepared, of course—can be just as important for the organism as any internal treatment. As will be clear to you from what I just said, we must simply know *how* we should use it, because it does make a difference whether we apply a plaster to one part of the body or another in a particular situation. It is essential to evoke the effect that counters a damaging force by applying the plaster to the right part of the body. Simply placing it on the painful or otherwise irritated spot is not always the right thing to do.

LECTURE 13

ESPECIALLY with regard to three sets of facts that we must now begin to discuss, the more materialistic trend in medicine may possibly begin to turn toward our spiritual-scientifically oriented school of thought. This will most probably be the case with our observations of everything involved in tumor formation and possible cures for cancer, a truly rational view of so-called mental illnesses, and our knowledge of the therapeutic use of external remedies—liniments, ointments, and the like. We can scarcely hope that conventional physical examinations unguided by spiritual-scientific insights will suffice to approach subjects such as the development of growths that culminate in carcinomas. Connections are omnipresent in the natural world, and today's psychiatry is in such a sorry state because there is no human, conscious connection between it and conventional pathology and therapy—two fields that are perhaps the most receptive to spiritual-scientific viewpoints. It will be especially necessary to consider everything spiritual science can say about these topics. Today all that is needed is to consider my writings; you will find that they have already said quite a lot in this regard. We need to take into account all aspects of the etheric body's intervention in the human organism.

It should not be said that clairvoyance is absolutely necessary in order to be able to talk about the etheric body's activity in the human organism, because a great many processes that simply oppose the etheric body's activities demonstrate that the etheric body is not active, or at least not properly active, in a specific way. To come to valid ideas on this subject, we will need to look at inflammations and their con-sequences as well as at tumor development as a starting point for the destruction of the human organism, so to speak. In the case of tumor development, very justifiable attempts are now being made to avoid surgery. Because of social circumstances that will need to be changed—not outer conditions, but social circumstances in which medicine plays a part, namely, issues of public hygiene—this very jus-tified ideal cannot always be implemented. The important point here is to create a substitute for what the surgeon's knife does or does not accomplish—and it certainly is effective in some respects but fails to accomplish anything in others. There are undoubtedly many people who advocate surgery today simply because they have no way of knowing about anything else but who will immediately take the oppo-site approach as soon as information becomes available.

You do not need me to describe the character of inflammatory pro-cesses in their various specific forms organ by organ. I am sure this is well known, but what is not so well known is the overriding process common to all inflammatory processes. This common process can best be characterized by saying that in every true inflammation, whether very small or very large, and in everything that can lead from inflammation to ulceration, spiritual-scientific investigation will reveal that the human etheric body as a whole is still functioning. This means that we can count on being able to do something to normalize and redistribute the etheric body's effect, which has become sluggish in a single direction, so that the person's entire etheric body will then work in a healthy way. In inflammations, the etheric body's activity is guided only in specific directions, whereas the activity of a healthy etheric body extends into the organism in all the appropriate direc-tions. In essence, we can say that if the etheric body as a whole is still healthy but has become sluggish with regard to a particular organ sys-tem, we will be able to discover agents, which we will discuss later, that are capable of stimulating it to develop its universal activity, if I may call it that, in this specific direction.

It is different in tumor formations of any sort. In this case, certain processes in the physical body function directly as enemies of the etheric body's activity. These processes in the physical body simply rebel against the etheric body's activity. As a consequence, the etheric body is no longer effective in these areas of the physical body. The etheric body, however, has a great capacity for regeneration, and spiritual-scientific observation shows that if we can remove the obstruction and overcome the enemy that counteracts the etheric body's activity in a certain area, we will indeed be able to deal with the problem. With tumors, then, it is a matter of using natural processes to stimulate the removal of the physical processes opposing the etheric body so that it can once again work in a spot its effects formerly could not reach.

This will become very important in the treatment of carcinomas. If carcinomas are observed objectively, it is quite evident that in spite of their many different forms, they all constitute a revolt on the part of certain physical forces against the forces of the etheric body. The cornification that typically appears in internal carcinomas and is less prominent in carcinomas located nearer the surface—although the tendency persists—shows us that a physical formative process has overcome the etheric formative process that should be present at that particular spot.

A careful study of these two phenomena—inflammation and ulceration on the one hand and tumor formation on the other—eventually makes it obvious that they are true polar opposites. Having said that this is obvious, let me also ask you to recall your experience of carcinomas located close to the surface. What happens in such cases can frequently be confused with pseudo-abscesses, at least in certain respects. Above all, therefore, it will be important to study this polarity more precisely.

Medical nomenclature that is at least medieval, if not exactly ancient, is often very disturbing in such instances. I am not referring to the historical medieval period but to the Middle Ages of nomenclature that lie in the quite recent past. It is not totally correct to describe tumors as "neoplasms." There is nothing new about them except in the very trivial sense of not having been there before; they are not new in the sense of growing out of the ground of the skin-enclosed organism of their own accord. They come about because the physical body opposes the etheric body so strongly that the outer body aligns itself with aspects of outer nature that are inimical to the human being. Tumor development offers easy access to all sorts of outer influences.

Here again it is important to study the image that contrasts with all these processes. Let me point you first in the direction of studying the development of *Viscum* (mistletoe) in outer nature. Although we do initially need to pay attention to how *Viscum* species develop on other plants, this is not the most important consideration. The parasitic nature of mistletoe is certainly the most important consideration for botany, but as far as our study of the connection between outer, non-human nature and the human being is concerned, a much more important consideration is that mistletoe, because it grows on other plants, on trees, is forced to carry out its vegetative growth in a different annual rhythm. For example, it is already done flowering before the trees it grows on have begun putting out leaves in spring. It is a winter plant and rather aristocratic in its behavior. It uses the foliage of its host trees to protect it from the intense light of summer and does not expose itself to the most intense rays of the Sun. (In line with the processes we described the day before yesterday, we must always see the Sun simply as a representative of the effects of light, but this would need to be studied in the context of physics and does not belong in this discussion. We cannot completely avoid what has crept into our language as a result of somewhat inaccurate observations of nature.)

Mistletoe's whole way of growing and thriving by attaching itself to other plants is especially important because it allows this plant to acquire very specific forces that can be described more or less as follows. Thanks to the forces it acquires, it rejects the intentions of organizational forces that develop in a straight line and demands their opposite. Here, too, the situation will become clear only when we understand it in the following way. Here is a schematic representation [see blackboard drawing, p. 190] of a spot in the human body that uses its own forces to revolt against all the etheric forces working into it. The etheric forces are backed up and brought to a standstill, and as a result something that looks like a new growth comes about. Mistletoe is a remedy that counteracts the etheric pocket that has formed here. It pulls the etheric forces back into this spot where they did not want to go.

You could verify this situation yourself through observation if you ever have a coincidental opportunity to observe the effect of mistletoe on the expulsion of the placenta. In this case, you would be able to study mistletoe's tendency to oppose straight-line organization Mistletoe causes the placenta to be retained in the human organism; that is, in its own way it does the opposite of straight-line organization. The ability to cause retention of the placenta—that is, to bring the usual organizational process to a standstill—is one of the most important characteristics of mistletoe's effective processes. Of course, in the case of more subtle activities in the human organism that have the same basis as placental retention, this effect is much less readily apparent, but the same force that is strongly active when mistletoe counteracts the straight-line organizational tendency also confronts us in any other images we get of mistletoe's effect. Having noticed that mistletoe counters the etheric body's failure to take hold of the physical body to the right extent, if we then induce a specific mistletoe effect, the etheric body may take hold of the physical body too strongly, resulting in convulsions. In other cases, the effects of mistletoe can cause the peculiar sensation of being in constant danger of falling over. These consequences are also related to the fact that mistletoe essentially promotes pollution, for example.

You can see in every instance—even in connection with the development of epilepsy, for example—that mistletoe has the capacity of opposing the human organism. This ability has less to do with the fact that it is a parasite, however, than with the fact that it allows nature to "give it a free helping of sausage"—to use an expression that at least the Viennese among you will understand. It is granted a special favor, an exception to the rule, in that it refuses to thrive in the usual season, to flower in the spring and then bear fruit. Instead, it does these things in a different season, during the winter. By doing so, it retains forces that then counteract the normal course of events. If it is not too offensive, we may say that if we look at how nature behaves in the development of mistletoe, nature seems to have gone crazy. It does everything at the wrong time when it comes to mistletoe. This behavior, however, is exactly what we will put to use when the human organism goes physically crazy, which is what happens in the development of carcinomas. The point is to develop an understanding of such relationships.

There can be no doubt that mistletoe is the substance that, if potentized, will allow us to replace the surgeon's knife in treating tumors. It is only a question of handling mistletoe fruit in the right way—but in connection with other forces in mistletoe itself, of course—so as to turn it into a remedy.

Mistletoe's craziness is also evident in the fact that its continued existence and reproduction are always dependent on being moved from place to place by birds. Mistletoe would surely die out if birds did not repeatedly carry its means of reproduction from one tree to another. Curiously enough, its reproductive structures also choose to pass through the birds themselves, in that they are first taken into the birds' bodies and later evacuated so that they can sprout on another tree. All these findings, if observed objectively, lead to insight into mistletoe's entire process of development. The gluey substance in mistletoe, in particular, needs to be brought into the right connection with a triturating agent so as to gradually produce a very high potency of this substance.

Next, this substance needs to be specially adapted to different organs—I will go into detail later—in part by considering the origin of the mistletoe, specifically what kind of a tree it grew on. But it will also be important to produce remedies that are based on the interaction of this gluey substance with specific metallic substances, which can even be derived from the metal content of other plants. For example, the interaction that comes about by combining and potentizing mistletoe from apple trees with silver salts will result in a remedy that can be highly effective against all abdominal cancers.

You must understand that I need to speak cautiously about these subjects, because although the basic thrust of what I am saying is absolutely correct and well founded in spiritual-scientific research, actual therapeutic measures depend totally on how mistletoe's constituents are processed, and the knowledge needed to produce such remedies is scarcely available yet. At this point, of course, spiritual science would be able to work favorably only when it could actually constantly collaborate with the clinical process that is the basis of so much of what other physicians do. This is what makes the relationship between spiritual science and medicine so difficult. These two approaches—the opportunity for clinical observation and spiritual-scientific research—must still remain separated because of modern social conventions. It will become evident that we will get nowhere unless these two paths are brought together. The important point will be to gather empirical evidence, because the only way you will be able to impress the outer world is if you can at least supply verification in the form of outer clinical reports, and so on. The need for these proofs is more an outer than an inner one.

If we simply proceed methodically, we will be able to prove that the effect of mistletoe really is based on what I have just explained. According to what I said here a few days ago, tree trunks are more like outgrowths of soil substance, little hills in which the vegetative aspect is still present and which support the growth of everything else that belongs to the tree. When mistletoe also grows there, its roots grow toward the ground as it makes itself at home up there on the tree. Thus it is to be expected that if we conduct experiments with plants that have the same crazy aristocratic attitude as mistletoe but lack its bohemian parasitic quality, we will see similar characteristics, and this is indeed the case. If we begin to investigate winter plants with regard to their tendency to counteract normal tendencies of the human organism, and specifically normal tendencies to develop illnesses, we can expect that plants that find it appropriate to put forth flowers in winter will all have similar effects. For example, if we simply extend our experiments to include *Helleborus niger*, the common Christmas rose, we will find that it induces similar effects. We must take into account, however, the contrast between male and female that I have at least begun to characterize. With *Helleborus niger*, we can hardly expect to achieve clearly visible results in women, but results will be perceptible in cases of tumor development in men if we use a similar processing method but produce a higher potency than the one I indicated in the case of *Viscum*.

If we work in this way, we must consider relationships of this sort—whether a plant thrives in winter or summer, whether it derives its effect from behaving like mistletoe or whether it is more inclined toward the Earth. Mistletoe does not like to be close to the Earth, but black hellebore, or Christmas rose, does, and is therefore more closely related to the male system of forces, which in turn is more closely related to earthly factors, as I explained a few days ago. The female system of forces is instead more closely connected to supra-earthly factors. These differences absolutely must be taken into account. It will prove especially important to acquire a certain insight into the processes of nature. This is why, in the attempt to illustrate the forces in the outer world, I turned to concepts of character such as "bohemian," "aristocratic," and "crazy" (which can serve us very well and are not at all inadequate with respect to what we are considering) to show what these forces are like.

Having acquired such concepts, we will then encounter the characteristic difference between a remedy's external and internal effects. But before we take this difference into account, we must also look at ideas that can introduce it in the right way. For example, there is one thing that absolutely must be studied with regard to certain illnesses that are now appearing. In the case of these new types of illness, which I pointed out yesterday, we will have to study what happens, for example, when we expose *Carbo vegetabilis* to marsh gas for some time simply by leaving it lying in the gas; we proceed with trituration only after the carbon is sufficiently impregnated with gas. The result will be externally effective in some way, in the form of ointments and the like, especially if the trituration is performed in conjunction with substances that can enhance the effect further. It is simply a question of discovering the right technique. If triturated with talc, for example, according to certain technical methods that we will certainly be able to ascertain, the resulting remedy will be very effective if used externally in the form of ointments and the like.

The important thing for us now, however, is to understand such a process. We will not understand it if we do not first sharpen our vision by learning healthy thinking with regard to psychiatry. Please believe me that spiritual scientists are actually angered, if I may express myself drastically, by the use of the German word *Geisteskrankheit* ("spirit illness") for psychiatric illness. It is ridiculous to use this term because the spirit is always healthy and incapable of falling ill. What happens is that the spirit's ability to express itself is disturbed by the physical organism. There is never any real illness in the life of the spirit or soul. Symptoms appear, but that is all.

Now, however, we must sharpen our vision for concrete individual symptoms. Perhaps you will see the first indications and then the further development of something like religious mania. (As you know, these terms are not all precise because the nomenclature in this field is extremely confused. Nevertheless, we do need to use these words.) All this, of course, is merely symptomatic. But assuming that something like this develops, the important point will be to gain a picture of its entire process of development. Once we have acquired this picture, however, and encounter an individual with this symptomatology, we will have to look carefully at any abnormalities in the process of lung formation—not in the respiratory process, but in the lungs' formative process, in pulmonary metabolism. You see, the term brain disease is also not totally correct. If the term *Geisteskrankheit* is completely false, then "brain disease" is actually half false, because any degeneration in the brain is always secondary. The primary factor in all illnesses never lies in the upper part of the body, but always in the lower part, in the organs belonging to the four systems of the liver, kidneys, heart, and lungs. In the case of someone who is losing interest in outer life and beginning to brood and act out delusions, the most important concern is always to get an idea of the constitution of this person's pulmonary process. This is extremely important.

Similarly, if we observe someone in whom obstinacy, pig-headedness, and self-righteousness appear, indicating a certain immobility or rigidity in thinking, this should lead us to investigate the status of liver function in the person in question. In such people, it is always the inner organic chemistry that is not functioning properly. Even what we have become accustomed to calling "softening of the brain" in common parlance is entirely secondary. The primary factor in psychiatric disorders, even if it is sometimes more difficult to observe, always lies in the lower organ systems. This accounts for the often dishearteningly low rate of success of psychotherapy. In fact, psychotherapy can accomplish more in the case of organic diseases than it can in so-called psychiatric disorders. We will have to get used to treating psychiatric disorders with medications. This is crucial, and it is the second of two areas in which outer trends in medicine will have to find a way to approach spiritual science.

In this area, well-trained psychologists will always prove to be the best observers. An extraordinary amount lies hidden in our psychological life, with all its great variety and its frequently merely suggestive effects. We will gradually have to achieve a real capacity for observation in this field. It is not true that human beings are simple or simply constituted in terms of their abilities, by which I also mean the capabilities of the bodily state of organization, which is the tool of a person's spiritual organization. Let me give an example. Strange as it may sound, it is absolutely possible for someone we are obliged to describe as an idiot, as a feebleminded person, to have abilities that allow him or her to come up with comments that are witty and brilliant. This is truly possible, because feeblemindedness can make a person very open to suggestion, very receptive to reflecting the mysterious influences of his or her surroundings. There are very interesting observations to be made in the field of pathological cultural history. We must not name names in reporting the results of such observations, which would detract from their credibility. It is not right to name names, but it is an idiosyncrasy of the field of journalism in particular that people with feeble minds can become good journalists because their slow wit puts them in a position to reflect the opinion of the times rather than giving their own obstinate views. For example, dull-witted journalists reflect the opinion of the times to such an extent that their accounts are much more interesting than those of self-possessed, strong-minded journalists. We learn much more about what humanity as a whole is thinking from weak-minded journalists than from strong-minded ones, who are always intent on developing opinions of their own.

This is an extreme case, but it occurs over and over again. It is the ultimate disguise of the actual state of affairs. We fail to notice the presence of feeblemindedness because its initial manifestation can be quite brilliant. In everyday life such a circumstance doesn't make much difference. Ultimately, no harm is done if our newspapers are written by the feeble-minded, as long as they present only good things. In extreme cases, however, where the limit is reached and this tendency develops into a form of illness, we need to acquire a very unbiased eye for observing the soul conditions of people who then fall into the domain of psychiatry. Since we will not always be able to judge by the disguises their soul activity has assumed, we will have to make our assessments on the basis of deeper-lying symptoms.

We must always realize that it is easiest of all to succumb to error when we are observing psychological states, because the most important question is not whether the person expresses intelligent thoughts, for example, but whether he or she tends to repeat these intelligent thoughts more often than the context necessitates. *How* an individual expresses his or her thoughts is the important concern. Whether a person repeats thoughts very frequently or utters them without supplying transitions is more important than whether the thoughts themselves are intelligent or stupid. A completely healthy person can still be stupid—merely physiologically stupid, not pathologically stupid. It is also possible for someone to express a clever thought and still be predisposed to psychiatric illness and even succumb to it. We can see this most readily if the person in question suffers from omission of thoughts or frequent repetition of thoughts. The person who suffers from frequent repetitions always has a potential for illness that is related to a formative lung process that is not in order, while the one who suffers from omission of thoughts always has an inherent predisposition to a liver process that is not functioning properly. Other symptoms fall in between.

These questions, too, can be studied in real life. For example, in cases where a substance is used as a food for pleasure rather than as a medicine, at least in the ordinary sense, we can see that coffee has a very clear and pronounced effect on the entire symptomatic process of our psychological life (and, incidentally, I have often mentioned this before, as least in certain circles). We should not place any value on such effects, although they are indeed present, because reliance on them simply makes the soul sluggish. It is possible to compensate for deficient logic by consuming coffee; that is, coffee consumption predisposes the organism to release more forces for purposes of logic than is the case when a person does not drink coffee. Thus, drinking a lot of coffee should be one of the habits of modern journalists, so that they do not have to chew on their pens so much in order to connect one thought to another.

This is one aspect of the question. In contrast, tea consumption prevents us from always linking one thought to the next in a pedantic professorial fashion, which, if taken to extremes, is not at all witty but bores people because we are constantly subjecting them to the precision of our own logical processes. Certain professions are now in decline, but their old state of organization could have made good use of an external means of becoming as witty as possible without inwardly being so. Members of these professions should have been advised to drink tea. Just as coffee is a good drink for journalists, tea is an extremely effective drink for diplomats, who have great need of the ability to habitually toss off disjointed thoughts that allow one to appear witty.

Such things are important to know, because if we can acknowledge them properly and have the necessary moral soul attitude, we know as a matter of course that in a moral lifestyle, these abilities must be promoted in some other, nondietary way. Such connections are extraordinarily important as a means of educating ourselves about certain natural relationships. Similarly, in a cultural context, it is important to look, for example, at the very low sugar consumption that was once typical in Russia, in contrast to the very high consumption typical in the Western or English-speaking world. We will discover that where psychological development has not paralyzed such manifestations, people present a very clear imprint of what they ingest. Russians express a certain selfless devotion to the outer world and have less ego awareness, which they substitute for on a level that is theoretical at best. This is related to low sugar consumption. In contrast, the British possess a strong, organically based sense of self that is related to high sugar consumption. Here, however, it is less important to look at actual consumption levels than at people's sugar cravings, because the level of consumption always develops as the result of a craving, out of the longing to enjoy something. That is why it is especially important to take a look at such cravings.

Looking to the organ systems of the lower human body as the origin of so-called psychiatric disorders points you in the direction of interactions within the human being that should not be disregarded from the joint perspective of pathology and therapy. These interactions between what I have described in simple terms as the upper and lower areas of the human being must always be taken into account with regard to both pathology and therapy. If we neglect to do so, we will never achieve a proper view of the effect of outer influences through which we want to work on a patient. It makes a big difference whether we apply the effects of warmth or water to a patient's feet or head. But we cannot bring reason to bear on these questions without first becoming aware of the great differences in the functioning of the upper and lower parts of the human being. This is why we will now discuss outer effects on the human being, to the extent that our particular subject permits.

LECTURE 14

I have been thinking for a long time about how to approach today's topic in this lecture series, as I will be able to present it only superficially owing to the shortage of time. I have been pondering whether or not to include it and have decided to do so even though it will show us once again how easily such matters can be misunderstood. You see, for a long time now certain people have been launching their attacks on Anthroposophy by suggesting that anthroposophical statements are just confused nonsense. Now, however, the opinion seems to be emerging that it is no longer possible to make this suggestion, because belated research shows that the matters we discuss give all too strong an impression of agreeing with what can be derived from the ancient mysteries. So now people are inventing the objection that I am betraying the mysteries. It will always be possible for them to formulate their objections in a way that suits their purpose. If they can no longer say that the contents are false, they will at least claim that it is quite wrong to talk about them.

What I want to say first of all is this: We must realize that the physical perspective reveals only a small portion of any human being, for the obvious reason that the human being also includes the etheric body, the astral body, and the I, which are constantly and independently active and working on the human organism and which naturally elude external physical assessment completely. (I use the term assessment advisedly, in view of what I want to present shortly.) But this does not mean that it is impossible for individuals of goodwill to train their intellect and capacity for judgment to absorb aspects of what we might call clairvoyance. These individuals will not achieve clairvoyance of the sort that deals with clear images, but they will achieve a method of evaluation that is at least able to establish a strong and valid relationship to clairvoyant insight.

Please consider the following. Let us begin with how the I works on the human being. Because human beings are what they are in our present period of evolution, the I works first and foremost on the human physical body. In present-day humankind, it has relatively little ability to master even the etheric body. In childhood, the I still governs the etheric body in a relatively dull and unconscious way, but later it no longer controls the etheric body at all. It retains a very strong influence on the etheric body only in those whose imagination remains strong in later life. In general, however, in people who become intellectual in a dry and rational way, the I has a stronger influence on the physical body than on the etheric body.

If you imagine properly what I have described as the influence of the I on the physical body, you will be quite close to also being able to imagine that this I works on the physical organization, setting up a kind of scaffolding throughout. Our physical body really does incorporate something resembling a delicate scaffolding, which can be seen as a kind of phantom that is constantly present. We carry around within us a scaffolding that has been impressed upon us by our I-organization, a very delicate scaffolding that is incorporated into the organization of the physical body out of the forces of the etheric body. In the course of a lifetime, however, we gradually lose the strength to incorporate this scaffolding consciously, although it remains present in our imaginative creativity in a semiconscious, dreamy way.

You can easily see that to a certain extent, the scaffolding the I builds into the human organism is a foreign object, and so the human organism constantly defends itself against this scaffolding and attempts to destroy it every night during sleep. Even though we perceive very little of this scaffolding in everyday life, we must not forget that it tends to splinter or fall apart within the organism. For this reason, it is the constant mysterious cause of inflammations in the organism.

It is very important to consider that a phantom of sorts is built into the human organism by the I, that the organism defends itself against this phantom as if it were a foreign object, and that this foreign object constantly tends to splinter and fall apart within the human being's physical organization. You can get a more or less reasonable view of this scaffolding simply by studying the organization of human eyes from a psycho-physiological perspective. The entire interplay between the eyes and the outer world, or the interplay between the soul and the outer world that takes place through the eyes, is representative of the building of this scaffolding in its purest form. There is a relationship between the I-scaffolding and what comes about through the interaction of the eyes with the environment, and I have often studied this relationship in people who were born blind and in people who have become blind. This makes it very easy to compare the interrelationship between the one phantom, which is a normal phantom in most people and is incorporated into their organization simply through the fact that they see, and the other phantom, which is the consequence of I-activity in the organism.

To express these phenomena graphically, I might say that through seeing, through the visual process, a phantom scaffolding is incorporated into the organism [drawing, white]. The other scaffolding, which is incorporated through the I-process, simply lies a bit deeper within the organism [yellow] and gives a clear indication of physical forces. What the I builds into the organization is a nearly physical phantom, an actual scaffolding, while what the eyes supply is still etheric. It is interesting to see how close these two come to each other in nearsighted people, how what I have sketched here in white comes very close to the other scaffolding, the yellow. In contrast, in farsighted people the white scaffolding moves outward.

In short, if you study the organization of a person's eyes, you will be able to get a reasonable understanding of that person's etheric body, which is very similar to what I have described here as one of the scaffolds. There is no better way of training yourself to grasp certain aspects of a person's etheric body than by paying attention to the organization of that person's eyes. The rest will come by itself. If you develop the habit of paying attention to whether people are near- or farsighted and allow the observation to work on you, this habit trains you to be receptive to perceiving the etheric body. If you then also assist this process by meditating, it will no longer be so difficult for you to move on from dedicated study of what the organization of the eyes evokes in the human being to a study of the etheric body.

Next you will convince yourself of the following. The process that is related to the organization of the eyes is always present in the human being. It is a normal token of a tendency that can also appear in an abnormal form. It is a normal process in everyday life, but something similar appears in all inflammatory conditions. You can really say that if the scaffolding in the physical body, the one that is similar to the etheric body, emerges too strongly, it gives rise to inflammations and their consequences. The conviction that is dawning in you can be strengthened by experimenting with external applications of formic acid derived from the animal kingdom. This is easy to do. You simply obtain the highest possible dilution of formic acid and administer it to your patient in the form of baths. You are then met by a consolidation of this yellow scaffolding here [see drawing, p. 201]. Through the use of formic acid, the I is harnessed to and pervades the scaffolding. If your patient is predisposed to inflammations, this is how you can cope with them, because the scaffolding tends to fall apart and trigger inflammations only when it is not properly pervaded by the I, since the scaffolding and the I belong together. They can be brought together by using formic acid in baths, as I have just described, but the formic acid must be highly diluted because only then do its forces become fully available.

You must pursue symptomatology a bit if you become involved in such matters. You must observe, for example, whether your patients with inflammatory conditions tend toward obesity. You will achieve good results with the above-mentioned external therapy with animal-derived formic acid only if both predispositions are present—on the one hand, a tendency to inflammations and on the other, an inclination to obesity, which points to a certain syndrome. If you have reason to suspect a breakdown of this scaffolding, which you can recognize from various other symptoms we will discuss later, and if you are simultaneously dealing with a patient who is quite strongly predisposed to obesity, you will always achieve extremely beneficial results. This is what must be taken into consideration.

You see, in this case spiritual-scientific knowledge is very shocking to modern individuals. Spiritual science knows that the process that must occur in the human organism so that the eyes develop in the way that they must in human evolution—through a long developmental history, of course—is an inflammatory process that is constantly kept within normal limits so that it does not erupt into inflammation. If you imagine that the same process that is at work in inflammation is held back, slowed down, and compressed, you have the process that forms the eyes in the human organism. From the very appearance of a person's eyes, you can gain an impression of whether or not that person is predisposed to inflammatory conditions. You will be able to see it in people's eyes if you train yourself to observe it. What we can experience about people's vision really is intimately related to observing the human etheric body.

And when we speak of the presence of the etheric body, of learning to perceive the etheric body, there is of course the inner process that leads to actual clairvoyance by way of meditation. But there is also the possibility of self-education from the outside. By attempting to view natural processes in the right way, we acquire insight into them from the perspective of judgment. You see, the organs of clairvoyance must be developed from within, but we develop our capacity for judgment in conjunction with the outer world. If we do this on a more intimate level, our capacity for judgment meets up with the otherwise more intimate meditative process that moves from within outward.

You may be justified in raising the question of whether all this cannot be observed in the animal kingdom too. The situation is this:

204 ❖ INTRODUCING ANTHROPOSOPHICAL MEDICINE

We do not gain a good idea of what is at issue in the human being by studying the same thing in animals. In public lectures, I have often emphasized a point that I want to emphasize here as well, but in greater detail. You see, people think that eyes are eyes, organs are organs, lungs are lungs, livers are livers, and so on. This is not true, however. Human eyes are the same organs as the eyes that are present in an animal, but they are modified by the fact that the I is incorporated into the human being, and the same is true of all the other organs. And with respect to what happens in an organ—which plays a very great role in a human being who is ill, by the way—the fact that it is pervaded by the I is more important than the aspect that also appears in the animal kingdom, where the organ is not pervaded by the I. This is a circumstance that is never taken into account sufficiently. People really never cease to judge these issues on this basis: Here is a knife, and there is a knife. A knife is a knife, and I insist that these are both knives on the basis of how they were made. Yes, but if one knife is a piece of silverware and the other a straight razor, it becomes impossible to insist that a one knife is the same as the other.

It is the same when someone comes along and insists that human eyes and animal eyes can be explained in the same way. It is simply nonsense to attempt to derive the principle that explains something exclusively from that thing's external appearance. This approach leads nowhere, especially if we base a study on mere outer appearances. Animal studies prevent us from examining certain circumstances in humans in the right way, because we can properly call these circumstances to mind only when we are conscious of the fact that the human being's most peripheral organs are the most thoroughly pervaded and shaped by the I.

Human ears are formed in a completely different way from the eyes. We can also comprehend human ears, however; we can train ourselves to understand them objectively in a way that is similar to how we train ourselves to objectively understand the eyes. (This latter type of self-education brings us close to clairvoyant perception of the etheric body.) We can school ourselves to see the facts in the right way, namely, that the ears are incorporated into the human being just as they are in the animal, but that in the human being their formation is then pervaded by the I-organization. If we study the formation of the ears, we discover that they are related to a somewhat more internal aspect of the human organism, just as the etheric body's formation of the eyes is related to a more peripheral aspect. We become able to direct our powers of observation toward ear formation and to say that the I has a role in this process, just as it also has a role in forming the eyes.

The I also incorporates a scaffolding into the organism that is somewhat different from the scaffolding described earlier. This one is related to everything that underlies ear formation in the organism. I will sketch this second scaffolding in here, in blue [see drawing, p. 201]. It lies deeper within the organism than the yellow one and has less of an organizing effect as it extends into the limbs. If we were to extract it from the human being, we would find that it has only stumps instead of arms and legs. We might call it a scaffolding that has remained as an infant in its development. It is also much less differentiated in the direction of the head than the other scaffolding. Once again, we discover a correspondence, this time between the second scaffolding and the organizing forces in human ear formation and all that underlies this process. I will draw it here in violet so that it corresponds to the white [see drawing, p. 201].

Like the first scaffolding, the second one also possesses a certain idiosyncrasy within the human organism. It, too, can become abnormal, so to speak, when the I is working too strongly—in this case, when the I is working too powerfully in the interior. We dealt earlier with the case of the I working with too much force at the surface. Once again, here is a circumstance that can help you study this subject properly. Pursue a bit of symptomatology and consider people who tend to be excessively or even slightly underweight, who have no tendency to put on weight. In such people, the I works too strongly toward the interior and strengthens this second scaffolding. But in contrast to the first scaffolding, this one has a different peculiarity. It tends to proliferate internally while the first one tends to splinter and fall apart. This one needs to be developed in two directions in particular. It needs to be developed in such a way that the proliferation that results from the I slipping out of it does not occur. (Proliferation and breakdown in these scaffoldings are both due to the fact that the I is not properly contained within them and slips out.) If the I slips out of this scaffolding but it is strong enough to maintain itself within the organism, psychological and physical consequences will develop. The psychological consequence is hypochondria; the physical consequence is constipation or similar symptoms.

This is one possibility. It is also possible, however, for the I to be too weak to hold together when it slips out. It may fall apart as an I, so that the cause of the breakdown is the I itself rather than its correlate, the physical scaffolding. Imagine what a strange state of affairs this is! In this instance, the I is so weak that fragments of it establish themselves in the organism. This is the true fact of the matter. These fragments become established because when people with this type of organization fall asleep, they are not able to take everything that slips out of the scaffolding with them. Part of it remains inside and proliferates as an I on the soul level. Human organisms subject to proliferations of the soul-I, which appear especially strongly during sleep, are predisposed to tumor formation. We are looking at an infinitely important process: People who are predisposed to tumor formations do not sleep properly because fragments of the I remain behind in the organism when these people fall asleep. Here we confront these I fragments, which are the triggers of malignant tumors and which are related to the entire syndrome I have just described. It is truly as if on the one hand we have hypochondria and constipation and, on the other, the organism—if it cannot help itself by turning the person into a constipated hypochondriac—proliferates internally, and malignant tumors appear. We will talk about this at greater length, but for now the point is simply to look at the principle.

You can also convince yourself outwardly of the facts of the matter by taking a different view of a topic I discussed earlier, namely, that the first formative process we mentioned can be dealt with by externally administering finely dispersed animal formic acid in the form of baths. Try administering an appropriately potentized preparation of the same formic acid internally and observe the effect it has, especially on thin people. In thin people, it influences tumor formation, driving out the tendency to tumor formation.

These effects absolutely must be observed on the macroscopic level. They demonstrate the importance of acquiring an eye for the macroscopic, for seeing a person's entire status and all aspects of his or her constitution in conjunction with what appears when the person is ill. They also give us a real sense of the need to separate a remedy's external and internal effects. If we trace the efficacy of the same remedy in its external and internal applications, we discover very interesting information. Once again, spiritual science is tremendously informative with regard to this second aspect of the human organization. It tells us that all of the forces that shape human ears lie on the same path as the forces that ultimately lead to internal tumor formation if they go too far. Our ear formation is the result of a process that is normalized by holding back the tumor-forming force at the right stage. The ear is an internal tumor in the human being, but kept within normal limits.

In the process of human development, the factor that shapes the eye is related to the inflammatory process, while the factor that shapes the ear is related to the tumor-forming process. Here we see a wonderful connection between health and illness in the human being. We are dealing with the same activities in both health and illness, but in one instance they take place at the right speed and in the other at the wrong speed. If you were to do away with the inflammatory process in nature, not a creature would be able to see. Sight is possible simply because the inflammatory process is integrated into nature as a whole. It has a specific tempo, however. If the wrong speed is imposed on it, it turns into the pathological process of inflammation in the human being. Similarly, the tumor-forming or proliferative process is significant in the natural world when it takes place at the correct speed. If you were to do away with this process, not a creature in the world would be able to hear. If you give it the wrong speed, however, you end up with everything that takes place in the development of myomas, carcinomas, and sarcomas. We will have more to say about these matters later.

If we are not in a position to seek out the healthy counterpart of each individual disease process, we cannot incorporate the disease process into the human organization in the right way, because it is simply true that this human organization is based on centrally internalizing certain processes that are scattered about on the periphery in nature as a whole. Instead of many of the subjects that our modern physiology beats to death, we should be looking at other subjects. Although these other matters are studied, their great importance has not been recognized. Take another example. On a macroscopic and even trivial level you can trace how the skin that is spread out over the body turns inward so that its continuations cover all of the internal parts. This reversal of functions, which occurs between the cheeks or outer parts of the face and the inside of the lips, for example, is extremely important. Here we can still see, in the outer human being, the rudiments of a process that ought to be traced properly in embryology, where cavities and involutions are all-important. It would be tremendously instructive to pursue such topics simply by studying the differences in reactions when we apply formic acid externally to the skin and internally to the mucosae, noting the subtle difference that appears. Everything I have indicated here represents only details of something that appears on a fundamental level, as I have most recently described. If you conduct such studies, you will encounter the great difference between the aspect of human organization that simply turns itself inside out toward the outside (etherically, as well) and the internal centralizing aspect, which are polar opposites.

This is important to the following consideration. If you ask what the second phantom I described, the one sketched in blue [see drawing, p. 201], corresponds to, I will tell you that it is a physical scaffolding in the organism that simply has a tendency to proliferate . If it remains within normal limits, it is related to the development of the ear. Train yourself to observe the human being in a way that teaches you how to look at the organization of the human ear and especially at how it is entirely internalized, while considering the organization of the eye at the same time. Consider the fact that the visual process takes place in the etheric while the auditory process takes place in the air. This is a significant difference. Everything on the lower end of the series of tangibles and intangibles is more closely related to the factor in the human being that is centralized and shifted into the interior, while everything that is more closely associated with the etheric is related to the human factor that is shifted toward the periphery.

What I have sketched here in violet [see drawing, p. 201] contains nothing less than an indication of what lives within the human astral body. By studying the organization of the ear, you can train yourself to use your capacity for judgment to observe human beings. This observation is a substitute of sorts for clairvoyant perception of the astral body. Learning to observe sight trains us to observe the etheric body, while learning to observe hearing trains us to observe the astral body.

If we consider people who are born deaf and people who become deaf, it is possible to make very interesting observations, and more profound associations in nature are revealed. Take note of the following example. As early as childhood, the congenitally deaf would have been predisposed to the worst sorts of tumor formation if they had not been born deaf. This is another one of the natural aids nature creates, and it points beyond what can be understood as the individual human organization between birth and death to an influence that intervenes in repeated earthly lives, because that is where it is balanced out. If we trace such phenomena to a certain extent, we reach a point where we begin to grasp the reality of repeated earthly lives.

If you attempt to stimulate the human being peripherally, you will always strengthen what I characterized as the relationship of the I to its first scaffolding. If you find it necessary to strengthen the human I, you can choose either an educational route or a therapeutic route. If you note a predisposition to inflammations, you will always find that you need to strengthen the activity of the I in your patient. This I-activity simply needs to be incorporated into its phantom scaffolding in the right way, so that the scaffolding will not fall apart. The activity of the I can be significantly strengthened, so that it fits into its scaffolding very well, by having your patient take baths to which highly diluted oil of rosemary, the sap expressed from rosemary leaves, is added. The stimulation coming from the periphery via the finely dispersed rosemary sap enables the I to work within what approaches the person in this way. You will find that the most remarkable phenomena begin to appear.

Consider how the human eyes are incorporated into the organism. The process of seeing is based on the fact that the I is able to pervade what is extracted from the human organism at this spot. There is very little animal activity in the eyes; it is all shifted to the vegetative level, and the process of seeing is based on the fact that the human being, the inner human being of soul and spirit, pervades something that is no longer animal-like and can identify with what is external rather than only with internal factors. If you identify with a muscle, you identify with the human formative process from within outward, but when you identify with the eyes, you are identifying with the outer world. This is why I once said that an organ such as an eye is a gulf that extends from the outer world into the human being. It is a piece of the outer world that has simply pushed its way into the organism like a gulf.

Again, sense physiology makes a fatal error by totally failing to take such considerations into account, and this is the origin of those silly stories about subjectivity, and so forth. Objectivity pushes its way into us; in this objectivity, we participate in a bit of the external world process. This is not taken into account at all today. For centuries, or at least for a century and a half, all sorts of sense physiology has been based on the subjective, because no one thought about how the outer world pushes its way in through its gulfs, as it were, so that we participate in it through our senses.

If you grasp this correctly, you will also have a correct understanding of what happens when a very finely dispersed substance works in from outside. If this is the skin with its pores and all the processes that are played out in connection with the pores, and if droplets of

rosemary are finely dispersed in a bath, it will be easy for you to see that an interaction comes about between the skin and the finely dispersed rosemary droplets. This interaction evokes something similar to the stimulation of a sensory process, and this stimulating sensory process works on the human I, incorporating it into its scaffolding. We can even go so far as to prevent the peripheral process of hair loss—if it is not too late, of course; if it is done in time—by supporting the scalp through the stimulating effect of rosemary droplets finely dispersed in liquid. It is simply a question of doing this correctly. This is an example of an effect working on the surface, on the periphery of the human organization.

Let us assume that the orderly interaction between the I and the human organization is broken through from outside. The I is really not just a point, it is a point that affects its surroundings, which means that the human organization's formative force, the I-organizing force, spreads throughout the human being and pervades everything. If injury occurs from outside to some part of the body, interrupting the interaction between the I and the force of the human organization, what you will need to summon to this spot must come from the astral organization, which is one stage lower than the I and pervades the human being in a way that makes it easier for the I to develop its therapeutic powers at the place where external injury has taken place. If you want to tell the astral body—which I have described as being located deeper in the interior, as even its phantom indicates—to come to a particular spot and help, you do not administer a bath. Instead, you wrap arnica in a woolen rag and apply an arnica compress to a sprain or similar external injury where the effect of the I has been weakened. In this way, you summon the astral body from the interior to come to the aid of the I. This is an example of a remedy working as a balancing factor on the surface or periphery of the human being.

This gives us a real basis for comparing different substances in the outer world in terms of whether their readily dispersed constituents aid the periphery, which means that these dispersing substances must be administered in the form of a bath that directly supports the I, or whether other substances, including arnica in particular, must be applied in order to summon the astral body, which supports the I indirectly. We discover the effects of such substances only by asking the I and the astral body to help. As you see, this is knowledge that can really lay the foundations for a theory of external and internal therapy.

LECTURE 15

Y ESTERDAY, someone who is very competent in this regard commented to me that of all anthroposophical lectures, these are among the most difficult to understand. I would like to begin today by addressing this comment. Within certain limits, we must certainly admit that it is true, but we will also have to admit that the difficulties are almost unavoidable.

In my opinion, however, the very fact that this comment is justified can teach us a great deal. Let us take a case where what I have to say is very easy to understand—or even two cases, one of which is very near at hand and the other somewhat less accessible to modern humanity.

With regard to the first, more obvious example, people of our current cultural epoch are justified in experiencing difficulty in understanding subjects like the ones that are presented here. A blackbird, however, has no such difficulty. A blackbird would find all of this readily understandable and would even offer practical proof of being able to comprehend it. Blackbirds—which are not, after all, totally ascetic animals—occasionally eat cross-spiders.[45] But when a blackbird eats a cross-spider and begins to feel very uncomfortable—which is what happens when blackbirds eat cross-spiders—it heads straight for a henbane plant. If there is a henbane plant nearby, the blackbird will go straight to it to get the appropriate remedy. If no henbane is

---

45. Cross-spider (*Epeira diadema*) is a common European garden spider with a crosslike marking on its back.

214 ❖ INTRODUCING ANTHROPOSOPHICAL MEDICINE

available, the blackbird develops convulsions and dies a terrible death.[46] Its own healing instinct, however, protects it from this fate; it immediately begins pecking away at henbane, the appropriate remedy. This is the very obvious example.

Another related process, however, is less accessible to modern human beings. At a certain time in the distant past, humans developed healing instincts like this, and these instincts encompassed aspects of what we encounter in a more or less concentrated form in Hippocratic medicine. It is interesting to study the wisdom of blackbirds (or of other birds, who can do the same thing in many instances) with reference to the very justified comment that was made yesterday. What is actually going on when a blackbird eats a cross-spider? The cross-spider's entire organization is closely linked to certain cosmic relationships in supra-earthly nature, and this connection gives rise to its overall limb development as well as to its markings. If I may put it in this way, the cross-spider has a lot of planetary life in it. In contrast, birds have lagged behind in experiencing planetary events, which they have shifted toward the interior of the organism.

When a bird swallows a cross-spider, the planetary forces make themselves felt inside the bird. These planetary forces, which still have the tendency to assume form, attempt to pervade the bird, which then has to combat this process. As soon as the bird has consumed the garden spider, its inner will becomes a copy of supra-earthly life, and it goes straight to a specific plant. This plant has become similar to earthly factors, the opposite of the planetary factors, because of the very way it grows out of the Earth—specifically, because of its inability to fully process a substance influenced by the planets, which it retains as a poison instead. The bird goes straight to this plant for help because as soon as the spider toxin begins to work in the blackbird, it summons up the bird's counter-instinct, its defensive instinct. There is an immediate transition from instinctive response to injury to the defensive instinct, so the entire phenomenon is nothing less than a very elastic elaboration on what we ourselves do if a fly gets in one of our eyes and we blink or move a hand in a simple reflex gesture.

---

46. Henbane (*Hyoscyamus niger*), black henbane, or stinking nightshade.

It is extremely important for us to observe these processes in the plant and animal kingdoms because it cures us of the belief that reason and common sense are contained only within our own skulls, when in fact they must also be flying around outside, since very rational behavior is evident in the bird's instinctive self-defense against injury. We human beings simply have the gift of being able to participate in the workings of outer reason and common sense. We engage in them, but it is nonsense to imagine that we carry them within ourselves. A bird does not yet participate in these workings in the sense of having a specific body part for acquiring the instinct to respond defensively to injury. To understand what is inside us, we humans use the head system, whereas birds still use the lung system for this purpose to a greater extent. Because a bird's thinking is less peripheral and lies closer to the core of its being, its lung system produces the defensive instinct against *Hyoscyamus*. In contrast, we humans have forcibly removed our thinking from our lungs and rhythmic system. Perhaps we will have time to speak more specifically about what human beings use for thinking, but in any case we no longer think so centrally. Unlike birds, we do not think with our lungs and heart, and so on—our thinking is no longer so connected to the cosmos. We must relearn such cosmic thinking.

If you ask what eliminated the final remnants of the instincts that connected us to nature, we must say that our schooling and our university education did this to us. Such things are fundamentally predisposed to preventing us from living in harmony with nature as a whole. They drive us into refined intellectuality on the one hand and refined sexuality on the other. In modern humankind, something that was central to primeval humanity is simply driven apart into these two poles. You see, in order to find our way back to a proper understanding of the universe, we must regain our health in the realm of scientific activity. Unfortunately, many subjects are currently being studied only by means of an unhealthy science. They will have to be studied by pursuing science in a healthy way.

Next, in connection with what I said yesterday, we will concern ourselves a bit with observing the human being in a way that points directly toward the relevant healing process. This mode of observation was so highly developed among primeval human beings that the appearance of anything abnormal in an individual immediately directed them to the appropriate healing process. This ability has been lost to modern human beings. Our intuition is unlikely to discover what primeval human beings discovered through instinct. This is simply a matter of evolution, which proceeds from instinct through intellectualism to intuition. Physiology and medicine, however, are among the fields that suffer most in the purely intellectual stage of evolution and are least able to flourish in the atmosphere of intellectualism.

Let us take a concrete example, a case of diabetes. As an abnormal development, what does diabetes represent? First of all, we can acquire true insight into diabetes only when we recognize it as weakness of the I—an inability of the I-organization to cope with the whole process of sugar formation as it is meant to take place. We must simply interpret the phenomena in the right way. It would be totally wrong to believe that because sugar is being excreted, we are dealing with an I that is too strong. No, in this case the I does not participate forcefully enough in the organic process to be able to supply and pervade the individual's organization with sugar in the appropriate way. This is the initial phenomenon, and everything that works to promote diabetes is related to it. We can perceive a first sign of diabetic illness if someone simultaneously eats too many sweets and drinks alcohol. This first sign may disappear again, of course, but it does show how the I-weakening process is initiated. The I cannot cope with what really ought to be taking place.

At the moment, it is important for us to look at these phenomena. This leads me to a concept that has not come up much in the course of our studies. Since it does appear on many of your lists of questions, we will enter into it in more detail in the remainder of these lectures. Your questions will all be considered, but first appropriate preparation is necessary. The concept I am approaching here is that of hereditary predisposition, which plays a major role in diabetes in particular. This hereditary predisposition does indeed have an effect on a weak I. We can always confirm the connection between a weak I—or rather, an I that is not functioning with all of its complexes of forces—and predisposition to inherited illnesses. If it were simply a question of hereditary predisposition, we would all be suffering from illnesses of this sort. That this is not the case is essentially due to the fact that someone with a well-functioning I is less likely to suffer from them.

On the other hand, we must not overlook the fact that psychological causes are often present in diabetes to a greater or lesser extent and that its appearance can be linked to stressful stimulation in high-strung individuals. Why is this so? When the I is weak, it tends to restrict its activity to the periphery of the organism, where it develops a strong intellectualism via the brain. This weak I, however, is not capable of penetrating deeper into the organism and specifically into those parts of the organism where protein is processed, where plant protein is transformed into animal protein. The activity of the I does not extend to this process. In its place, the astral body becomes all the more active, because the astral body's activity is greatest where digestion, blood formation, and respiration interact in the middle organizational process. Because of the lability of the I, this middle process is left to its own devices and begins to develop all sorts of obstinately independent processes that relate only to the middle region of the human being rather than to the totality.

We can say that predisposition to diabetes occurs if the I excludes itself from internal processes. These internal processes, especially that of secretion, are strongly related to the development of feelings or emotions. All of this secretion, which as you know is an oscillating and circulating activity, is neglected while the I is focusing its chief activity on the brain. As a result, the person in question loses control over certain psychological influences that assert themselves in the form of emotional influences. Why can we remain calm when something exciting occurs around us? It is because we have the ability to send our reason into our guts, because we are really in a position to engage the whole person instead of remaining only in the brain. While we are thinking, we cannot do this. While we are busy in the one-sided intellectual way that comes from the brain, the inner part of the body is engaged in its own movements; we are then extremely susceptible to stressful stimuli. Consequently, these stimuli also evoke their organic processes intellectually while they should be doing something else. Stimuli that work on our feeling life should not evoke their organic processes without first being pervaded by the intellect. They should be

218   ✣   INTRODUCING ANTHROPOSOPHICAL MEDICINE

subdued by reason before working on the interior of the human being.

It is important to realize that in a situation like this, we are encountering a labile I, and that the I is related to the most supra-earthly factors in the human being, to the factors that are most peripheral to the Earth. In reality, everything that is active in our I approaches us from far beyond the Earth. Thus we must try to become familiar with activities that are related to these supra-human processes having to do with our I, so that we become able to shift the I into a realm where it learns to participate appropriately in supra-earthly factors.

Within the earthly element, the equivalent of the supra-earthly influence that leads the I to work on its inner, central organization causes either the mineral part of the Earth or its plants to form etheric oils, or oils of any sort. Just as the human I becomes active in the eyes, coming into direct connection with the outer world through this gulf, it must also be brought into connection with the oil-forming process. We can probably do this best by attempting to incorporate finely dispersed oil into therapeutic baths. It would be very desirable to investigate what degree of dispersion is required, how often the baths should be administered, and so on. This is how diabetes' devastating attack on the organism should be counteracted. You can see here how observing an outer process and associating it with an internal human process creates a human/supra-human physiology that is also a therapy at the same time. This is the path we must take if we want to achieve anything at all in this regard.

After we acquire some additional, more concrete concepts, I would like to point out once again how human beings actually relate to the environment. Please consider how the totality of the Earth's plant life grows upward, dispersing its forces in the flowers and gathering them together again in the fruits. Consider, too, all the thousands of strange variations of this process that exist. Perhaps something that ordinarily shoots entirely into the seeds is retained in leaf development, making the leaves thick and cabbage-like, or perhaps the seedpods thicken because certain forces are held back at the very last minute. There are all kinds of possible variations.

The process of plant development, however, should truly not be considered only from the perspective of the physical effects of the

Earth and the countereffects of light. While it is certainly true that a plant incorporates a physical and an etheric body and is entirely subsumed by them, it is equally true that up where the supra-earthly collides with the earthly, there is a cosmic astrality related to this plant. We might say that the plant grows upward toward, but cannot attain, an animal process of development. The interior of the Earth is saturated with the plant-forming process while the atmosphere toward which plants grow is saturated with an animal-forming process, which plants approach but cannot attain. The process we see taking place here weaves above the flowering plant world, where it has a circumferential or peripheral relationship to the entire Earth. This same process, however, is centralized and internalized in animals. Animals split off and incorporate the activities that take place above plants. The organs that animals have and plants do not are nothing other than what animals claim for themselves. Something that is otherwise developed on the periphery and directed at plants from outside is developed from a central point outward by animals.

This animal-forming process is also present in human beings but is located closer to the center of the physical human organization. It tends more in the direction of the interaction of digestion, blood formation, and respiration, where the process shaping the human being is most similar to today's animal-forming process. This is also why the interior of the physical body is the part of the human being most closely related to the vital processes of the plant kingdom, and why we can always count on being able to treat the interior of the human body with derivatives of vital processes that manifest in the plant kingdom. Human beings, however, have an advantage over the animal kingdom. This advantage is based on the fact that humans undergo not only the interaction that takes place in animals between the plant and astral elements but also one that takes place between the mineral element and an element that is super-astral—that is, even farther out on the periphery than the merely astral element. Thus we can say that the specifically human attribute at the present stage of the Earth's evolution is to participate in the mineral-forming process. Just as protein transformation takes place in animals, another process—one that science does not take into account at all—takes place in human beings. This process tends more toward the periphery than the animal activity of transforming protein, happening—if we may put it like this—between the heavens and the mineral kingdom. If we want to have a term for it, we can call it a desalinizing process, in accordance with its chief characteristic.

You see, in the human organism, a desalinizing process is continually taking place, a tendency to transform salt formation into its opposite. This is the true basis of our humanness and especially of our human thinking, which transcends animal existence. In our peripheral aspect—although not in our central aspect, which is similar to animal formation—we resist the formation of salt. We counteract salt formation just as animals counteract the ordinary earth-forming forces of plant protein. We must seek out the forces inherent in this counteraction, preferably in the mineral kingdom, in order to be able to cure certain conditions in human beings that we cannot successfully treat with phytotherapeutics. I might say that we see human beings as mere animals if we attempt to treat them exclusively with plant-derived remedies. We respect people's humanness by asking them to take part in the fiercer battle against the mineralization of the Earth, a battle that goes on in the Earth's surroundings, and by allowing the I to participate in this battle when we make it possible for an individual to become involved in it.

Each time we treat a person with silica, we are appealing to that person's silica-splitting forces, to the ability to overcome this hard mineral. By doing so, we enable the I to engage vigorously in a process that no longer takes place on Earth at all. The forces prevailing outside the earthly sphere attempt to fragment everything that is earthly and solid in universal space. The universe has the peculiarity of smashing to pieces everything that aggregates and solidifies in the planetary realm. In everyday life, we seldom participate in this process, which is usually confined to universal space. The people who participate in it the most are mathematical personalities, people who are accustomed to living in the world of numbers and thinking in terms of mathematical forms. Their kind of thinking is based on smashing the mineral element to pieces. In contrast, people with a certain distaste for mathematics want to restrict themselves to a mere desalinizing process and cannot become agents of internal destruction. This is the difference between mathematical and non-mathematical personalities. Counteracting the Earth's mineralizing process is the basis of many ideas about the therapeutic process.

Once again, these are things that were simply part of primeval humanity's instinctive defensive response to injury. When primeval human beings noticed any sign of their thinking becoming weak, they turned to some mineral substance, which they took. By breaking down this mineral substance internally, they once again acquired the ability to be in harmony with supra-earthly factors that are very far removed from the Earth. It is possible to trace processes in the natural world outside the human being in a way that permits direct observation of the validity of statements such as this. Let us do this by considering a plant that is extremely interesting in this regard, *Betula alba*, or white birch.[47]

White birch counteracts or refuses to participate in the normal process of plant development in two ways. The usual process of plant development would come about if you could mix what happens in birch bark with what happens in birch leaves, especially the young spring leaves that still have a trace of brown in them. If you could mix these two separate processes and make the active principle in birch bark work together with the active principle in birch leaves, you would get a wonderful herbaceous flowering plant. The birch tree comes about simply because the processes that arise during the living formation of protein are carried into the leaves to a greater extent than is normal. The protein-forming process is concentrated in the leaves, while the process of potassium salt formation is preserved in the bark. In a plant that remains herbaceous rather than becoming a birch tree, the process of potassium salt formation mingles with the process of protein formation in the plant's roots. In the birch tree, what the roots take from the Earth is forced outward into the bark, while the leaves receive what a herbaceous plant would mingle with what comes from the Earth.

---

47. The European white birch is now called *Betula pendula*. *Betula alba* can refer to either that (more likely) or to *Betula papyrifera* (American white birch—paper or canoe birch).

Thus, the birch tree works on the human organism from two different directions. Through its bark, which contains the appropriate
potassium salts, it works in cases where the patient's desalinizing processes need to be stimulated, as in skin rashes, for example. What
shoots outward into the bark in the birch tree also shoots outward in
the human being, where it has a therapeutic effect. But if you take the
leaves, which preserve the protein-forming forces, you get the birch
factor that influences the center part of the human being, where it
proves to be a good remedy for gout and rheumatism. If you want to
further enhance the process, you can take the mineral aspect of the
birch's development by producing charcoal from birch wood. Then
you get therapeutic forces that work in a strong internal and external
way on the outside of the human interior—that is, on the intestines,
and so on.

We must learn to see a plant's effect on the human being from its
external form. If you study *Betula alba*, you can say that if we wanted
to transform this birch into an image in the human being so that it
would make the entire human being healthy, we would turn it inside
out and incorporate the forces that surge into the wood and bark into
the human skin, the periphery, while we would take what the birch
sends outward and apply it to the interior of the human being. We
would turn the entire birch tree inside out in the human being—as an
image, mind you; this is meant to provide you with an image—in such
a way that we can trace the healing forces it offers to the human being.

When you look at plants with very pronounced root development—
plants that develop very strong root forces that then deposit potassium
and sodium salts in the plants—you find that this tendency to hold
fast to the roots has a healing effect on internal bleeding and also on
the formation of kidney stones, and so on. Shepherd's purse, *Capsella
bursa-pastoris*, is one plant that might be useful in these conditions and
everything lying between.

Think your way as well into a plant such as *Cochlearia officinalis*,
common scurvy grass or spoonwort. This plant is also interesting to
study. Through the sulfur contained in its oils, it is able to work
directly on its own proteins. In the mineral realm, sulfur works on protein by enhancing its formative forces. If the process of protein forma-

tion is too sluggish, it can be speeded up through the addition of the sulfur process, which is essentially what a plant such as spoonwort develops in an organic form. The fact that spoonwort grows in specific locations, that it is introduced into nature in a very particular way, condemns it to develop excessively sluggish protein processes. A wonderful instinct of nature balances this with the plant's sulfur-containing oils, which counteract sluggish processes of this sort.

A protein process that has been speeded up is something different from a protein process that proceeds at a natural pace. We must always take this into account. You can find protein forming processes in many different plants that proceed just as quickly as those in spoonwort, but they do not come about through the interaction of a sluggish principle and an accelerating principle. A constant interaction of this sort in the growth of spoonwort makes it inwardly related to and especially suited for use in diseases such as scurvy, because the process that takes place in scurvy is extremely similar to the one I have just described.

I believe we can actually get quite far by training ourselves to think of outer natural events in conjunction with events within the human being in this particular way. This thinking leads us to these extremely important relationships, but it also leads to an understanding of the human being that cannot be acquired in any other way, because the human being can be understood only from the perspective of what is external to the human being, while the external can be understood only from the perspective of the human being. We must be able to study these two things in conjunction with each other.

I hope you will not find it extraneous if I conclude today's lecture with a topic that will help us with subsequent observations, namely, the peculiar way the spleen functions in the human organism. Human spleen function tends very strongly toward the spiritual aspect. This is why I once said in a lecture cycle on esoteric physiology that, if you remove the spleen, the etheric body—that is, the etheric spleen—takes its place very easily, so that this is one of the human organs that can be most readily replaced by its etheric counterpart.[48] The spleen, however,

48. These lectures took place March 20–28, 1911 in Prague (CW 128).

224 INTRODUCING ANTHROPOSOPHICAL MEDICINE

is less closely related than the other human abdominal organs to metabolism as such.

What is the spleen actually? To spiritual-scientific research, the spleen presents itself as the organ that is called upon to create constant harmony between crude metabolism and all the more soul-like or spiritualized processes in the human being. The spleen—and this is basically true of all other organs to a greater or lesser extent—is a strong subconscious sensory organ, and it reacts extremely strongly to the rhythm of food intake. Constant eating induces a totally different kind of spleen activity than leaving intervals between meals. We can observe this particularly in the irregular spleen activity that develops in children who snack constantly. We can also see it in the fact that when eating does not intervene—after we fall asleep, for example— the spleen comes to rest to a great extent, but only in its own particular fashion. The spleen is the organ of sensation that allows the more spiritualized aspect of the human being to perceive the rhythm of food intake, and it speaks to the human subconscious, telling us what needs to be done to mitigate at least in part the damaging impact of unrhythmical eating.

Thus, spleen activity works less in the direction of metabolism as such and more in the direction of the rhythmic processes. It participates in rhythmic processes that must take place between food intake and respiration. An intermediate rhythm provided by the spleen is simply interposed between the rhythm of respiration and the intake of food, which otherwise does not tend to be especially rhythmical. Respiratory rhythm enables human beings to live within the strict rhythmicity of the cosmos. Our irregular food intake constantly disrupts this strict cosmic rhythm, and the spleen is the mediator.

This state of affairs can actually be confirmed by simply observing the human being. Please do study anatomical and physiological details. You will find all of this is confirmed down to the smallest detail. On the one hand, you will find proof of what I have said in how the artery to the spleen is almost directly connected to the aorta and also externally in how the spleen is incorporated into the organism. On the other hand, you will find evidence that the spleen mediates in the direction of food intake in how the splenic vein is placed within the entire organism; it leads to the portal vein and is in direct connection with the liver.

Here a rhythm that is half outer and half inner aligns itself with the lack of rhythm so that they regulate each other. The activity of the spleen is interposed between the rhythmic human being and the metabolic human being. Many symptoms that are related to improper spleen function can be put in order by building on the knowledge we have acquired about the connection between the respiratory system and the metabolism or between the circulatory system and the metabolism as mediated by the spleen. It is not at all surprising that the physiology of the spleen is largely ignored by materialistic science, which knows nothing about the threefold human being—the metabolic human being, the circulatory human being, and the neurosensory human being.

LECTURE 16

YOU will see that the answers to the questions you so kindly gave me now begin to appear in the lectures. It was simply a matter of creating the foundation for a rational response. Today I would like to link up with the last topic we talked about yesterday, when I was able to draw your attention to the significance of spleen functions in the human organism. These functions are the regulators of our subconscious soul life and must be addressed as such. We misunderstand the entire nature of the human being if we believe the spleen to be an organ of secondary importance. Admittedly, it is not difficult for this error or misunderstanding to arise because the spleen is such a highly spirit-pervaded organ that its functions are very easily taken over by only the etheric spleen, and other organs can also be called upon to step in and take over its functions. You will see, however, that the effect of the spleen becomes more curious the more it is lifted up out of the subconscious into consciousness.

At this point, we come to a certain method of healing that has attracted interest recently, which, strangely enough, takes the effect of the spleen as a starting point—spleen massage. You will be convinced that gently massaging the area of the spleen initially has a balancing effect on human instinctual activity. When people receive gentle massages to the area of the spleen, they develop better instincts in some respects. For example, it becomes easier for them to discover what foods suit them and generally what is useful or not useful to their bodies. But there are immediate limits to massaging this area. As soon as the effect grows too strong, it becomes capable of completely undermining instinctual activity once again. A curious pause ensues here at the null point. This massage must not be taken too far.

What is this actually related to? Gently massaging the spleen—the area of the spleen, that is—drives something into that area that is otherwise not there. In a certain way, the consciousness of the person being massaged is projected in that direction. A great deal depends on this shift and flow of consciousness. The limitations of our language sometimes makes it difficult to express adequately such subtle workings in the human organism. But strange as it may sound, there is a strong interaction between the unconscious activity of reason and common sense, which is mediated by the spleen, or rather by the spleen's functions, and the human organism's conscious functions. And what are these conscious functions? All physical processes in the organism that are accompanied by higher conscious processes, and especially by ideational processes, have toxic effects. This must not be overlooked. The human organism is constantly poisoning itself through its ideational activity and is continually counteracting these toxic conditions with unconscious states of will. The center of unconscious states of will is located in the spleen. If we pervade the spleen with consciousness, influencing it through massage, we work against the highly toxic effect that emanates from our higher consciousness.

Spleen massage, however, does not always have to be external massage. It can also be internal massage. You may argue that this should not be called massage, but the important point is that we understand each other. Spleen massage can also be implemented like this: If we see that a person has a strong inner organic activity that stems from toxic conditions, we can influence the spleen's abnormal state of consciousness by telling that person to eat as little as possible at mealtimes and to eat more frequently, dividing up the meals so there is less time between them. Dividing up the activity of eating massages the spleen internally and has a profound effect on its activity. Of course, there is a certain catch to this, just as there is always a catch to such processes. You see, in our hurried times, people—or at least many people—are always involved in external stressful activity that has an extremely strong influence on spleen function. People do not do as certain animals do, which stay healthy by lying down after eating and refusing to allow their digestion to be disturbed by outer activity. These animals spare the functioning of their spleen. People who are engaged in outer, nervous, hurried activity do not do this. As a result, spleen activity is gradually becoming highly abnormal among all of civilized humanity, and it is becoming especially important to relieve the functions of the spleen by using the methods that I have just spoken about.

Being attentive to subtle forms of massage, such as internal and external spleen massage, points very neatly to the connections between the human organs that are the vehicles of the unconscious and those that are the vehicles of consciousness. This leads us to discover the importance of massage, or at least makes it easier for us to understand its entire significance. Massage has a certain importance, and under some circumstances it can also have a strong healing effect, although its primary effect is on the regulation of rhythmical activity in the human being. But if we want the massage to be successful, we must know the human organism well.

For guidance on this path, consider the tremendous difference between the arms and the legs in the human organization—not in the animal, but in the human being. In human arms, which are relieved of the burden of gravity and move freely, the astral body is much more loosely bound to the physical body than it is in the feet. In human feet, the astral body is very closely bound to the physical. We might say that in the arms, the astral body works more through the skin, from the outside in. It envelops the arms and hands and works from the outside inward. In a sense, it has a swaddling effect. In the legs and feet, the will works through the astral body in a way that is very strongly centrifugal, radiating from the inside out. This is the reason for the considerable difference between arms and legs. Consequently, if we massage a person's legs and feet, we are doing something fundamentally different from massaging the person's arms and hands.

When we massage someone's arms it draws the astral body in from outside. This makes the arms much more into instruments of the will than normal, which has the effect of regulating the internal metabolic exchange between the intestines and the blood vessels. In this way we work more on blood formation when we massage the arms and hands. In contrast, if we massage the feet and legs, the physical aspect is transformed into an ideational one to a greater extent. This has a regulating effect on the metabolic processes of elimination and excretion. In this extension of the effects of massage, moving in one instance from the arms toward the inner anabolic realm of metabolism and in the other instance toward the catabolic realm, we see what a complicated creature the human organism really is.

If you investigate these issues rationally, you will discover that every part of the body has a specific connection to other body parts. Understanding this inner interaction in the appropriate way is the basis of effective massage. Massaging the abdomen can always have beneficial effects, even with regard to respiration. It is especially interesting to note that abdominal massage has a particularly good influence on respiratory activity. When we massage directly below the area of the heart, respiration is influenced more strongly, whereas if we move further down it influences the organs in the throat. The action is reversed when we massage the torso—as we move farther, it has a greater effect on the upper organs. For example, we can enhance an arm massage by also massaging the uppermost part of the torso. I might say, these things illustrate the connection between individual members of the human organism. In particular, we can see that this interaction between the upper and lower parts of the human being, or in general between related parts that are sometimes quite far apart, appears in conditions such as migraine.

In truth, migraine is nothing but the shifting of digestive activities, which should actually have their seat in the rest of the organism, into the head. This is why anything that makes too many demands on the rest of the organism—such as menstrual periods, for example—also affects migraines. We can say that when misplaced digestive activity takes place in the head, the cranial nerves are burdened with something they are normally freed from. The very fact that only highly regulated digestive activity in the form of absorption takes place in the head frees up the cranial nerves to become sensory nerves. When the above-mentioned unregulated activity takes place in the head, they lose this quality and become inwardly sensitive and receptive to things that the internal parts of the organism should not be able to sense. This is the basis for the pain of migraine and all similar conditions. It is quite understandable how someone must feel when suddenly forced to perceive the interior of the head instead of the outer world.

If we understand this condition properly, however, we will be able to suggest only that the best cure for migraine is sleeping it off in peace, or something like that. Everything that people take for it, or which they are sometimes forced to take, has harmful effects. By taking the usual allopathic medications, you anesthetize the neural apparatus that has been sensitized, meaning that you impair its activity. Let us say that someone suffers a migraine attack shortly before having to go on stage and chooses to put up with a certain amount of damage rather than not being able to perform. In this case it is especially easy to observe the anesthetization of something that should not be anesthetized. Such instances demonstrate that the human organism is extremely subtle and that one is often forced to sin against its demands simply as a consequence of being socially entangled in life. This is self-evident and should not be disregarded. Sometimes we may simply have to accept the damage that results from a person's situation in life and attempt to cure its inevitable consequences later.

The great subtlety of human bodily organization also becomes evident if we investigate color and light therapy in the right way. Therapy of this sort should certainly be taken into account to a greater extent in the future than has been the case in the past. We also need to explore the difference between the effect of color, which appeals entirely to the upper part of the human being, and the effect of light, which is more objective in scope and appeals to the whole human being. A direct effect on an organ can be achieved by bringing someone into a room where objective color and light shine upon the entire person or where a specific body part is exposed to the purely objective effect of color or light. This is something that definitely affects the person from outside.

If, however, the exposure is brought about in a way that engages the impression of color or the presence of the color (which is otherwise engaged only by consciousness), the effect is different. That is, if instead of allowing colored light to shine on a person, I bring that person into a room that is totally decorated in a certain color, the effect is different and pervades all the organs leading up to the organs of consciousness. Subjective color therapy of this sort invariably affects the I, while objective color therapy works on the physical system, through which it only indirectly affects the I. Please do not say that because blind people are unable to receive visual impressions, it is irrelevant to bring them into a room decorated in a certain color and that the inevitable result will be the total absence of any effect on them. This is not the case. In this instance, certain effects that emanate from perceptible things but lie below the level of perceptibility emerge very strongly. Even if the people I bring into a room painted red or blue are blind, the color still makes a difference to them. It makes a significant difference, and it must be said that the effect of bringing blind people into a blue-walled room is to shift the entire organization, their entire functioning, away from the head and toward the rest of the organism. If I bring them into a red-walled room, their functioning shifts away from the rest of the organism and toward the head.

From this discussion you can see that the rhythm induced by allowing one color to alternate with another must be the essential factor when the surroundings are objectively suffused with color. Whether the room we bring people into is blue or red is less important than whether we bring them into a blue room after first experiencing a red one or vice versa. This is of crucial importance. If I see a general need to bring about improvement in the rest of a person's system by strongly stimulating that person's head functions, I move that person from a blue room into a red one. If I want to improve someone's head functions by way of the rest of the organism, I move that person from a red room into a blue one. I believe that such matters will become very important in the not-too-distant future and that color therapy, as opposed to light therapy, will have an important role to play.

It is important to allow a role in any future therapy for the interplay between the conscious and unconscious. This will help us to develop healthy judgment concerning the peculiar way that substances work on the human being through baths, for example. It makes a great deal of difference whether the impression made by external applications is cold or warm. It must be understood that a cold impression—a cooling effect of a compress or bath—indicates that the substance itself is the active therapeutic principle. It is the effect of the particular therapeutic substance that is important in this instance.

It is not the substance itself that is important, however, if the effect of an application such as a compress is warming rather than cooling. The substance used is almost irrelevant in this case, since it is the warming effect that must be considered. The origin of the warming effect is irrelevant to the effect itself. In the case of cold compresses, then, we must always pay attention to how we can tincture the fluid or water being used with a substance. We can elicit the effectiveness of these substances when we are able to make them work in cold water— that is, if they are soluble at low temperatures. In contrast (unless we are using etheric substances, or highly aromatic substances, which constitute a somewhat different case because their effects are also present at high temperatures), we cannot produce any significant direct effect from solid substances that do not dissolve easily. We will not be able to induce real healing effects with warm compresses or baths. On the other hand, if substances similar in nature to sulfur or phosphorus (such as sulfur itself) accompany a warm bath, they will be especially able to develop their corresponding therapeutic effects.

The important point here is the subtle observation of relationships such as those I have just presented. At this point I would like to say that you will find it very useful to establish an archetypal phenomenon of some sort. It is interesting to note that this method played a great role when medical knowledge, and so on, were still cultivated on the basis of the mysteries to a greater extent. In those times, issues were stated in terms of archetypal phenomena, rather than theoretically. For example, one such statement was, "By taking honey or wine internally, you strengthen the forces of cosmic origin that work in you." We might also say that this strengthens the forces of the I, which would be the same thing. I think such a statement makes it very easy to gain an overview of the subject. Also, "By rubbing an oily substance into your body, you weaken the harmful effects of the earthly forces within you"—that is, of the forces that counteract the effect of the I in the organism. And, "By finding the balance between sweet strengthening from the inside and oily weakening from the outside, you will live long." The physicians of antiquity also said, "Rub yourself with oil to remove the damaging influences of the Earth and—if you are able to do so, if your organization is not too weak—strengthen the forces of the I with honey or wine. Thus, you strengthen the forces that lead to old age." Any statement such as this was meant to express the archetypal phenomenon of the matter. It was intended to point people in the right direction through facts rather than through theorems or dogma. We must make our way back to this approach because it is much easier to get your bearings among all the many substances of the outer world if you can refer back to archetypal phenomena rather than to abstract, so-called natural laws, which leave you in the lurch whenever you want to tackle anything concrete.

I would like to present you with a few of these archetypal phenomena that are easy to state: "By putting your feet in water, you evoke abdominal forces that promote the formation of blood." Here you have an archetypal phenomenon that points you strongly in the right direction. "By washing your head, you evoke abdominal forces that regulate elimination." These archetypal phenomena are very informative, because they encompass the lawfulness and reality of the issues. The human being is present in statements such as these because, of course, they would make no sense if I were not thinking about the human being. The fact that I am thinking about the human being is very important in all these areas.

Once again, these things point to a more spatial interaction of forces in the human organism. A temporal interaction is also present, however, and we encounter it clearly when we observe people who have been mishandled in their childhood or early adolescence to such an extent that for the rest of their lives they can cultivate only things that should actually be cultivated in adulthood rather than things that should be cultivated in adolescence and childhood. Let me express myself more clearly. During adolescence, human beings develop certain forces that shape the organism during that same period. Not everything that takes shape during adolescence, however, is immediately put to the right use. Shaping the organism during adolescence also serves to store up something that becomes effective only during adulthood. I might say that certain organs that are built up during childhood should not be used then and there. Since in adulthood, however, it is no longer possible to build them up, they are kept in reserve for later use.

For example, people should be educated through imitation up to the second dentition, after which authority should play a big part in their education. If this is not taken into account, organs that should remain in reserve for adulthood may be called upon prematurely. With modern materialistic ways of thinking, people may object and say that how we use imitation or authority could not possibly be so important. In fact, however, it is tremendously important because the effect carries over into the organism. For example, it is very important to allow children to grow into liking a particular food by imitating the sympathy their parents or teachers have for that food. That is, you bring the imitative principle into connection with developing an appetite for a particular food. An extension of the imitative urge is then present in the organism. Later, the same is true of authority.

To put it briefly, if organs—these are very delicate structures, of course—that are meant to be held in reserve for adulthood are called upon during childhood, the terrible illness that we call schizophrenia appears. Since this is the real basis of schizophrenia, appropriate education is an excellent preventive. At the moment, what we are attempting in the Waldorf school can be implemented only after the age of six or seven and cannot yet be extended to early childhood education; but (as I described in my booklet *The Education of the Child* [49]) schizophrenia will disappear if it becomes possible someday to place education as a whole in the service of the knowledge that comes from spiritual science. Shaping education in this way prevents people from calling on their adult organs prematurely. This is something that must be said with regard to appropriate education.

The opposite also exists in life; it involves saving organ effects for later that should unfold only during adolescence. Throughout life, there are demands placed on organs that exist primarily for the benefit of childhood and adolescence; but the consequences of such demands

49. Contained in *The Education of the Child and Early Lectures on Education*, Anthroposophic Press, Hudson, NY, 1996.

are damaging unless they gradually diminish. In this area, a great variety of causes permit such practices as psychoanalysis to intervene in human thinking as a whole in a confusing way. It is in fact true that the most damage is caused not by major errors (which are soon revealed as such), but by those that contain kernels of truth, since they may be taken to extremes and misused.

What is the phenomenon behind the rise of a view such as that of psychoanalysis? It is this: Because of today's lifestyle, which is frequently unnatural and fails to adapt human beings sufficiently to the outer environment, much of what impresses people during childhood remains unprocessed. Such impressions simply remain a part of our psychological makeup without being appropriately incorporated into the organism as well. The slightest effect on the psychological level extends (or should extend) also into the organism. But a child today receives many impressions that are highly abnormal, so that they must remain psychological impressions and not become immediately transformed into organic impressions. They continue to work as psychological impressions. Instead of participating in a person's entire development, they remain as isolated soul impulses. If they were to participate in bodily development as a whole, they would not remain isolated soul impulses and would not place demands later in life on the organs that exist only for the sake of adulthood and are no longer present to make use of adolescent impressions. Thus an inappropriate situation arises: The individual as a whole is forced to permit isolated soul impulses to act on organs no longer suited to this purpose.

The symptoms that then emerge can be diagnosed by means of a properly applied psychoanalytic method. By questioning the patient, it is possible to discover certain things that are still present in his or her soul life, impressions that simply have not been processed and have devastating effects on organs that have become too old to do this processing. The important point here, however, is that this route leads only to diagnosis but never to therapy. If we use psychotherapy simply as a diagnostic method, we are doing something that is somehow justifiable if conducted tactfully. Many letters that have been written to me, however, claim that psychoanalysts use their receptionists like spies to unearth all kinds of issues on which they then question their patients. This happens so frequently that all of psychoanalysis has been tainted by this nonsense. But if we disregard these unfortunate incidents—and it really all depends on the moral stance of the people involved—we can say that from the perspective of diagnosis, there is some truth in psychoanalysis, but it is never possible to be therapeutically effective by taking the psychoanalytic route. Once again, this is related to a phenomenon of our times.

The tragedy of materialism is that it leads us away from actually recognizing matter, prevents us from acknowledging matter. Materialism is less damaging to the recognition of the spirit itself than to the recognition of the spiritual aspect of matter. Preventing the view that spiritual effects are omnipresent in connection with matter, preventing us from looking for spiritual effects in matter, blocks many considerations that should not be blocked for the sake of a healthy view of human life. If I am a materialist, I cannot possibly ascribe all the properties we have discussed here to matter. Materialism considers it sheer nonsense to ascribe these properties to matter even though they are properties it does indeed possess. This means that we move away from the possibility of acknowledging matter for what it is. We no longer speak of phosphoruslike or saltlike phenomena, and so forth, because all this is seen as nonsense. We move away from both the possibility of acknowledging the spirit in matter and the possibility of studying formative effects properly. Above all, we move away from the insight that each human organ has the dual task of being oriented toward consciousness and toward its own solely vegetative process.

This view has been lost in one area in particular that we will now discuss, namely, how we consider the teeth. From the materialistic perspective, teeth are seen as mere chewing instruments, more or less, but this is not all they are. Their dual nature becomes evident from the very fact that while a merely chemical investigation suggests that they are related to the skeletal system, from a phylogenetic perspective they actually develop out of the skin system. The teeth in particular have a dual nature, but their second nature is extremely well concealed. If you compare animal teeth to human teeth, you will see that what I said in the very first lecture about the element of weight, which the entire ape skeleton presents, is especially strongly expressed in the structure of an animal's jaw and teeth. In a certain way, we see the effects of uprightness even in the human mouth.

This is related to the fact that teeth are not merely chewing implements but also very important suction devices. On the one hand, they have an outer mechanical effect, but on the other hand they also have an inherent inner suction effect that is very delicate and spiritualized. At this point we are forced to ask what the teeth actually draw in. For as long as they can, they draw in fluorine. They are suction devices for drawing in fluorine. We human beings need very small quantities of fluorine in our bodies, and—at this point I am going to say something that may shock you—if we do not have it, we become too intelligent. We become so intelligent it almost destroys us. Fluorine's effects tone us down to the appropriate level of stupidity that we need in order to be human. We need fluorine in small quantities to constantly counteract the process of becoming too intelligent.

Early dental decay, which is a lessening of the effects of fluorine, points to excessive demands that are being made on the teeth's ability to draw in fluorine. It points out that something is making the person in question defend him- or herself against stupidity. (We will speak about these issues later, although there is not much time left.) The person in question is destroying his or her teeth so that the effect of fluorine does not cause excessive stupidity. Just think about this extraordinarily subtle connection: Our teeth decay so that we don't become too stupid. This shows you the intimate connection between effects that are useful to human beings and the damaging effects that are the opposite pole of the pendulum swing. Under certain circumstances, we need the effects of fluorine so that we do not become too intelligent. We can also do ourselves damage, however, by making these effects too strong, in which case we destroy our teeth through the activity of our organs. These are issues I ask you to ponder carefully, because they are related to extremely significant processes in the human organism.

To the extent allowed, and on the basis of the content of the last lecture, I will have to summarize a few topics that will shed real light on this whole issue and make it bear fruit. Consequently, although this can be only a beginning, it is good that we can take two days to address this matter.

In relation to what I said yesterday about dental development and tooth decay, I would like to say a few things that are also generally appropriate to illuminating the matter of the healthy and the sick individual. It is not good to take discussions such as those we engaged in yesterday in an overly materialistic sense, because it is important to see an external process such as tooth decay as only the outer symptom or consequence of a specific inner process that is concealed from outer perception.

You will understand the entire process of tooth formation if you look at it in conjunction with other processes in the human organism that appear to be quite far removed from it. Consider, for example, a familiar phenomenon that we assess properly only if we know how to think about it in connection with the process of tooth development. It is well known that young women can have perfectly healthy teeth until the delivery of their first child, and then their teeth decay. This is extremely enlightening with regard to the connection between toothache or tooth decay and the organism's entire constitution. In addition, we must also consider the very interesting connection between what is going on in someone's teeth and that person's predisposition to hemorrhoids. These are all connections that prove that the most strongly mineralizing effects in the human being, on the one hand (because tooth formation is one of the most mineralizing processes) are intimately related to the individual's entire organizational process on the other and are revealed in relationships and dependencies that go all the way through to the opposite end of the human being.

Our view of the process of tooth development is very much influenced by the undeniable fact that at the conclusion of this process, when the teeth have emerged from the gums and their outer covering has developed, a living human structure is turned over to the external world as a mineral entity. The enamel that covers the teeth is almost completely closed off, and anabolic processes no longer take place there. In a certain sense, what we encounter there has become totally inorganic in character. I believe I pointed out yesterday that the building-up process is less relevant than the continuous breakdown that occurs in teeth throughout a person's lifetime. Although we must acknowledge that our internal organization, with its anabolic activity, can do very little at the outer boundary of the human organization where the tooth's outermost part develops, we must bear in mind that this internal organization is also related to catabolism, the process of destruction, and that the question of how to delay the onset of this breakdown in the individual is much more important than the other matter [the building-up process]. It would be totally erroneous to believe that tooth decay is entirely the result of outer damage. This needs to be taken into consideration.

Furthermore, what I said yesterday about the function of fluorine in relationship to tooth formation applies essentially to the period of childhood when tooth development is proceeding from the inside out. Most of this period is only the preparatory stage of tooth formation, because the second teeth develop deep within the organism, within the entire organism, before becoming outwardly visible. Fluorine's formative process culminates when fluorine achieves some kind of stable state of equilibrium in a substance on the surface of the teeth, when it is bound to this substance and is at rest, in a certain sense. Its rest is disturbed, however, when the teeth begin to decay and to move in the direction of breaking down. There is a subtle process that emanates from the teeth and is related to a formative process brought about by fluorine. This latter process, the fluorine process, pervades the entire organism and persists throughout the person's life.

Prophylactic treatment of this syndrome is predicated on what I have just said. For example, I might say that much of what has found its way into Waldorf education (apart from other factors that influence a child's healthy development) is calculated to prevent premature tooth decay in those attending the Waldorf school. Strangely enough, with regard to such health prerequisites of the body's periphery, a great deal depends on appropriate education during childhood. Unfortunately, at present the point at which Waldorf education can begin to influence tooth formation is a little too late in terms of the prophylactic dental process that needs to be implemented; it would actually have to begin somewhat earlier. Nonetheless, since the teeth appear gradually rather than all at once, and since the effects of the inner process persist for a long time, something can still be achieved even though the children come to us only at age six or seven, but it is not really enough.

It is both possible and important, however, to do what I told you earlier, namely, to carefully check the quality of tooth development as the first tooth is appearing. There is reason to object that this presents certain difficulties, since the process of tooth formation begins well before the crown breaks through in its finished form. This is correct, but the teeth themselves are not the only evidence of the state of tooth formation. We will find that children who are clumsy with their arms and hands and legs and feet at age three, four, or five—that is, who do not easily learn to use their arms and legs, or especially their hands and feet, in a coordinated way—will also tend to have difficulty incorporating the process of tooth development in the right way. In the functioning of their arms and hands and legs and feet, we see the same pattern that emerges in the process of tooth formation. This is why the tooth-forming process is regulated to a great extent if we encourage children at the earliest possible age to run in a way that makes them move their feet artistically—for instance, in the Kiebitz-step, where they have to brush their feet against each other as they walk.

In addition to foot dexterity, training children's fingers to be skillful greatly promotes the process of tooth formation. In our handwork classes in the Waldorf school, you will find the boys learning to knit and crochet along with the girls. Everything is done equally by boys and girls, and even the older boys are still enthusiastic about knitting. This is not done on a whim; it is all done to make the children's fingers dextrous and skillful, to drive soul into their fingers. By driving soul into their fingers, we especially promote everything related to the process of tooth formation. It makes a difference whether we let children sit all the time and be lazy or encourage them to run around, whether we permit their hands to remain clumsy or encourage them to become skillful. It makes a difference because later everything we have neglected in this regard appears in the form of premature tooth decay—more in the case of some individuals and less in others, of course. We can say that the earlier we begin training people in this way, the more we are able to influence and slow down the process of tooth decay from this direction. Because it is so difficult to intervene in any way in anything related to tooth development, we will find that we need to consider processes that seem quite far removed.

I have been asked how fluorine is absorbed into the organism. Does it come in through the enamel from outside or through the saliva, through the dental pulp or the bloodstream or the like? You see, fluorine as such is a process that shapes the human being, and spending a lot of time agonizing about how the substance is absorbed is not at all the important issue. As a rule, we need to consider only the usual process of nutrition; that is how compounds containing fluorine are absorbed. We simply need to delineate the very ordinary process of nutrition in order to see how fluorine compounds are brought from the periphery to the places where they are to be deposited. The important point is that fluorine as such is much more widespread than we think. A great deal is present in various plants (relatively speaking, of course, since we really need very little). The fluorine-forming process in particular is present in plants even when fluorine is not evident in chemically detectable amounts. We will discuss this in more detail shortly. Fluorine is always present even in any water we drink, so there is no need to make a special effort to get enough. The important consideration is that the body is organized in a way that permits it to master the specific and extremely complicated process involved in fluorine absorption. But to put it in conventional terminology, you would have to say simply that the bloodstream transports fluorine to the right place.

Then there is the question of whether the enamel of fully erupted teeth continues to be nourished. It does not. This is clear from what I explained earlier. But we do need to pay attention to something else that takes place there. We might say that spiritual-scientific investigation of the area where the teeth form and the surrounding area reveals an extremely vigorous activity of the etheric body, which is free and only loosely connected to the physical organization at this point. The activity that can be observed here, this etherically mobile organizing that is constantly going on around the jaws, is by no means present in such a free form in the human abdomen, where it is most closely bound to physical, organic activity. This relates to several phenomena I mentioned earlier. Releasing the etheric body's activity from the physical organism, as happens in pregnancy, immediately calls forth significant changes in the other pole, in tooth structure, and hemorrhoids are similarly related to the fact that the effects of the physical body and etheric body are going in separate directions. But when the etheric body becomes independent in this lower end of the human organization, it is immediately pulled into the organization at the other end, where it is associated with the opposite effect, the destructive effect. Enhancing and intensifying normal, healthy organic activity on the lower end—which happens in a healthy sense in pregnancy but in an unhealthy sense in a sick person—works regressively or destructively on the teeth in particular. It is especially important to take note of this effect.

It is possible to raise the question of whether therapeutic intervention is necessary in cases where everything I told you about education and the outer effects of fluorine does not work adequately. The human organism is so complicated that medical treatment must sometimes intervene in place of mere education. From a macroscopic perspective, hand and foot coordination are fluorine effects. The effect of fluorine is not what our imagination imposes on it when we think in atomistic terms; it is the constitution a person develops when his or her fingers become supple and dextrous, when the legs become agile. The effect of fluorine appears on the surface of the human organism and continues toward the interior. It is the inner continuation of what happens in external activity. Not only the teeth but also the fact that a child doesn't know how to do anything and cannot become skillful shows us that the child's education has been bad. Then we need to intervene prophylactically in the organism in some way. It is very interesting to note that if we experiment with an aqueous extract of the sap of horse chestnut bark—that is, with an esculin extract—and administer a very high dilution internally, it is possible to regulate tooth preservation, if we do not start too late.[50]

This is another interesting connection. The sap of horse chestnut bark actually contains a substance that builds up our teeth. We can always find something in the macrocosm that is important in some way for our internal organization. This effect is related to the fact that esculin expels chemical activity from the substances it works in—it renders their chemical activity ineffective. Strangely enough, when we beam a spectrum through an esculin solution, the chemical effects are expelled from the spectrum. The elimination of chemical effects is also what we see when we give the organism a very dilute aqueous extract—it must be an aqueous extract—of esculin. Then we see that the process of overcoming chemical activity and working toward mere mineralization is the same as the tooth-forming process in the organism. The only difference is that this process, which otherwise takes place on a merely external level when chemical activity is eliminated, is permeated by the organizing forces present in the human organism.

Even ordinary chlorophyll works in a similar way, although it is administered differently. The force inherent in the bark of horse chestnut and some other plants is present in chlorophyll in a different form. In this instance, however, we must try to extract the chlorophyll with an etheric substance, and then we need to apply it externally to the

---

50. *Esculin*—a glucoside $C_{15}H_{16}O_9$ that absorbs ultraviolet light; obtained from the inner bark of the horse chestnut (*Aesculus hippocastaneum*) and the roots of the yellow jessamine (*Gelsemium sempervirens*).

abdomen in the form of a liniment instead of administering it internally. If we massage the abdomen with etherized chlorophyll, the effect on the organism with regard to tooth preservation is the same as when we administer esculin internally. These therapies need to be tried out. Presenting the statistical results would surely have a significant impact on the outer world. Once the dental pulp is dead, we must attempt to make the entire organism receptive to absorbing fluorine, but this is no longer a matter for general dental treatment.

All this shows how strongly dental treatment—to the extent that it is possible to treat the teeth at all—is related to all the growth forces of the human organism. What I have explained about esculin and chlorophyll points us in the direction of forces that are essentially related to very subtle growth processes tending toward mineralization. The simple fact of the matter is that our higher development toward the spirit is purchased at the expense of our teeth. We pay for it with a general regression of the tooth-forming process. This is also true from the phylogenetic perspective. In comparison to the process of tooth development in animals, this process regresses in humans. It shares this regressive character, however, with the regressive processes that are omnipresent in the organization of the human head.

I have guided you here to modes of observation that can become significant in assessing the whole process of dental development. We can now add another perspective that will be the basis of a few more discoveries. At this point I am going to interject a seemingly unrelated subject, namely, the issue of diet, which also has to do with what we have just been discussing. Dietary questions are extremely important because their significance is social as well as medical. We could spend a long time debating the significance and validity of various peculiar diets, but the main consideration is that any dietary restriction makes people antisocial. This is where the social and the medical aspects collide. The more special needs we have in terms of nutrition or, the more inclusive they are with regard to the outer world's influences, the more antisocial we become. The significance of the Last Supper was not that Christ gave each disciple something special, but that he gave them all the same thing. The possibility of coming together as human beings to eat or drink is of great social significance, and anything that tends to interfere with this healthy social aspect of our human nature needs to be handled with some caution.

When individuals are left to their own devices, they develop all kinds of dietary likes and dislikes, not only on the conscious level but also with respect to internal processes on the organic level. In this sense, it is really not so important to look at people's likes and dislikes, tolerances and intolerances, in the usual way, because by learning to tolerate something that he or she could not tolerate before— that is, by overcoming a dislike in the broadest, organ-based sense— an individual achieves more on behalf of his or her organization than could be achieved by any amount of abstention from foods that are not well tolerated. Inherent in overcoming something we cannot tolerate is the literal, not figurative, production of an organ that has been destroyed, or even of a new organ, if we look at the etheric body. The organ-forming force is inherent in nothing other than the overcoming of dislikes and intolerances. Beyond a certain point, catering to the appetite causes the organs to hypertrophy or degenerate rather than benefiting them. Thus, further damage is caused whenever too much is done in terms of accommodating what the damaged organism wants to ward off. However, when the attempt is made to gradually accustom a person to something that seems poorly tolerated, the bodily organization is always strengthened.

In this respect, contemporary science has obscured almost everything we would need to know by subscribing to the external principle of natural selection and the survival of the fittest, which is really quite superficial, at least initially. Roux extended it to the struggle among the organs in the human being, but that is very superficial indeed.[51] This principle becomes important only when you can actually examine what is going on internally. And then it must be

---

51. Wilhelm Roux (1850–1924), German zoologist considered the founder of modern experimental embryology; professor at Halle (1895–1921); *Der Kampf der Teile im Organismus* (1881) [The struggle among the parts of the body]; *Über die Zeit der Bestimmung der Hauptrichtungen im Froschembryo* (1883) [Timetable for the development of the primary directions in the frog embryo]; *Über die Entwicklungsmechanik der Organismen"* (1890) [The developmental mechanics of organisms).

said that strengthening a single human organ, or in fact any organ in the phylogenetic series, is always based on overcoming an antipathy. The shaping of organs takes place as a result of overcoming antipathies, while the growth of an existing organ is due to indulging in sympathies—which, however, must not be taken beyond a certain point. Sympathy and antipathy do not exist exclusively on the tongue or in the eye; the entire organism resonates with sympathy and antipathy. Each organ has its own sympathies and antipathies. An organ develops an antipathy to what built it up under particular circumstances. It owes its development to the very thing to which it then develops an antipathy once it is complete. This phenomenon would lead us much deeper into phylogeny if we would simply consider that the initial impact of the environment is to stimulate inner defenses, or a discharge of antipathy, against it and that this process progressively perfects the organization. In the realm of organisms, the fittest in the struggle for survival is the organism that is the most able to overcome inner antipathies and replace them with organs. This is part and parcel of the organ-forming process.

Considering this provides us with a clue to how to look at dosages of remedies. In the organ-forming process itself, you see a constant oscillation between sympathy and antipathy. The genesis of the human organization is essentially connected to the development of sympathy and antipathy and dependent on the alternation between them. The relationship of sympathy to antipathy in the organism is the same as the relationship of lower potencies, in which actual material effects of a substance are utilized, to higher potencies. The effect of the high potency is the opposite of that of the low potency. This fact is related to the overall organizing force. In a certain sense, it is quite true, as I mentioned yesterday from a different perspective, that certain effects that are active in the organism in a particular way during the first period of life are reversed in later stages or may also be postponed. As I told you yesterday, this is the basis of schizophrenia on the one hand and on the other of the development of isolated areas of the soul that take hold of the organism in inappropriate ways later on in life.

We will be able to cope with these conditions only when our science has again been spiritualized a bit, when we have reached the point of no longer attempting to cure psychiatric disorders by soul-spiritual means, and when we are willing to ask what is out of order in the organs when a particular mental illness appears. In the reverse situation, strange as it may sound, we have much more reason to turn to psychological factors in so-called physical illnesses than in so-called mental illnesses. In mental illnesses, psychiatric findings are never helpful much beyond the diagnostic stage. They must simply be studied in order to discover the possible location of the problem in the organism. The ancients equipped us with the terminology for these connections. It was not for nothing that they gave the mental symptoms of hypochondria thoroughly materialistic names such as "abdominal boniness" or "cartilaginous abdomen." Even if the hypochondria worsened to the point of insanity, they would never have turned to anything other than abdominal disease as the primary cause of such a condition that appears on the psychological level. We need to progress to the point of being able to see all so-called matter as a spiritual entity.

We are suffering tremendously today from the fact that the materialistic way of thinking is the extension of a Catholic asceticism that attempted to achieve the spirit by despising nature. Our modern worldview has chosen to take up certain aspects of this ascetic trend. Consequently, it assumes that the processes taking place in the lower body are crudely material and need not be taken into account. In actuality, this is not true. The spirit is at work in all these things, and we need to know how it is working. If I link the spirit at work in the human organism to the spirit at work in some external substance or activity, spirit works with spirit. We must get away from despising nature. We must once again reach the point of being able to imagine all of nature as spiritualized. Right now, when materialism is at its height, we are seeing the emergence of a desire to use all sorts of hypnosis and suggestion to treat individuals with so-called abnormal conditions. Don't you find this striking and tremendously significant for an overall reform of medical thinking? Concerns that seemed far removed from materialism are appearing in this materialistic age, when we have lost the possibility of educating ourselves about the spiritual aspects of mercury, antimony, gold, or silver. The crucial point here is

248 + INTRODUCING ANTHROPOSOPHICAL MEDICINE

that we have lost the possibility of educating ourselves about the spiritual aspect of matter. This is why we want to treat the actual spiritual aspect as such, which is what happens in psychoanalysis, where we attempt to guide the spiritual aspect. Healthy views on the spiritual properties of matter must once again assume their rightful place.

Keeping alive this belief in the spirituality of outer material substances is by no means the least of what the homeopathic tradition accomplished during the nineteenth century. Because superficial allopathic medicine, unfortunately, has turned more and more to the belief that we are dealing only with material aspects, with outer material effects of substances external to the human being, this is one of homeopathy's most important accomplishments. It leads us to pay attention to the patient's psychological state when we are diagnosing so-called physical illnesses on the one hand, and on the other to look for physical damage when an abnormal psychological state is strongly apparent. Actual physical illness should always raise the question of the patient's temperament. If we find that the patient tends to be a hypochondriac, this by itself will lead us to treat the person in a way that has a strong impact on the lower part of the body. This means that we must use materially active substances—that is, lower potencies—to treat this particular person. In contrast, if we find that a person, apart from his or her current illness, has a lively mind and a sanguine temperament, we will need to resort to higher potencies from the very beginning.

In short, we need to ascertain the patient's psychological state, especially with regard to physical illness. We encounter this overall psychological state even in children in a certain way. If the child does not already have phlegmatic tendencies, if we cannot clearly perceive the potential for this temperament—which should appear only at a later stage of life, and even then only to a limited extent—then schizophrenia is unlikely to appear. Making the distinction between inner activity and inner passivity is especially important. Just think, when we make use of hypnosis in our so-called psychotherapy, we are placing someone entirely within another person's sphere of influence and preventing independent activity. Blocking a person's activity or inner initiative has consequences in outer life that are important for the person's entire biography. If we observe the corresponding phenomenon in children, it plays into their dental history with consequences later in life. We will talk about this more tomorrow.

For example, I may consider it necessary for myself to avoid certain foods and emphasize others. (After what I said earlier, it is important to take this into account.) I may consider it important to adhere to a particular diet, which may be very good for me. It makes a considerable difference, however, whether I have arrived at this diet through independent experimentation on myself or whether I simply let the doctor prescribe it for me. Please don't be offended by this bald statement. From the materialistic point of view, it looks as if a diet that is good for me serves the same purpose regardless of whether I have taken the initiative to work it out on my own, possibly under my doctor's guidance, or whether I simply let the doctor prescribe it. Ultimately, however, the effects of the diet the doctor prescribes, although initially helpful, will be damaging in that they make it easier for me to succumb to age-related dementia than would otherwise have been the case, while my active collaboration will make it easier for me to remain intellectually spry in old age, although of course there are other contributing factors.

In any form of hypnotherapy, this interplay of activity and inactivity is largely suppressed because I enter a state of dependency, relinquishing not only my own power of judgment, in that I do what the other person suggests, but also the power to direct my own will, which I hand over to the other person's judgment. For this reason, the use of hypnotherapy should be restricted as much as possible. It can be used only if we are certain that, for other reasons, the person in question will not be harmed by this will impairment, which is present in everyone who is treated in this way, and that the impairment is outweighed by the greater service we are doing this person by helping him or her with hypnosis for a time. In general, however, spiritual science must recommend the therapeutic effects of substances, of the atmosphere, and of movement in the human organism—in short, of everything other than direct spiritual influence. Therapeutic effects should emerge actively from either the consciousness or the subconscious of the person in question on the basis of independent initiative.

These things are so very important because they are the most sinned against in this materialistic age and infected by prevailing views. It is terrible to experience today how all these tendencies toward hypnosis and suggestion are being carried over into education. This is a terrible trend, and we may be able to see clearly in this regard only once we can answer the question of how the activities of the human organism that wake it up work in contrast to those that put it to sleep. When people go to sleep and dream, they imagine movements that are not obeyed by voluntary actions. In this instance, people are at rest with respect to the outer world, while their conscious experiences are in motion. The reverse is true in eurythmy. Eurythmy brings about the exact opposite of going to sleep, namely, a stronger waking up than the ordinary manifestations of consciousness. The hypertrophied imagery of dreams is removed, and in its place a healthy development of the will is driven into the limbs. The will organization is driven into the limbs. If we begin to study how differently the vowels and consonants of eurythmy affect the lower and upper parts of the human being, we realize that a significant therapeutic element can be sought in eurythmy.[52]

---

52. See Rudolf Steiner's *Curative Eurythmy*, (CW 315), Rudolf Steiner Press, London, 1983. This course was held one year later during the second course for physicians (April 12–18, 1921), *Anthroposophical Spiritual Science and Medical Therapy*, (CW 313), Mercury Press, Spring Valley, NY.

LECTURE 18

DORNACH, APRIL 7, 1920

I believe that our scientific medical education truly needs an infusion of what might be called a return to the true causes of pathological phenomena. In recent times, the tendency has become ever more pronounced to disregard actual causes and to look at surface occurrences. A phenomenon related to this superficiality is the fact that whenever we begin to read or hear a description of any type of illness, current medicine or pathology almost always informs us about what has invaded the human organism, about what kind of bacillus provokes the illness in question. It is terribly easy, of course, to repudiate any objections to the idea of lower organisms invading the body for the simple reason that it is no longer necessary to first prove that these lower organisms are present. Since distinct forms of microorganisms are indeed evident in different illnesses, the tendency to suggest a connection is quite understandable.

But even on a superficial level, this view gives rise to an error that actually completely distracts us from the main issue. If bacilli appear in large numbers in a certain part of the body in the course of an illness, they naturally provoke symptoms, as do any foreign bodies in the organism. As a result of the presence of these bacilli, all kinds of inflammations appear. But if we then attribute everything to the activity of the bacilli, directing our attention only to what the bacilli are doing, we are distracted from the true cause of the disease, because any habitat that lower organisms find suitable for their own development within the human body is brought about by the primary causes. For once, we need to pay attention to the domain of primary causes. In order to do so, we must briefly turn our attention again to modes of observation that we have already begun to use.

Consider once again the plants that cover the surface of the Earth, the sum total of the Earth's vegetation. We must be clear that the vegetation growing up out of the Earth toward cosmic space is not simply sent forth by the Earth. It is also pulled upward by forces that are just as much a part of plant growth as the forces working into it from out of the Earth. In plants, there is a constant interaction between the Earth's forces and the forces of the supra-earthly cosmos. What is the effect of these nonearthly forces, which are always present in our environment? If these forces that work in from the cosmos came to full expression and took hold of the plants totally—that is, if the planets did not ensure that these forces could also withdraw—plants would have the tendency to turn into animals as they went on growing from the stem toward the flower and the seed. The tendency to turn into animals is always present. What works in from the cosmos is counteracted by the tendency that works out of the Earth, the tendency to suppress plant existence and to become mineral within the plant kingdom. What I am drawing your attention to here is the fact that plant existence as such holds the balance between the tendency toward mineralization or salt deposition in plant tissue and the tendency toward inflammation or becoming animal-like.

This process is always present in outer nature, but it is also present in an internalized and centralized form in the human organism. Because it possesses lungs, the human organism is a real little Earth, and everything that works out of the lungs works downward in the same way that the forces that work from the Earth out into the plant organism work upward. The effect of everything that works via respiration and cardiac activity to counter the internal metabolism of the lungs and so forth is similar to the effect of this cosmic factor out here [see drawing on following page].

In the human organism, everything that is concentrated in cardiac activity needs to be kept separate from what is organized and concentrated in the lungs' internal metabolism. These two activities must be kept separate. They can be allowed to affect each other only through

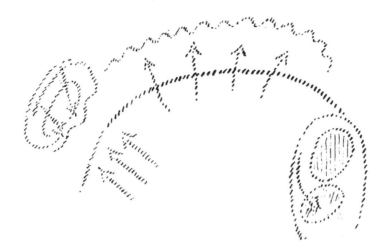

an etheric or astral diaphragm inserted between them. At this point we must raise the question of whether this diaphragm exists, since I am using this word only to suggest an image. Is there a diaphragm that prevents the activity of the head, throat, and lungs from mingling with the activity of the abdomen and chest in any way except through the external rhythm of respiration? Such a diaphragm does indeed exist, and it is the external rhythm of respiration itself. At this point, you begin to see how harmony is achieved between the upper and lower regions of the human being. What we call rhythmical activity in the human being, the rhythmical trembling that is expressed outwardly and physically as respiratory rhythm, extends into the activity of the etheric and astral bodies and separates the earthly forces of the upper part of the human being, which are concentrated in the lungs, and the heavenly forces of the lower part, which work from below upward through the activity expressed in the heart, just as they work from the periphery of the cosmos toward the center of the Earth.

Imagine that this rhythm is not working properly. The metaphorical diaphragm, which, though not physically present, is created by these rhythms striking against each other, is out of order. What happens then is analogous to what happens when the Earth's activity becomes too strong in plants, when earthly salt-forming activity affects the plants too strongly and they become overly mineralized. What happens then is that an "etheric plant," which is built into the lungs and grows up out of them just as physical plants grow up out of the Earth, becomes the cause of pulmonary hardening or the like. Here we find that the mineralizing tendency that is present in plants can also become too strong in the human organism.

On the other hand, the animalizing tendency can also become too strong. When this happens, it creates a domain in the upper part of the organism that should not be there. The organs of this part of the body become embedded in an etheric domain, as it were, that is favorable to an activity that should not be promoted in the organism, namely, the life of microscopic plants or animals. Where they come from need not concern us, but we do need to be concerned about the creation of the habitat that supports them. This favorable habitat should not be present. Its activity ought to extend throughout the organism rather than becoming a special enclosed domain. When it extends throughout the organism, it supports the life of the entire organism, but when it takes the form of a little enclosed domain, it becomes a life-supporting medium for the microscopic plants or animals whose presence we can confirm in everything that causes illness, or at least in much of what causes illness, in the upper areas of the human being.

To solve the riddle of how bacilli influence the human organism, we must return to rhythmical activity and its disturbance and see whether a special domain is created in place of a general domain extending throughout the organism. Without returning to the spiritual causes, we will never be able to solve this riddle. Exactly the same thing that affects plant life here—above the Earth's surface, that is— also affects the outer life of animals and human beings. Like plants, humans and animals are also influenced by certain forces that come from the cosmos above the Earth and counteract the forces arising from within [see left of drawing on p. 253]. The forces coming from within the Earth are localized in certain organs in the upper part of the human being, while the forces streaming in from outside are localized in abdominal organs. Once again, if I may put it in this way, a dividing wall must be erected between their respective activities. Normal regulation of this separation is accomplished by human spleen activity. This is another example of how rhythm is active in the human organism. But this time the rhythm is different from respiratory rhythm, which takes place in little oscillations and runs through the entire life of the human being.

If respiratory rhythm is not in order, diseases having exclusively to do with the upper part of the human being will arise. But since digestion extends both downward and upward, it is also possible for diseases that are caused down below to be present in the upper region of the human being. We must distinguish between these two types of illness. We must not think of the human being as divided according to some rigid scheme, because individual systems intermingle. However, there must be a dividing wall between what works from above, as if coming from the Earth, and what works from below, as if coming from heavenly space. In fact, our upper regions send their forces out to meet the forces of the lower human being, and in each human individual the rhythm between the two must be regulated. This rhythm is expressed in the right proportion of waking to sleeping. Each time we wake up is one beat of this rhythm, and each time we fall asleep is another beat. This rhythm of waking/sleeping, waking/sleeping incorporates other rhythmical processes, smaller peaks that are brought about simply because even in the waking state we are awake in our upper parts but asleep in our lower parts. The rhythmical activity that is continually taking place between the upper and the lower parts of the human being is caught up in larger rhythms only through the alternation of waking and sleeping.

Imagine that a breach occurs in the boundary that consists of this rhythm between the upper and lower parts of the human being. In this case, the activity of the upper part of the human being usually breaks through into the abdomen from above. An etheric breach occurs, and etheric activity that ought to take place only in the upper human body begins to occur in the lower part. Certain finer forces break through. Once again, this results in the creation of a domain that should not be there. Instead of being localized in the abdomen, this domain ought to be distributed throughout the human being. As a result of a breakthrough of this sort, the abdomen is poisoned, in a sense. When upper-body activity intervenes in this way, abdominal activity can no longer take place as it should. In addition, however, the new domain that is created here provides a habitat for microorganisms. You might say that a breakthrough from above provokes typhoid fever in the human being. The concomitant phenomenon of the appearance of an abdominally localized milieu creates what the typhus bacillus requires in order to flourish.

Here you see a clear separation of primary and secondary factors. This separation will also enable you to see the need to distinguish between the ultimate causes of such an illness and the symptoms of inflammation that appear simply as a consequence of the presence of a whole army of intestinal fauna or flora, especially in the small intestines. All the physical symptoms in the small intestines—including bacilli, including the activity of these plant or animal microorganisms—are simply reactions to upper functions breaking through into the lower functions of the human organism. Again, we need not discuss where these bacilli come from, because they would not be able to lead their animal or vegetable existence there if the right milieu had not been created for them. All these phenomena are mere consequences. The important point is to aim for the primary factor rather than secondary ones when we are looking for therapeutic procedures. We will speak more about this later, because we can talk about these matters only once we are in a position to go back to their true origins. This is almost impossible for modern conventional medicine because it excludes any view that shifts from a material process to a spiritual process. Everything material, however, is underlaid by spirit.

You will easily be able to explain the characteristic clinical picture of typhoid fever, for example, if you take a good look at what I have just discussed. Keep in mind that this illness is very often coupled with symptoms of pulmonary mucosal inflammation and disturbances of consciousness. Pulmonary symptoms develop because an activity is withdrawn from the upper body in order to appear down below. Once the breakthrough has taken place, what has appeared in the lower part of the human being is no longer present at all up above. Similarly, the upper organs that are the vehicles of consciousness can no longer work effectively when what is supposed to mediate their activity has penetrated the lower parts of the body. The entire clinical picture of typhoid fever appears before your mind's eye if you really look at this primary cause.

Under certain circumstances, this collection of unrelated outer symptoms—something we otherwise always look at only from outside—appears so forcefully in an individual's subconscious that it even becomes possible to paint it on the basis of its existential connections. The urge to objectify it prophetically comes about before it paints itself upon the interior of the organism. Then the person in question feels the urge to record what is slipping away from the upper body as blue spots and what is slipping away from the abdomen as red spots on canvas. Imagine an individual who feels called upon to be an artist instead of a tailor or a shoemaker but has little experience in painting techniques. If this person is also robust enough—and this does not require outer robustness—to constantly suppress abdominal illnesses that are attempting to arise within, you can experience how this person objectifies these abdominal illnesses on canvas rather than allowing them to gain a hold on the body. You can find the products of this strange activity in much of expressionistic painting, where you can see the artist's state of health with regard to the lower body in the red and yellow colors. Try to see everything you find there in blue and purple as a poetic expression of the state of the artist's upper body, of the lungs and everything that accompanies lung activity as it moves rhythmically toward the head.

If you take a close look at examples such as this, you will find a remarkable harmony between an individual's general actions and the internal state of his or her organization. From how an individual presents him- or herself, you will develop a certain intuition or image of how that person's body is functioning. It is totally false to believe that a person's outer actions and appearance, the soul activity he or she undertakes in the outer world, is dependent only on the nervous system. It depends on the entire human being; it is an image of the entire human being. Simply by recalling the childhood appearance of someone condemned to carry all of the damaging consequences of delayed growth over into later stages of life, we can develop intuitive insight that enables us to observe in the child what the intellectual adult of advancing age will be like. What prevents him or her from growing upward makes this person appear ungainly but strong. Whether a child appears heavy or light will allow you to get an intuitive idea of how that child will grow. Numerous similar phenomena point out how the entire gesture of the way a person presents him- or herself is nothing more than the interaction of the inner parts of the human organism, an interaction that has been brought into movement.

It would be desirable to include such considerations in medical curricula. Just think, the most favorable prerequisites are already present. It is easiest for young people in their early twenties to immerse themselves in such subjects. As soon as we reach our thirties, we lose this gift and it is no longer so easy to find our way into such matters, although it remains possible to acquire intuitions of this sort through very strict self-education. Certain potentials that persist in spite of the destructive drill that takes place in our secondary education, and especially in higher education, also make it possible for us to find our way back to any active forces remaining from our childhood and train ourselves to see the human being in this way. But placing the right value on a more subtle, sculptural study of anatomy and physiology for medical students would do a lot to improve medical treatment as a whole for humankind.

Illnesses that appear in the form of epidemics must also be considered in terms of their primary causes. The rhythm between head and chest, which has its crudest expression in the rhythm of respiration, is easily damaged in individuals who also tend to allow certain atmospheric or supra-earthly phenomena to influence them strongly. Others, whose respiratory system is healthily organized from the start, will tend to resist such influences. It is always possible for other disruptive causes to intervene, of course, but let me choose an example that will help us understand what this all depends on. Suppose that during a particular winter the Sun's activity—note that I said the Sun's activity, not the effects of light—is strongly influenced by the outer planets— Mars, Jupiter, and Saturn. Sun activity that can assert itself independently because Mars, Jupiter, and Saturn are at a distance would have a different effect from this particular winter constellation.

During a winter like this, we can notice that the atmospheric phenomena are different. In susceptible individuals, this has an unusually strong influence on the rhythmical activity taking place between the chest and the head, whose crudest expression is the rhythm of respiration. We can say that this constellation significantly strengthens the tendency to regularize this rhythm in people who were born in healthy circumstances and are internally robust, although outwardly, of course, they may be quite frail. In these people, respiratory rhythm is very strongly regulated, as is the general rhythm between the head and the chest. An internally reinforced rhythm such as this is not easily affected by outside influences, and severely damaging factors are required in order to influence it. An influence such as the one I described, however, has an exceptionally strong effect on people in whom this rhythm is irregular in some way, because an already damaged rhythm tends to permit further damage. All predisposed individuals who live on parts of the globe that are particularly affected by this heavenly constellation are candidates for so-called influenza. These influences absolutely must be present to lay the groundwork for an illness like influenza.

In a different case, something more complicated is present. Even though each individual rhythm is an independent entity—both the ongoing rhythm that finds its crudest expression in respiration and the rhythm influenced by sleeping and waking—human rhythmical activity as a whole is such that these rhythms, taken together, form a unity in the entire human rhythmic system. The lower rhythm may assert itself too strongly, relatively speaking, because the upper rhythm, the head-chest rhythm, is weakened. When the upper rhythm is too weak and deviates from its proper position, it is susceptible to being made even more irregular by the lower rhythm. In this case the lower rhythm, which emanates from the activity of the spleen and from other organ activity that we will speak about later, works upward too strongly, creating the predisposition to hypertrophy of the upper digestive process with all its concomitant symptoms. Once again, a domain is created that especially favors the growth of certain lower organisms. The total picture that then appears is one of symptoms of inflammation and paralysis creeping into the upper organization while the beginnings of organ malformations or new organic growths also appear there. In short, we have the symptomatology of diphtheria. I might call this is a breakthrough, from below upward, in the opposite direction from the breach that occurs in typhoid fever from above downward. This second type of breakthrough is essentially provoked by what I have just described.

In all of these issues, the age of the person in question must also be considered. During childhood, the entire interaction of the upper and lower parts of the human being as well as the rhythmical activity that mediates between them is totally different than it is in later life. In childhood, for example, the upper region of the human being must exert a much stronger influence on the lower region than is the case later on. In reality, children "think" much more than adults do. Strange as this may sound, it is nonetheless true. Instead of becoming conscious, children's thoughts simply go into the organism and appear in its growth and in the forms it is developing. This application of thought activity to the body's formative forces is especially pronounced in the first years of life. Once the body no longer needs to use so much of the formative forces for its own purposes, they are held back and become the force that forms the basis of memory. Therefore, memory appears only after the organism's demands on the formative forces are reduced, because the forces that underlie memory on the organic level are transformed forces of growth and development, which are especially called upon to shape the organism during the very first years of life.

Everything is based on metamorphosis. What we encounter on the mental or spiritual level is only the respiritualization of an activity that worked on a bodily level when spirit was moving into matter. This explains why children have strong forces of resistance to many abdominal symptoms. Heavenly factors, supra-earthly factors, appear principally in the abdomen. Here again, imagine that a strong reflection occurs in the human abdomen as the result of a particular supra-earthly constellation of the Sun to other planets. What will the consequences be? There will be little effect on adults, in whom the rhythmical activity between the upper and lower parts of the body has already settled down to some extent, but children will have to forcefully resist the cosmic factor that wants to be reflected in the abdomen. And when a particular cosmic constellation affects a child's lower body very strongly, the upper body must resist exceptionally strongly. This convulsive, overly strong application of forces in the upper part of children's bodies causes epidemic cerebrospinal meningitis. This process certainly provides insight into how outer, nonhuman nature sends these influences into the human being. I might say that if you take this as a background for your observations, you can paint a picture of the entire symptomatology of meningitis, right down to the stiffening of the neck muscles. Because of the exertion taking place in the upper part of the child's body, inflammatory symptoms must appear in the upper organs, in the meninges of the spinal cord or brain, which then result in the other symptoms.

It is especially necessary to sharpen our eye for seeing the human being in the context not only of the interactions taking place between different parts of the body but also of the interactions taking place between internal human factors and natural factors external to the human being or even external to the Earth. To my way of thinking, astrology in its present form is highly suspect, so of course I do not want to see it get out of hand as a result of views like this. It is enough to be aware of where such conditions come from, and we will indeed find this awareness necessary with regard to healing in particular. But it is really not so important to say that some illness or other is brought about by the quadrature of this star to that star. Under certain circumstances, this can be useful with regard to a cosmic diagnosis, but it is not the point. The point is to be able to heal.

Tomorrow, we will move on from today's considerations to the substances in outer, nonhuman nature that have a defensive effect, that contain forces opposing what intrudes into the human organism in this way. In this context, recognition of the upper and lower areas of the human being really must assume more of a place in medical science, because in my opinion the strength of this recognition would enable physicians to collaborate in the interest of human health. When physicians specialize, they lose interest in the human being as a whole. I do not mean at all to say that physicians should not specialize. The techniques that appear over the course of time simply do bring about a certain degree of specialization. While this is happening, however, collaboration among specialists should also increase.

This becomes evident when we consider pyorrhea, for example, which was mentioned in one of your questions. When it appears, we are dealing with not only a local problem, as many people believe, but with a predisposition—or worse—that involves the entire organism and is simply localized in the gums. For example, it would be very helpful if dentists who note the appearance of pyorrhea in their patients would make a habit of alerting other physicians to the fact that these people are likely candidates for diabetes. What we have already described to a certain extent as coming to expression in diabetes is easy to treat as long as it remains in its germinal stages in the upper part of the human being, as pyorrhea. Much too little attention is paid to the fact that the lower part of the human being can overcome the upper, resulting in inappropriate impoverishment or enrichment of either the upper or the lower part. If the tendency to inflammation appears first in the upper region, the disease takes one form. If it appears in the lower part of the human being, it assumes the opposite or polar form of the illness. A very great deal depends on making this distinction.

For this reason, it will also seem quite understandable that the etheric body, which contains all of an individual's forces for growth, must work differently during childhood than at a later age. In childhood, the etheric body must intervene in physical functioning to a much greater extent. It needs organs that provide it with direct points of contact. This is especially important during the fetal period, but it is still the case in the first stage of childhood, when both growth and form development are taking place, when sculptural forces need to take effect as growth continues. This is why we need organs such as the thymus gland, and to a certain extent also the thyroid gland, whose tasks are greater in childhood. Later, these organs regress and may degenerate if physical forces take hold of them too strongly.

Chemical activity within the organism simply must be stronger during childhood. Later this chemical activity tends to be replaced by the action of warmth. I might say that a change human beings undergo in the course of a lifetime is symbolized by the spectrum, or more than symbolized, if we look first at the more chemical portion of the spectrum (blue, violet), then at the light portion (green, yellow), and finally at the warmth portion ((red). Human beings undergo

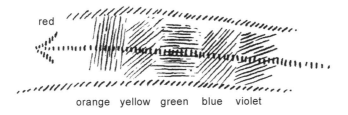

red

orange yellow green blue violet

a process of organization in this same direction [see drawing]. In childhood, we are more dependent on chemical action, but then we move on to light action and later to the effects of warmth. The organs that make it possible for the etheric body to promote chemical activity in the physical body are glands such as the thyroid, thymus, and adrenals. Because these organs are in some way bound to chemical activity, the flesh tones of human skin are related to their activity—that is, to the underlying etheric activity—to a great extent. One of the effects of the adrenals, for example, is to make a person either pale or red-cheeked and so on. Adrenal degeneration has to be expressed in the coloration of the skin. To see deeply into these connections, simply recall that patients with so-called Addison's disease, which is due to adrenal degeneration, turn brown. This points toward a certain chemical activity in the organism. It is especially relevant to the fetal period, while the action of light comes into consideration more in life after the age of about fourteen. Later still, we move more into the action of warmth.

All this constitutes an important indication with regard to the course of an individual's life. Childhood, especially the fetal period, represents a preponderance of the salt process, while the middle portion of life that is still somewhat closer to childhood represents a mercurial process of sorts and later life a sulfur process, in the context I have just described. In childhood, we must pay the most attention to the salt process, in midlife, to the mercurial process, and at a later age to the sulfur-like or phosphorus-like process, regulating each in its turn. If you look at the fact that the human organism also includes the trinity of organized chemical activity, an organized light process, and an organized warmth process—that is, organized salt, mercury, and sulfur processes—you will also get an idea of how life as a whole organizes the human being. In the child, lifestyle—by which I mean not merely nutrition, but everything the person does—works through chemical activity, intervening strongly within the organism. In the very young person, the light process, which I might say is stronger, intervenes in the entire organism in a way that can also sow the seeds of psychological disturbances of all sorts, because adolescents are most susceptible to impressions of the outer world. Whether the outer life that enters us strongly at this age is built up logically or illogically is of great importance for our entire soul constitution in later life. We will continue talking about these questions tomorrow. In particular, we will move on from the pathological aspects we have discussed today to therapeutic aspects.

LECTURE 19

DORNACH, APRIL 8, 1920

I will attempt to elaborate as much as possible today and tomorrow. In the case of a very preliminary stimulus such as this, which was all this course could provide, the important concern is to become more familiar with how spiritual science describes the route by which outer substances enter the human organism and also with the countereffects of these substances. Having a complete overview of how any substance takes effect points the way to discovering its use as a remedy, and we can then judge for ourselves, which is much better than simply following guidelines stating that this is for this and that for that.

Today I will once again have to begin with a topic seemingly very far removed in order to arrive at something very close at hand. One question that appeared repeatedly, a question that necessarily interests all of you, is the question of heredity. It plays an exceptionally large role in assessing both the healthy (or at least relatively healthy) individual and the sick individual.

It must be said that modern materialistic science studies heredity only on a very abstract level, without many practical consequences for real life. Strangely enough—or at least "exotericists" find this strange, because to esotericists its laws are readily apparent—when we begin to study a subject like heredity seriously, we find that everything that is important for people to know about cosmic connections is outwardly revealed and quite visible at some point or other. In each instance, an outer manifestation of some sort reveals the forces that are present in external nature but hidden, although very active, in the human being.

We must keep these forces particularly in mind as we study heredity, because everything related to heredity is constantly being negatively influenced and veiled in illusions so that we cannot assess it properly. Having arrived at a conclusion about heredity, we find that it does not concur with other phenomena. This is because the facts of heredity in particular are so shrouded in illusions, which in turn is related to the fact that male and female are involved in heredity in ways that are very lawfully governed but are difficult to *determine*. Heredity is indeed governed by laws, but the manifestations of these laws are such that their regulating principles cannot always be apparent immediately. The horizontal position of the beam of a scale is governed by laws, but if we keep adding weight so that it tilts to the right or to the left, it is difficult to adhere strictly to the principle.

Something similar is true of hereditary phenomena; their governing principle is akin to the forces that bring the beam of a scale into the horizontal position. As it manifests, however, this lawfulness is extremely variable, because male and female are always involved in specific ways in heredity. The male always transmits what human beings owe to earthly existence and earthly forces, while the female organism is more oriented toward transmitting what comes from the supra-earthly cosmos. We might say that the Earth constantly makes demands on the man, organizing him through its forces, and that it is also the root of the development of male sexuality. In contrast, the heavens are constantly making demands on the woman and bringing about her form. Their influence predominates in all of her internal organizational processes.

This distinction points back to something I have already said. If conception results in a female being, she tends to be taken up by the heavens, if I may put it like that, to become ever more incorporated into supra-earthly processes, while a male being tends to be claimed by the Earth to an ever-increasing extent. Thus, the Earth and the heavens work together, because what I am saying should not be interpreted as meaning that only the heavens work on the female and only the Earth works on the male. Both influence both, but the balance tilts toward the side of the heavens in the woman and toward the side of the Earth in the man. The laws governing this balance, although very strict, are also variable.

This variability has certain consequences, however. There is something intrinsic to the woman's organism that continually resists earthly factors. But strangely enough, this is the case only within her own organism and does not apply to the embryo she carries. In the female organism, the heavens' struggle against the Earth is restricted to all the organizational processes that lie outside the formation of the ovum—that is, outside of what is incorporated into the reproductive processes. This means that the female organization is always withdrawing from the forces inherent in the reproductive process. In the woman, everything surrounding reproduction withdraws from these forces. We can say that while the man has some tendency to pass on all that is inherent in the reproductive forces—that is, everything that can be passed down via heredity—the woman, although she tends to withdraw from heredity herself, has a stronger tendency to transmit hereditary characteristics through her egg-forming forces

For this reason we can ask the question, how can we work within human society to counteract destructive forces of heredity? It is indeed true that the forces of heredity do not come to a halt in the face of either so-called spiritual or so-called physical factors. This is apparent, for example, in the fact that diabetes can very easily appear in the next generation of a family that tends heavily toward psychiatric illnesses in the present generation, so that a metamorphosis in direction occurs between generations. How to rescue people from destructive effects of heredity is indeed an exceptionally important question. The only way to do so is to make sure that womankind remains as healthy as possible, because healthy women will draw supra-earthly influences into our earthly processes, and, as a result, the processes that work to transmit hereditary damage by means of the embryo will be constantly combated from within the female organism. Therefore, a society that pays close attention to women's health resists the damaging influence of earthly forces on heredity by appealing to the effects of balancing forces that work in from above the Earth. The female organization acts as the only earthly accumulator of these forces. It is extremely important to take this into account.

What I have just said is universal; it applies to all earthly and supra-earthly forces. It becomes very visible, however, when we are dealing with hemophilia, with blood diseases. It is important to point out the fallacy of talking around the subject of hereditary phenomena in general terms. We must study those instances where the facts obviously point to hereditary. Please study the manifestations of heredity in hemophiliacs. You will discover a strange phenomenon that is familiar to all of you but which is only an outer expression of what I have just explained. You will find that in the bloodline of a family, hemophilia is transmitted only *to* male individuals *by* female individuals—that is, a woman who is the daughter of a hemophiliac tends to transmit the disease to her male off-spring even though she herself does not have it; she simply carries it because she belongs to that family. The men, in contrast, become hemo-philiacs, but if they marry women who can be proved not to come from hemophiliac families, their disease is not transmitted.

If you analyze this tendency, you will find it to be a clear manifesta-tion of what I have just said. The phenomena among hemophiliacs demonstrate the actual processes of heredity much more clearly than any of Weismann's recent experiments.[53] We must also regard these circumstances as important to an overall assessment of the human organization, which needs to be assessed in accordance with what can influence it.

What is the real basis of hemophilia? Even superficial consideration reveals the answer. The clotting ability of the blood is absent, so that even the slightest opening toward the outside can make a hemophiliac bleed to death. As a rule, clotting sets in at the wound site after a nose-bleed or a dental operation, for example, but in hemophiliacs this does not happen. All their symptoms are entirely due to deficient clotting ability. There must be a factor in their blood that counteracts clotting and works too strongly, so that it is not negated by the forces that begin to work in from outside when blood clots. When blood clots, we are dealing with forces that work in from the outer world. If there is something inherent in the blood that does not allow these forces to prevail, the blood tends to be too fluid.

53. August Weismann (1834–1914), first a physician, then professor of zoology in Freiburg. He postulated that acquired characteristics cannot be inherited. *Die Kontinuität des Keimplasmas als Grundlage einer Theorie der Vererbung* (1885) [The continuity of germ plasma as the basis of a theory of heredity]; *Das Keimplasma* (1892) [Germ Plasma].

You will easily discover that a strong tendency toward excessively fluid blood is related to the entire development of the human I, but not in a superficially apparent way. It is related not to the ideational process but to the will that is active in the human I. Thus, the organization that causes excessive fluidity in the blood is associated with everything that strengthens or weakens a person's will. Let me give you a nice historical example that once again demonstrates that we can discover certain secrets of nature if we interpret them correctly. It was not nature alone, however, but history that presented the famous case of the young women of Engadin, which you may have heard of.[54] These two young women represent a phenomenon that can thoroughly illuminate the understanding of the human being that medicine needs. These young women, who came from hemophiliac families, made a firm decision not to marry; they went down in history as personal opponents of the transmission of hemophilia.

We must make sure that we are looking at the right thing in such a case. It is certainly not characteristic of all young women from hemophiliac families to abstain from the urge to reproduce. Doing so requires the cultivation of a strong subjective will of the sort that works in the I rather than in the astral body. This strong will must have been present in these two young women, which means that what they had in their I, in their will, was in some way related to the forces that are active in hemophiliacs in particular. Consciously strengthening these forces is easier among hemophiliacs than among non-hemophiliacs. If this fact is acknowledged in the right way, it provides a certain insight into the blood's intrinsic forces and enables us to recognize their interaction with what lies outside the human being. By studying the forces in the blood that are related to conscious will, we discover the nature of the human will's entire relationship to forces outside the human being. The fact of the matter is that certain external forces have this particular inner relationship to human forces of will, because the last thing expelled into the natural world in the

---

54. There is no documentation of any such case in Engadin. The incident referred to may well have occurred in Tenna in the Safien valley, which (like Engadin) is also in Graubünden. See the novel by Ernst Zahn, *Die Frauen von Tannò* [The women of tannò], 1911; "Tannò" is a poetic variation on the name *Tenna*.

course of evolution had to do with conscious human will or with human will in general. This was the last thing to be forced out into the natural world.

It is important to study such processes, which shaped the human being but have been forced out and are now present in external nature. These excluded processes have intrinsic qualities that show how they relate to the process of shaping the human being. One such phenomenon has been studied for a long time. It is extremely difficult to get an overview of it because modern intellectual people have difficulty reenlivening the forces that preserved atavistic medicine even into the seventeenth and eighteenth centuries. This phenomenon that has been studied for so long is antimony and everything related to it.

Antimony, you see, is a very strange material, which is probably why some people who dealt with it, such as the legendary Basilius Valentinus, studied it so intensively.[55] Certain characteristics of antimony immediately reveal that it is very strangely enmeshed in the processes of nature. Possibly one of the least of antimony's characteristics is that it has an exceptional relationship to other metals and other substances, frequently appearing in conjunction with them, especially in other substances' sulfur compounds. In the natural world, sulfur, as you know, has a specific effect that we have discussed, at least briefly. Antimony's affinity for the sulfur compounds of other substances demonstrates how it is enmeshed in nature. This is even more emphatically evident, however, in another of its characteristics, namely, that whenever the opportunity arises, antimony appears in the form of bundle-like crystals—that is, it wants to turn into a line and move away from the Earth. Wherever antimony accumulates in linear formations, we can literally see the supra-earthly forces of crystallization entering the earthly domain. Crystal-forming forces that otherwise appear in more regular forms are active in these bundled, needlelike antimony formations. The substance of antimony itself reveals how it is enmeshed in the overall activity of nature. Similarly, the smelting process that yields

---

55. It is said that Basilius Valentinus (Basil Valentine) lived at about the end of the fourteenth and the beginning of the fifteenth century. Writings attributed to him include *The Tract of the Great Stone; Concerning Natural and Supernatural Things;* and *The Triumphal Chariot of Antimony.*

antimony in the form of fine filaments points very strongly to antimony as a revealer of crystallization forces.

Another quality of antimony is that it can oxidize and even burn in a certain way if it is heated until red-hot. The white smoke that forms has an affinity for cold objects, to which it adheres, producing the well-known "flowers of antimony."[56] Again, this is an example of how the force of crystallization is discharged in conjunction with other bodies.

The strangest characteristic of antimony, however, is its ability to ward off certain forces that I have described, over the course of the days we have spent here, as being subearthly in some respects. These are the forces at work in electricity and magnetism. If antimony is subjected to a specific type of electrolysis that makes it precipitate at the cathode, and if this antimony deposit is then touched with the tip of a metal rod, the antimony explodes. It creates little explosions. The resistance to electricity that antimony develops if we simply give it a bit of help is quite characteristic of this substance. Here we can see how antimony fits into the context of nature. Other substances do not demonstrate their place in nature so forcefully.

We can understand what an obvious natural example is attempting to show us only when we assume that the forces present in nature are at work everywhere but are simply exceptionally evident in substances where they are concentrated and localized. The force working in antimony, for example, is actually present everywhere. To coin a

---

56. "Flowers of antimony" is the white smoke from an alchemical fusion process that produces antimony. Basil Valentine stated: "The flowers of Antimony ... may be prepared in different ways, which all students of alchemy know. Some mix them with salt ammonia, drive them through the retort, and then wash out the ammonia. These flowers are of a beautiful white colour. Others sublime them over a strong fire, and, by placing three alembics on each other, they manage to prepare white, yellow, and red flowers at the same time.... But the most potent and efficacious flowers of Antimony are prepared as follows: Mix red flowers of Antimony with colcotar of vitriol, and sublime the mixture thrice. Then the essence of vitriol ascends with the flowers, and they become more effectual. Extract the flowers with spirit of wine, remove sediment, distil spirit of wine in Bath of S. Mary, till there remains a dry powder, which represents the purified flowers of Antimony.... These flowers act as a gentle purgative; they cure tertian and quartan fever, and most other diseases..." (*The Triumphal Chariot of Antimony*, Vincent Stuart Publishers, London, 1962, pp. 122–124).

phrase, the "antimonizing" force is at work everywhere. This anti-monizing force also has a regulating function within the human being, but human beings in normal health draw this force in from outside the Earth. In a normal state of health, we turn not to the anti-monizing force in the earthly element or to its concentrated form in the substance antimony but to the external, supra-earthly force of antimony. The obvious question is, what is this antimonizing force in the supra-earthly domain?

From the planetary perspective, it is the interaction of Mercury, Venus, and the Moon. When these planets work together rather than separately, their effects are not mercurial, silvery, or coppery. Instead, they work just as antimony works in the Earth. This effect can be investigated simply by looking for the effects on human beings of con-stellations in which the three forces of the Moon, Mercury, and Venus neutralize each other through the appropriate oppositions and quadratures. When they work together in this way, their interaction is related to the effect of earthly antimony. The force that works out of the Earth from all of its antimony is the same as the force that works down on the Earth from these three planetary bodies above the Earth.

This leads me to mention another point. You see, the makeup of the Earth is such that it is actually incorrect to speak of an individual piece of antimony. All of the antimony within the Earth's organization forms a unity, as does all of the silver or all of the gold. The individual piece is not very important. If you take a bit of antimony out of the Earth, you are simply rummaging around in the antimony body that is incorporated into the Earth. The bit belongs to the entire antimony body.

Having said this, we have described one aspect of what becomes vis-ible through the effects of antimony. In nature, however, any effect is always opposed by a countereffect, and objects are given form through the alternation between effect and countereffect. Now we need to look for the opposing forces. They reveal themselves as soon as we recog-nize that antimony forces are acting on the human being whenever anything regulated in the interior pushes its way outward. These same antimony forces are at work in the clotting of blood. This is where the antimonizing factor is active. Wherever the blood shows a tendency to pause and clot in its ongoing existence and flow, the antimonizing force is present. Wherever the blood attempts to evade the force of clotting, the opposite effects are present. As curious as it may seem, we always encounter anti-antimony forces in hemophiliacs; we find these anti-antimonizing forces in them. These forces, however, are identical to what I would like to call the proteinizing forces, if you will—the forces that form protein, whose organizing effect promotes protein formation. I repeat, the protein-forming forces are what prevents blood from clotting.

In this way, we develop a knowledge of the connection between antimonizing and proteinizing factors in the human organism. I must say, I believe that studying the interaction between these factors would yield fundamental insights into disease processes and healing processes, because proteinizing activity takes all the forces that sculpt and shape in the natural world and incorporates them into the human or animal organism for purposes of building up substance. Antimonizing forces are the sculptors, as it were, that work inward from the outside to give shape to the substances that build up our organs. Thus, the forces of antimony have a certain relationship to our organs' internal organizing forces.

It is important to distinguish between these two processes when you consider the internal structure of an organ such as the esophagus. You can trace its internal structure in a certain way without first taking into account the type of process that takes place there—how semiliquefied food moves along the esophagus, and so on. Along comes the esophagus and works together with what is entering the human organism. On an abstract level, we can separate the processes taking place in an organ's internal structure and what happens when the organ works together with what enters the human being from outside. These are two different processes. In the organ itself, the antimonizing force is at work in the human being. The human being is antimony if we exclude from consideration everything that is introduced from outside. The human being is antimony. The important thing is not to overburden the normal, vital internal organ-forming force with this antimony-forming force. We must not introduce it into life's normal processes or we will poison the organism through overstimulation. When it needs stimulating more strongly, however, we must administer something that we ordinarily should not.

At this point you turn to the effect of antimony, which results from the qualities of antimony that I described earlier. This effect varies in specific ways depending on whether you apply the antimony externally or internally. When you administer antimony internally, you must try to use such a high dilution that it can penetrate into the upper part of the human being. If you are successful, this will have an exceptionally strong stimulating effect on disturbances in organ development or internal organ processes. For this reason, highly potentized antimony will play a major role in certain forms of typhoid fever. In contrast, when antimony is applied externally in the form of ointments and the like, the effect is somewhat different and is achieved by using lower potencies. Under certain circumstances, of course, we may also need to appeal to the power of more highly potentized antimony for the sake of external parts of the body. In general, however, its external effects are induced by using lower potencies.

This example demonstrates that an exceptionally useful therapeutic substance such as antimony is interposed into what I described as a lawfully regulated course of events oscillating between two poles. For this reason, you will have to restrict the internal use of antimony to patients who are very strong-willed and external applications to individuals who tend to be weak-willed. You will have to make this distinction. As you see, the antimony in the mineral kingdom manifests as something that has an inner relationship to human will, in that the more conscious human will becomes, the more it feels the need to bring about an effect opposite to that of antimony. Human will has a destructive effect on all the forces that I described earlier as constituting the characteristic action of antimony. In contrast, antimony supports everything that has an organizing effect in the human being and is influenced by thought forces, especially the subconscious thought forces that are still active in children. Antimony's forces work together with these particular forces. Thus, if I introduce antimony into the human organism arbitrarily and it makes its own forces strongly felt, it develops a powerful phantom within the human being. The inner forces of the organs are immediately stimulated, and nothing is left over to allow them to work together with what has been introduced into the organism. The result is vomiting and diarrhea, which are due to the fact that the action is confined to the organs themselves and does not extend to their surroundings, as the countereffect also attests.[57]

If your constitution permits, you can counteract the damaging effect of antimony by means of a drug that is the instinctive choice of people who enjoy anything that supports and regulates their circulation and other rhythmical processes. Drinking coffee has a balancing effect on these rhythmical processes. I am simply recounting the facts here; my intention is not to recommend this practice, because in a different connection it can be very harmful to take the regulation of these rhythmical processes away from the I itself. But that is not what I want to talk about here; I simply want to discuss the facts. Drinking coffee brings a certain order into the rhythmical processes when the soul of the person in question is not strong enough to do this itself. This is why coffee is an antidote of sorts to the toxic effects of antimony. Coffee reestablishes the rhythm between the internal action of organs and what lies outside them. This interaction is also maintained by a particular rhythm. The real reason for drinking coffee is to bring about an ongoing rhythmization between our internal organs and what happens to ingested foods in the vicinity of these organs. All of this brings us back to a different activity, namely, the proteinizing process. It and all the processes on this other side are strengthened—not the side of the organs' own internal power of organization, but the side where digestion occurs as the result of the organs' outer action. Everything that happens on a mechanical level in the movement of the intestines and everything else that takes place in digestion is in intimate interaction with the proteinizing forces, the forces that build up protein and are the opposite of the antimonizing forces.

---

57. Critical to understanding this section is the concept of digestion as an external process that moves *through* the human body—a process that is essentially the same as (though more complex than) the digestive process of a single-celled organism when it secretes enzymes into its environment and absorbs the dissolved nutrients. The human digestive tract may be viewed as surrounding, not "containing," the food passing through, which is still "outside." Thus "outer" in this case should not be thought of as outside the body in the usual sense.

I must now point again to something I indicated earlier. The oyster with its shell formation is a very instructive object—or subject, if you prefer. To a lesser extent, the same process is present in the calcium excretions that produce eggshells. What is the basis of this? What is a shell such as an oyster shell or an ordinary eggshell? It is a product that the egg or oyster tissue has to get rid of by forcing it to the outside, since its continued internal presence would kill the egg or the oyster. The development of such a shell is based simply on the need to maintain life. If we eat oysters, we are also eating the life process that manifests in external shell formation. I can put this to you in these terms, I hope, although I would have to speak somewhat more selectively if I wanted to please modern science. In any case, along with the oyster, we eat this life process, a proteinizing activity that opposes the antimonizing process. By doing this, we promote everything in the human being that leads to the development of typhoid symptoms.

Eating oysters is an exceptionally interesting practice. It promotes the formative force, the proteinizing force, in the human abdomen. By doing so, however, it frees the head of certain forces, removes them from the head. As a result, someone who has eaten oysters feels less weighed down by the forces that want to work in the head. In a certain respect, eating oysters makes the head empty. We must develop these proteinizing forces constantly, because we cannot allow the head to be burdened with form-giving forces. People who eat oysters, however, take this too far, striving passionately toward empty-headedness and also increasing the possibility that certain forces will break through in the direction of the abdominal organs, as I described yesterday. That is, the tendency to typhoid fever is encouraged. You can imagine how this tendency, if present, calls for treatment with antimony. We will be able to successfully summon up what is needed to internally combat the tendency to typhoid fever by implementing simultaneous internal and external treatment with antimony, especially by rubbing in antimony ointments while administering high potencies of antimony internally. This therapy would work from both sides to counteract the tendency toward typhoid.

You see how we always attempt to consider the human being in the context of the cosmic environment. The significance of this view becomes apparent when you investigate the human being's connection to what happens in the natural world when the direct forces of the Earth are opposed in a particular way. Plants are able to resist the direct forces of the Earth and to save up many of their formative forces for the time when flowers and seeds develop. The usual process of plant formation that underlies edible plants is based on the use of a very specific total amount of earthly forces in building up the plant. If a plant resists these earthly forces, it is exposed to supra-earthly forces as it approaches its culmination in the development of seeds and fruits, and it then begins to want to look out into the world in the same way as higher beings. This plant is greedy to perceive but has no organs to support perception. It remains a plant, but it wants to develop an organ similar to the human eye. It cannot develop an eye, however, because it has the body of a plant rather than that of a human or an animal. As a result, this plant develops into deadly nightshade, *Atropa belladonna.*

I have tried to vividly describe the process that takes place in the development of deadly nightshade. Because it evolves into deadly nightshade, and because the forces with which it ultimately imbues its black berries are already present in its roots, this plant is related to everything in the human organism that moves in the direction of the type of form development that can happen only in the domain of the senses, to something that lifts human beings out of the domain of their internal organization and into the domain of their senses. The process that takes place when tiny potentized amounts of deadly nightshade are ingested is extremely interesting, because it is very similar to the normal version of this same process, namely, the waking-up process that is mingled with dreaming. Waking up—the state when we are still not quite perceiving with our senses and sensory perception is still directed inward, pervading our consciousness with dreams—is a type of deadly nightshade process within the human being. Deadly nightshade toxin evokes the same activity that otherwise takes place when our waking is pervaded with dreams, but makes it permanent. In nightshade poisoning, this process is not subsumed by consciousness, and the transitional phenomena persist. We see an interesting circumstance here: If evoked at the right times, processes that may also be symptomatic of poisoning are quite at home in the human organization.

As I just described, the development of deadly nightshade is a plant's mad desire to become human. We might say that human waking has something of the character of this process of developing into nightshade, but it is toned down, kept within limits, and restricted to the moment of awakening. Thus, if you want to relieve the body of inner proteinizing processes, to make excessively strong proteinizing processes withdraw and to deflect the physical aspect into the soul, so that what otherwise works in the body's substances works in the form of hallucinations, you administer potentized belladonna. In this instance you relieve the body of an activity by shifting it to the soul. This is what we encounter in the usual macroscopic effects of belladonna, although—as I said at the beginning of this lecture—there they are confused and pervaded with illusions. If you push people to remain in the waking-up stage instead of moving on to full wakefulness, you kill them. People are always in danger of losing their lives when they wake up, but they wake up so quickly that this danger is overcome. There are interesting connections here between a so-called normal process, one contained within normal limits, and a process that becomes abnormal as soon as it transcends normal limits.

These are processes that the physicians of antiquity repeatedly attempted to trace, or so it seems to me. When they spoke of engendering the homunculus, this more or less meant that in the clairvoyance they still possessed, they could see something like the antimony phantom. The proteinizing forces that oppose antimony appeared to them, projected out of their own being, in the external formative process they carried out in their laboratories as antimony forces developed. They externalized a force that normally remains within the human organism. They saw the homunculus appear in the course of the process in which antimony assumes its various forms. In the process that was played out there, they saw the homunculus.

LECTURE 20

I F the education of physicians is to continue in ways that are healing for humankind, certain things that I have attempted to point out in these lectures really must gain ground, specifically the ability to think of the entirety of the healthy or sick human organism in conjunction with outer, nonhuman forces, substances, and effects. This way of thinking will bridge the gap between the scientific direction in medicine, which increasingly amounts to nothing more than the recognition of diseases, and the effort to create remedies and therapeutic effects. To travel this route successfully, however, we need to acquire an overall view of the human being, a view illumined by spiritual science, starting with the present status of the human being in relationship to the external world. As you know, our connection to the outer world is most highly developed in the interaction between our outer senses and the environment. Our more outer senses, such as the sense of sight, have little to do with internal physical effects, but as soon as we enter the domain of the lower senses, such as smell and taste, we see that our human exterior and our external interaction with the environment have been internalized.

Up to a point, human digestion is nothing other than an extension and transformation of sensory activity. Until the intestinal processes surrender nutrients to the functions of building up lymph and blood, and even during this transition, the entire process is something of a metamorphosis of sensory activity. The lower down this activity takes place, the more organic its effect. Up to this point, we must recognize the digestive process as an extension of the process of perceiving taste.

By giving this fact its due, we can lay the groundwork not only for dietetics as a whole but also for understanding all the healing factors that are necessary in order to be effective in this particular field. This combination will also allow us to gradually and systematically recognize the damages that can occur here. Suppose you trace the effect of ammonia salts, for example, on the human organism. A believer in modern science will say that ammonia salts such as ammonium chloride affect the motoric nervous system of the cardiac muscles. This entire so-called motoric nervous system, however, is a nonentity. As I have already emphasized sufficiently, there is no difference between sensory nerves and motor nerves, so this whole idea is nonsense.

The important concern here is something essentially different. As long as the effect of ammonia salts persists—say, within the domain extending from the tasting process to the process of blood formation—an internal continuation of the effects of tasting is also present. This continued effect is also an astral body process. In the astral body, it triggers a reaction such as sweat excretion, for example. Being able to grasp this first phase of human digestion as an extension of the tasting process gives you direct insight into both the excretion of sweat and, in a certain way, the excretion of urine. Please consider this situation as follows: When we look at the main events of this phase, we are essentially dealing with nutrient absorption as a result of internal secretion of body fluids. This is the main factor. Everything that comes into consideration here can be reduced, more or less, to the dissolving effect body fluids have on food. The opposite of this dissolving effect consists in the activity of the liver and spleen, which is why we had to list liver and spleen activity as belonging to the activity of water or fluids. But in contrast to the dissolving effect that occurs in the first phase of digestion, liver activity has the effect of enclosing and surrounding things, of transforming again what was accomplished in the first part of the process.

We can form a fundamental image of what we encounter here by simply looking at two processes side by side. The first is what happens when I throw salt into warm water—the salt dissolves, yielding an image of what happens up to the point when nutrients are absorbed into the lymph and blood vessels. Next to this I place a couple of rounded drops of mercury, which attempt to create enclosure, to round off, organize, and create forms. This is an image of the process that begins with the absorption of nutrients into the lymph and blood vessels, a process that is governed by the liver and its relationship to the human astral body. We need this type of insight into what is going on, because it encourages us to study how the outer world behaves in the formation of salt and mercury. If we always consider the human being in connection with the outer world, the outer world literally allows us to decipher what needs to be active in the interior of the organism.

If we trace the path of ammonia salts further, as they make the transition to blood formation, we find that they alkalize the blood. Farther along in their journey, they begin to act from the lower part of the human being and influence the upper region, where they evoke responses. The interesting point, however, is that a complete reversal takes place—the processes are reversed completely. We can characterize this reversal somewhat. Whereas the upper area of the human being initially attempted to perceive within the digestive tract through tasting, now the entire situation reverses; the lower part of the human being tends more toward perception, and the upper part tends more toward what now influences perception. Consequently, while previously a certain reaction set in (which I characterized as proceeding from the astral body), the process is now reversed. The response—that is, what corresponds to the response—goes from below, while what would correspond to the initial action begins from above. Thus, above, the movement of the ciliated epithelia is stimulated, for example, and pulmonary secretion is promoted. The inverse of the original direction is in effect here. Initially, the dissolving process causes movement of the liver, but then the liver's enclosing function induces dissolution, dispersion, and stimulation in the pulmonary functions, which are localized above the liver. Instead of dissolution taking place down below, secretion is induced in upper organs.

Within the human organism, this is the route leading from the acquisition of substances via dissolution, via the salt process, to the formative process and on to dispersion, which is comparable to the processes of evaporation and combustion. To provide an image of the phosphorus or sulfur effect, where inorganic substance is ignited, imagine a simmering liquid that is continuously and actively evaporating. Juxtapose this with the droplets of mercury. This is the activity that develops both in the opposite organs—that is, in the lower part of the human being—and in the lungs and related organs in the upper human being.

Having understood these internal processes, we can also gain an idea of what can be introduced into them from the outer world. The concepts we acquire are quite far-reaching, extending even to the following activity. If you recall what we said a few days ago, you will realize that tooth development is a very peripheral activity in the human organism and that as such it soon becomes the completely external, mineralizing process I described. Please do not misunderstand this statement; I think it has been slightly misunderstood. I said that because tooth formation is such a peripheral process, technical, external attempts to repair the teeth through mechanical dental therapy are justified if we are dealing with deterioration of the teeth after the mineralization process has set in, because that is all that can be done from outside. Mechanical treatment, including everything that is done externally to fix the teeth and so on, is all we can do for structures that have become outwardly mineralized. We are justified in having teeth replaced when they become defective, because after a certain point we cannot take care of our own teeth from within. We must take care of our own fluorine-forming process, however, because it has to be there. The entire organism needs it. With respect to the fluorine-forming process in the organism, a substitute must be found for what the teeth do as long as they are still sound. There is a way of creating this substitute, but in doing so the process of reversal that I have just characterized must be taken into consideration in the right way.

What is this entire process of tooth development, if we consider the reality of the situation? It is the mineralizing process moving outward from within. Once the second teeth have all emerged, the goal of pushing the mineralizing process toward the outside has been accomplished. It is then countered by the sexualizing process, which moves inward once again. Tooth formation and the development of sexuality are two opposing processes that work against each other as if in a rhythm. To the same extent that tooth formation is completed, the process of sexualization proceeds in the other direction.

But if you look at the situation in this way, you will also realize that a different process in the human being, namely intestinal peristalsis, which is directed inward and toward the rear, is also diametrically opposed to the direction of the tooth-forming process and has a great deal to do with it. These two processes are intimately related; that is, everything belonging to peristalsis is intimately related to everything that brings about tooth formation in the opposite direction. This intestinal movement is intimately associated with the human organism's use of fluorine. We might say that whenever intestinal movement takes place more quickly and intensively than the person's individuality warrants, it has consequences in tooth decay and especially in everything that fluorine normally ought to be doing in the human organism. Consequently, any dentist who notices that someone's teeth are in very poor condition needs to recommend that the movements of digestion be performed slightly less intensely, which can be accomplished by prescribing either rest (in the purely outer mechanical sense), if the person's occupation permits, or remedies that calm down the digestion, specifically by slightly reducing the intensity of intestinal movement.

The regulation of this activity is particularly important and is promoted by limb activity that obeys orderly laws, especially, as I have already pointed out, by activity of the arms and hands and legs and feet and by eurythmy, which imbues movement with soul. It can also be said, however, that if the gymnastic element becomes too strongly physiological, the pendulum swings back in the wrong direction, making it very easy to bring about the opposite effect. This also makes it understandable why activities such as ordinary dancing, to which girls in particular subject themselves, can have a damaging effect on the process of tooth formation, so you really must not ask why girls who do a lot of dancing have worse teeth than boys. The point is that this dancing needs to be ensouled and not taken to excess. And with regard to hand activity, simply overdoing the actions involved in knitting and crocheting is enough to produce the opposite effect of using this activity properly.

284 INTRODUCING ANTHROPOSOPHICAL MEDICINE

We can see here how a reversal takes place already in the domain of mechanical, visible movement. In the first place, a reversal of the process of tooth formation takes place in digestion. But it is also very important for the movement imposed on the digestive process to be transposed into the human movement that serves locomotion, the ability to move in a forward direction. This inversion has aspects that are tremendously important in building up the human being. It means a great deal that human beings are able to walk forward and that their digestion is stimulated to move toward the rear. We can bring about beneficial results by accustoming a person with sluggish digestion to walk backward a lot in gymnastics, which has the effect of promoting digestive activity. From being a mere collection of empirical notes, all these phenomena are transformed into inner insight if we use spiritual science to illuminate the entire constitution of the human being.

I would now like to draw your attention to another matter. If we move on to *nux vomica,* we can certainly see that it has a wonderful effect on the human being. What is the basis of this effect? If we simply take advantage of the appropriate opportunity to study nux vomica, we will gain inner insight into it. If you simply study nux vomica in people with hangovers, you will see what kind of an effect it has there, and this makes it easier to gain an overview of all of its other effects.

In a hangover, there is a real reversal of all of human organic activity. A hangover is an extension of the process that takes place primarily in the first phase of digestive activity. After overindulgence in wine, beer, or champagne, a hangover sets in when what occurs up to the point where substances are absorbed into the lymph- and blood-forming processes continues on into these processes themselves. Then the domain of the human organism whose real task is to dissolve substances is transformed into a sensory organ of a sort. Instead of directing the major part of their sensory activity toward the outer world, instead of entering into communication with the outer world and encountering the Earth and its processes, people who are hung over condemn themselves to perceive internally, because what is now inside them has become very, very similar to the Earth's external activity. They begin to sense the Earth's rotation, and the bed begins to spin.

An earthly activity of a sort, an internal outer world, is present beyond their intestinal activity, in the activity of lymph and blood formation. These people have transformed themselves into an internal outer world and have horrible perceptions of processes that do not bother them at all when perceived externally. The interior of the human being is not suited to becoming an Earth. On the contrary, it is meant to withdraw from the Earth. Now, however, these people create a real Earth inside themselves. It would be more appropriate to shift this Earth to the outside and surround it by sensory perceivers who could view it externally, but instead these people are forced to perceive it with the outer portion of the human interior.

Until a strong natural healing process sets in, which it usually does, nux vomica counteracts the symptoms that arise by suppressing sensitivity to this outer thing that has been internalized. At the same time, this suppression does not disturb the internally located outer process. This relates to one of nux vomica's healing effects, which is to weaken the extension of the metamorphosed process of taste so that it no longer disrupts what is located beyond it. This weakening brings about a cure of sorts.

Now assume that the opposite situation is present. The extended tasting process—that is, the dissolving process—is impaired rather than enhanced, so that it does not go far enough. Let us assume that this situation exists: The interior proves to be too weak to adequately dissolve what is taken in from the outer world and involve it in the salt-forming process. This first phase of digestion is working the way we want it to when we administer nux vomica, but it is doing so naturally, through a different process to which the inadequately dissolved substances attempt to adapt. They cannot find the way out; they cannot cross the boundary between the process of tasting and digesting on the one hand and the process of blood formation on the other. Consequently, they look for a way out in the opposite direction, which gives rise to all the symptoms that can be alleviated simply by promoting the dissolving process that nux vomica suppresses. Everything that is looking for the wrong way out can be counteracted with *Thuja*. We have just deduced the polarity between nux vomica and *Thuja* from the constitution of the human being, which also demonstrates that we always need to look at the overall organization of the human being, because it is important not to underestimate the polarities present there.

The functions that drive the activity in the lower part of the human being up toward the upper part are all intensified during sleep. We must be very careful about how we attempt to characterize sleep. While it is indeed true that sleep is one of the best remedies, this is true only when sleep lasts exactly long enough to meet the needs of the human individuality in question, neither longer nor shorter. Sleeping too long makes a person sick because it causes excessive percolation through the boundary I have just described. Too much moves from the first phase of digestion over into the lymph- and blood-forming process. We are constantly exposed to this danger, because the lower part of the human organism is always asleep and therefore continually subjects us to the sickening of the blood. We carry the antidote around within us, however, although this antidote is of course attuned only to the normal process that constantly attempts to sicken us through sleep, the process that is balanced out by the iron content of the blood. Iron is the metal that is most important to human beings. It works inside us, equalizing any excess that moves from one process into the other. What I have just said explains both the diseases that result from iron deficiency in the blood and the fact that iron, if it is administered in a potency high enough to be related to the homeopathizing process that is evoked each time by the upper part of the human being, can always help the organism overcome the intrinsic disruptive processes that work from below upward. As you have already seen, human processes substitute for the other main metal processes relevant to the human being.

In this context, I would like to briefly summarize what arises out of the whole spirit of my lectures here. Today we have once again pointed to lymph and blood formation in the human being. This process has a relationship to copper in that it is the polar opposite of copper's mineralizing tendency. We would need to make it clear to ourselves that this activity still belongs to the lower region of the human being (specifically, to the uppermost portion of this lower organism) and that its relationship to copper therefore tends very strongly in the direction of the Earth's copper-forming force, since everything related to the lower part of the human being is related to earthly processes. In working with copper, the golden rule is generally to use it in low potencies—not in doses large enough to be harmful to humans, of course, but in proportions that are still fairly similar to its naturally occurring concentrations in the Earth.

Just as the inner activity of lymph and blood formation is related to copper, everything standing at the transition between the outer digestive process and the internal digestive process of lymph and blood formation is related to the liver and especially to mercury. It relates to mercury in the same way that the other process relates to copper, with the reservation that mercury's rounding, balancing aspect already links it somewhat to the interaction between these two processes. But the processes that human beings must develop so that not too much gets into the blood—the processes that nux vomica induces and *Thuja* suppresses—are regulated by the action of silver.

At this point the field is open to investigate outer nature with these constituents in mind and to see nature as a dismembered human being, as it were. In this way, we put the human being, whether well or ill, entirely into the context of the environment to which we are so closely related through the lower parts of the human organism. What rises into our upper parts from below through the copper-related process is regulated and balanced out by the opposition of iron. This demonstrates that human beings need iron; we always need an excess of iron processes or, chemically speaking, iron. All the other metals are present in human beings in the form of processes. In a certain respect, the human being is a sevenfold metal, but only iron is present as such, while the other metals are present only in the form of processes.

Just as everything that works together with lymph and blood formation in our organs is related to copper, everything that moves outward from the lungs, opening up in the larynx and so forth, is related to iron. Similarly, the portions of the brain that serve internal functions, that are more similar to the brain's digestive activity and therefore correspond to the process of transition between the intestines and the lymph and blood vessels, are related to the tin-forming process, which works to ensoul and regulate the digestive process in the area I have just described. In contrast, nerve fibers and related structures that represent the extension of the senses in the upper region of the human being are related to lead, which in turn corresponds to the processes of sweat and urine excretion.

I might say that these things illuminate the human being and simultaneously point to how we can extract therapeutic benefits from the opposite effects in the substances surrounding us. We must recognize the need for spiritual science to point out how so-called psychiatric disorders are seated in the organs in many respects and how organic diseases are very strongly related to effects of soul and spirit. This is a difficult chapter. On the one hand, materialism proceeds purely on the basis of mechanics or chemistry in dealing with so-called physical illnesses, treating the human being more or less like a mechanical device; on the other hand, it has reached the point of being unable to provide more than a mere description of psychological symptoms in so-called psychiatric disorders, because it has lost the ability to see the connection between the soul/spirit and the physical body.

The intimate connection between these two aspects becomes evident when we investigate the interplay between psychological and bodily states of health in a concrete way. What promotes psychiatric illness? In the first stages of an illness, pain and other subjective symptoms appear. These symptoms are most apparent in acute illnesses and are transformed in chronic illnesses. They constitute the response of a person's soul and spirit to any type of organ damage, the withdrawal of soul and spirit from the organs in question. Pain is simply the withdrawal of the I and astral body from the physical and etheric bodies. Pain may also be linked to a withdrawal of the etheric body, but the essence of the sensation of pain lies in the astral body and the I. As a rule, the I is still strong enough to perceive the entire subjective, conscious process that is the opposite and counterpart of the one taking place in the physical organ. As the illness becomes chronic, this conscious process gradually withdraws from the I. As a consequence, what is happening on the level of the soul is now restricted to the astral body; the I no longer participates in what the astral body and etheric body are suffering. A disease of the organs moves on to become chronic; acute illness becomes chronic.

This is a question of conscious symptoms on the soul level, which retreat. If we want to pursue symptomatology, we must study the individual in greater depth. Instead of asking how someone feels or where it hurts, we must ask whether he sleeps well or badly or whether or not she feels like working. What we regard as symptoms in chronic illnesses must extend over longer periods of time and have more to do with the entire process of a person's development, while immediate subjective sensations can be considered symptoms in cases of acute illness. When it comes to chronic illness, we must look more at the person's biography than at immediate symptoms.

Ordinary, physical chronic illness occurs when the whole process can be contained within the organ in such a way that the astral body and etheric body still participate properly in the organ's activity, sending as much as is needed into it. If the patient's constitution permits him or her to tolerate the astral body's disordered effect (by way of the etheric body) on the organ in question, it will also permit the patient to take the astral body's abnormal connection to the liver, for instance, beyond a certain critical point, so that the liver no longer notices that the astral body fails to work into it in the right way. In this case, I would say that the liver recovers but becomes accustomed to the disordered effect of the astral body. If this goes on long enough, it will make its way into the soul in the reverse direction. Something the liver ought to pull into the physical body is pushed into the soul instead, resulting in depression. In a certain respect, then, the seeds of so-called mental illness are sown by overcoming chronic illnesses to the point of tolerating an abnormal connection to the astral body.

Someday, when these matters are generally studied in this way, we will go beyond merely describing the pathology of mental illnesses. There is a lot of talk today about irregularities in processes of ideation or will activity, but as long as we do not know how the curious interaction of the liver, spleen, and other abdominal organs supports what ultimately appears in its highest form on the soul level as human will, we will not be able to find the physical counterparts of the pathological symptoms we describe. Especially in so-called psychiatric disorders, it should occur to us to implement physical methods of treatment. It may seem contradictory that spiritual science would lead, on the one hand, to physical treatment in so-called psychiatric disorders, while, on the other, pointing to the soul's role in recovery from physical ailments. But this is related to the great contrast between the upper and lower parts of the human being. It is also related to the reversal that occurs when sensory activity introduced from outside becomes inner sensory activity, which is the case in the extension of the tasting process, or when something that is present in the interior discharges outwardly in cilial movement or the potential for ciliary movement. If understood correctly, this can lead to a certain goal.[58]

Now I have tried to expose you to quite a lot in these twenty lectures. When I was preparing them and getting an overview of everything that would be relevant, I realized that giving these lectures would be difficult—where should we begin? If we began with elementary subjects, we would not get very far in twenty lectures because we would have time only to point out the route that needs to be taken. But if we began upstairs, as it were, and introduced all sorts of occult facts, it would not be easy to bridge the gap to modern medicine in a certain direction, and even more time would be required. Wherever we observe the extensive damage done by materialism today, we also see the need to counteract this damage from the other direction. Please understand what I am saying as a friendly comment rather than as taking sides in any particular direction. It is not my intention to be partisan in any way; I simply want to present the facts objectively. One thing, however, may and must be said: If we survey modern allopathic medicine, we invariably find that it tends to evaluate patients with a

---

58. "Through the sense of taste, we penetrate one stage deeper into outer substantiality than ... through the sense of smell. In smelling, the substance itself approaches us and discloses its particular character. In tasting, it is the substance's effect on us that is perceived. The difference between them is best felt by visualizing how, in the sense of smell, a gas-like substance approaches us in a finished state so that we can perceive it as it is, while, in the sense of taste, we use our own fluid to dissolve the substance—that is, we cause a change in it—in order to delve into peculiarities of this substance that it does not reveal to us on its own. This means that the sense of smell is suited to perceiving the outside of the material element, while the sense of taste already, to some extent, goes inside material things. For the inside of an object to be disclosed, we must change its outside" (Rudolf Steiner, *Anthroposophy [A Fragment]*, Anthroposophic Press, Hudson, NY, 1996, p. 91).

view to the concomitant phenomena described by the bacterial theory of infection. This diverts our attention to a secondary issue. As a mere aid to recognition, the natural history of bacilli would be extremely useful. We can indeed learn a lot from the type of bacillus that is present, because a certain type always appears under the influence of a very specific primary cause. There is always plenty of opportunity to see this connection.

There is a tendency to mistake a secondary factor for the primary cause, as when, for example, we look at the extent to which bacilli affect human organs instead of the extent to which the human organism can become a habitat for bacilli. Such a tendency appears not only in allopathic medical theories concerning bacteria, but also in that whole way of thinking. Consequently, this tendency causes damage that I need not elucidate, since many of you have noticed it yourselves. You see, homeopathic medicine has at least certain advantages in that it always aims at the human being as a whole, keeps an image of the overall effect in mind, and attempts to build a bridge to the discovery of remedies, but we also cannot always be satisfied when we scrutinize homeopathic medicine because of another idiosyncrasy of homeopathic medical literature.

Please forgive me for saying this, but if you look at this literature, especially the therapeutic literature, it can almost drive you to despair because you find the remedies listed one after the other, and each one is always supposed to help a whole army of illnesses. It is never easy to find anything specific. Everything is helpful for so many different conditions. I know that this is how things have to be, at least for the present, but it simply leads us astray. We can resist being led astray only by proceeding in the way that has been indicated here, at least on an elementary level. This is why I chose an elementary content for these lectures instead of beginning with the occult. The situation can be improved only when this method of studying human and nonhuman nature enables us to move on to restricting the usage indications of remedies, to delineating remedies. This is not possible unless, in addition to studying a remedy's effect on a person who is healthy or ill, we also gradually attempt to see the entire cosmos as a unity. For example, we must study the human being by tracing the entire antimonizing process, as I pointed out in one instance yesterday. We must attempt to see what antimony does outside the human being in connection with what it can accomplish inside the human being. This view delineates very specific domains in the outer world, which then have connections to the human being.

As I said before, such issues led me to emphasize elementary content in these twenty lectures. Of course, naturopathy, because it serves the instinct to reconnect human beings to their own healing processes in a natural way, makes it necessary to point out the true basis of these intrinsic healing forces, namely, the interaction between earthly and supra-earthly factors. For this reason, naturopathy is dependent on not becoming too strongly involved in materialism. Today it really is possible to see how all of the different partisan directions are tending toward materialism, which in a certain sense is common to all of them. Thus the important thing is to spiritualize this entire field. However, today's world is very opposed to any such effort. The antidote to materialism will also need to appear from the side of experts and professionals, because what we are attempting here, although it may be in its very beginning stages, must not be misinterpreted as fostering dilettantism. This prejudiced view of what we are doing already exists, and it is very damaging. That is why I want to emphasize how important it is for any of you who understand that we are attempting to work scientifically to contribute to combating this prejudice. At present, people take into account and enlist the help of everything that modern science has to offer, but they are unwilling to see what we are really attempting to accomplish.

I would like to mention one thing here in conclusion, just as an example. Such instances occur repeatedly. You see, it is possible to properly explain eurythmy's significance for the human constitution only to a physician. The reason this building [the first Goetheanum in Dornach] stands here can be explained only to a physician who is able to understand how the entire human organism turns first inward and then outward again, as we have discussed in these lectures. Today, what we say must be based on what completely opposes lay materialism and outmoded, traditional schools of thought. We must also consider something that I believe needs to be combated on a professional level; otherwise such blatant examples will simply proliferate. You see, our kind Mr. M., who left yesterday, attempted to put his goodwill into action by writing an article about the Dornach building and eurythmy for a Zürich newspaper. He received this response:

Dear Sir:

It is beyond comprehension that the theosophical anthroposopheum, with its tasteless mockery of the countryside, can lay claim to Goethe's name. We have seen more than enough examples of eurythmy here. Thanks for sending the material.

H. Trog
Editor

Now you see this curious opposition to the spiritual element that is intended to come into the world. This is what we encounter today, and the decadent substance of such materialistic troughs force us to pay some attention to them as they assault our noses with their contaminating stench.[59]

This is what I wanted to say in concluding this cycle of lectures, because it helps me to emphasize my request that you consider this cycle to be only a beginning. As I said to myself as I prepared: It was difficult to begin (owing to reasons I have already enumerated). But now that we are at the end, I must say that it is even more difficult to stop! Not to say what I could also have said is truly more painful. I beg you to consider all this in your assessment of what this introduction was able to provide. I hope that you and others will understand that I am speaking out of truly objective, not merely subjective, heartfelt feelings when I now say to you, whose attendance here has demonstrated your great interest in this beginning, "Until we meet again, on a similar occasion!"

---

59. There is a play on words here. "Trog," the name of the editor, means "trough"—presumably the kind used for feeding farm animals.

Dr. Steiner concluded following a participant's expression of thanks:

My dear friends, I have chosen this avenue as the only way that spiritual science will be of use to the art of healing. In future, too, you will find that for readily understandable reasons, I will adhere to the method I have used up to now. I want the necessary interaction of spiritual science and healing to remain a matter between myself and the healers. I myself, of course, never have intervened and never want to intervene in the practice of healing. This is left up to practicing physicians. Everything that needs the stimulus of spiritual science should exist on the basis of the give and take between spiritual science and physicians themselves. Any prejudice that might be added to whatever prejudice already exists can be more easily prevented by making it impossible for people to say that I am a charlatan who is actively involved in curing people. This is something I have always attempted to avoid.

Thank you very much!

RUDOLF STEINER'S COLLECTED WORKS

The German Edition of Rudolf Steiner's Collected Works (the Gesamtausgabe [GA] published by Rudolf Steiner Verlag, Dornach, Switzerland) presently runs to over 354 titles, organized either by type of work (written or spoken), chronology, audience (public or other), or subject (education, art, etc.). For ease of comparison, the Collected Works in English (CW) follows the German exactly. A complete listing of the CWs follows, with literal translations of the titles as they are in German. Other than in the case of the books published in his lifetime, these titles were rarely given by Rudolf Steiner himself, and were often provided by the editors of the German edition. The titles in English are not necessary the same as the German; and indeed over the past seventy-five years have frequently been different, with the same book sometimes appearing under different titles.

For ease of identification and to avoid confusion, we suggest that readers looking for a title should do so by CW number. Because the work of creating the Collected Works of Rudolf Steiner is an ongoing process, with new titles being published every year, we have not indicated in this listing which books are presently available. To find out what titles in the Collected Works are currently in print, please check our website: www.steinerbooks.org or write to SteinerBooks, 610 Main Street, Great Barrington, MA 01230.

Written Work

CW 78   Anthroposophy, Its Roots of Knowledge and Fruits for Life
CW 79   The Reality of the Higher Worlds
CW 80   Public lectures in various cities, 1922
CW 81   Renewal-Impulses for Culture and Science - Berlin College Course
CW 82   So that the Human Being Can Become a Complete Human Being
CW 83   Western and Eastern World-Contrast - Paths to Understanding It
        through Anthroposophy
CW 84   What did the Goetheanum Intend and What Should
        Anthroposophy Do?

Lectures to the Members of the Anthroposophical Society

CW 88   Concerning the Astral World and Devachan
CW 89   Consciousness - Life - Form. Fundamental principles of a spiritual-
        scientific Cosmology
CW 90   Participant Notes from the Lectures during the Years 1903-1905
CW 91   Participant Notes from the Lectures during the Years 1903-1905
CW 92   The Occult Truths of Ancient Myths and Sagas
CW 93   The Temple Legend and the Golden Legend
CW 93a Fundamentals of Esotericism
CW 94   Cosmogony. Popular Occultism. The Gospel of St. John. The
        Theosophy in the Gospel of St. John
CW 95   At the Gates of Theosophy
CW 96   Origin-Impulses of Spiritual Science. Christian Esotericism in the
        Light of new Spirit-Knowledge
CW 97   The Christian Mystery
CW 98   Nature Beings and Spirit Beings. Their Effects in Our Visible World
CW 99   The Theosophy of the Rosicrucians
CW 100 Human Development and Christ-Knowledge
CW 101 Myths and Legends. Occult Signs and Symbols
CW 102 The Working Into Human Beings by Spiritual Beings
CW 103 The Gospel of John
CW 104 The Apocalypse of John
CW 104a From the Picture-Script of the Apocalypse of John
CW 105 Universe, Earth, the Human Being: their Being and Development,
        as well as their Reflection in the Connection between Egyptian
        Mythology and Modern Culture
CW 106 Egyptian Myths and Mysteries in Relation to the active Spiritual
        Forces of the Present
CW 107 Spiritual-Scientific Knowledge of the Human Being
CW 108 Answering the Questions of Life and the World through
        Anthroposophy

CW 268 Soul-Exercises: Vol. 2: Mantric Verses, 1903-1925

CW 269 Ritual Texts for the Celebration of the Free Christian Religious Instruction. The Collected Verses for Teachers and Students of the Waldorf School

CW 270 Esoteric Instructions for the First Class of the School for Spiritual Science at the Goetheanum 1924; 4 Volumes

CW 271 Art and Knowledge of Art. Foundations of a New Aesthetic

CW 272 Spiritual-Scientific Commentary on Goethe's Faust in Two Volumes. Vol. 1: Faust, the Striving Human Being

CW 273 Spiritual-Scientific Commentary on Goethe's Faust in Two Volumes. Vol. 2: The Faust-Problem

CW 274 Addresses for the Christmas Plays from the Old Folk Traditions

CW 275 Art in the Light of Mystery-Wisdom

CW 276 The Artistic in Its Mission in the World. The Genius of Language. The World of the Self-Revealing Radiant Appearances – Anthroposophy and Art. Anthroposophy and Poetry.

CW 277 Eurythmy. The Revelation of the Speaking Soul

CW 277a The Origin and Development of Eurythmy

CW 278 Eurythmy as visible Song

CW 279 Eurythmy as visible Speech

CW 280 The Method and Nature of Speech Formation

CW 281 The Art of Recitation and Declamation

CW 282 Speech Formation and Dramatic Art

CW 283 The Nature of Things Musical and the Experience of Tone in the Human Being

CW 284/285 Images of Occult Seals and Pillars. The Munich Congress of Whitson 1907 and its Consequences

CW 286 Paths to a New Style of Architecture. "And the Building Becomes Human"

CW 287 The Building at Dornach as a Symbol of Historical Becoming and an Artistic Transformation Impulses

CW 288 The Manner of Forms of the Living-Organic

CW 289 The Building-Idea of the Goetheanum: Lectures with Slides from the Years 1920-1921

CW 290 The Building-Idea of the Goetheanum: Lectures with Slides from the Years 1920-1921

CW 291 The Nature of Colors

CW 291a Knowledge of Colors. Supplementary Volume to "The Nature of Colors"

CW 292 Art History as Image of Inner Spiritual Impulses

CW 293 General Knowledge of the Human Being as the Foundation of Pedagogy

SIGNIFICANT EVENTS
IN THE LIFE OF RUDOLF STEINER

1829:   June 23: birth of Johann Steiner (1829-1910)—Rudolf Steiner's father—in Geras, Lower Austria.

1834:   May 8: birth of Franciska Blie (1834-1918)—Rudolf Steiner's mother—in Horn, Lower Austria. "My father and mother were both children of the glorious Lower Austrian forest district north of the Danube."

1860:   May 16: marriage of Johann Steiner and Franciska Blie.

1861:   February 25: birth of *Rudolf Joseph Lorenz Steiner*

        Summer: the family moves to Mödling, Lower Austria.

1863:   The family moves to Pottschach, Lower Austria, near the Styrian border, where Johann Steiner becomes stationmaster. "The view stretched to the mountains...majestic peaks in the distance and the sweet charm of nature in the immediate surroundings."

1864:   November 15: birth of Rudolf Steiner's sister, Leopoldine (d. November 1, 1927). She will become a seamstress and live with her parents for the rest of her life.

1866:   July 28: birth of Rudolf Steiner's deaf-mute brother, Gustav (d. May 1, 1941).

1867:   Rudolf Steiner enters the village school. Following a disagreement between his father and the schoolmaster, whose wife falsely accused the boy of causing a commotion, Rudolf Steiner is taken out of school and taught at home.

1868:   A critical experience. Unknown to the family, an aunt dies in a distant town. Sitting in the station waiting room, Rudolf Steiner sees her "form," which speaks to him, asking for help. "Beginning with this experience, a new soul life began in the boy, one in which not only the outer trees and mountains spoke to him, but also the worlds that lay behind them. From this moment on, the boy began to live with the spirits of nature...."

1869:   The family moves to the peaceful, rural village of Neudorfl, near Wiener-Neustadt in present-day Hungary. Rudolf Steiner attends the village school. Because of the "unorthodoxy" of his writing and spelling, he has to do "extra lessons."

1870:   Through a book lent to him by his tutor, he discovers geometry: "To grasp something purely in the spirit brought me inner happiness. I know that I first learned happiness through geometry." The same tutor allows him to draw, while other students still struggle with their reading and writing. "An artistic element" thus enters his education.

1871:   Though his parents are not religious, Rudolf Steiner becomes a "church child," a favorite of the priest, who was "an exceptional character." "Up to the age of ten or eleven, among those I came to know, he was far and away the most significant." Among other things, he introduces Steiner to Copernican, heliocentric cosmology. As an altar boy, Rudolf Steiner serves at Masses, funerals, and Corpus Christi processions. At year's end, after an incident in which he escapes a thrashing, his father forbids him to go to church.

1872:   Rudolf Steiner transfers to grammar school in Wiener-Neustadt, a five-mile walk from home, which must be done in all weathers.

1873-75: Through his teachers and on his own, Rudolf Steiner has many wonderful experiences with science and mathematics. Outside school, he teaches himself analytic geometry, trigonometry, differential equations, and calculus.

1876:   Rudolf Steiner begins tutoring other students. He learns bookbinding from his father. He also teaches himself stenography.

1877:   Rudolf Steiner discovers Kant's *Critique of Pure Reason,* which he reads and rereads. He also discovers and reads von Rotteck's *World History.*

1878:   He studies extensively in contemporary psychology and philosophy.

1879:   Rudolf Steiner graduates from high school with honors. His father is transferred to Inzersdorf, near Vienna. He uses his first visit to Vienna "to purchase a great number of philosophy books"— Kant, Fichte, Schelling, and Hegel, as well as numerous histories of philosophy. His aim: to find a path from the "I" to nature.

October 1879-1883: Rudolf Steiner attends the Technical College in Vienna— to study mathematics, chemistry, physics, mineralogy, botany, zoology, biology, geology, and mechanics—with a scholarship. He also attends lectures in history and literature, while avidly reading philosophy on his own. His two favorite professors are Karl Julius Schröer (German language and literature) and Edmund Reitlinger (physics). He also audits lectures by Robert Zimmerman on aesthetics and Franz Brentano on philosophy. During this year he begins his friendship with Moritz Zitter (1861-1921), who will help support him financially when he is in Berlin.

1880:   Rudolf Steiner attends lectures on Schiller and Goethe by Karl Julius Schröer, who becomes his mentor. Also "through a remarkable combination of circumstances," he meets Felix Koguzki, an "herb gatherer" and healer, who could "see deeply into the secrets of nature." Rudolf Steiner will meet and study with this "emissary of the Master" throughout his time in Vienna.

1881:   January: "… I didn't sleep a wink. I was busy with philosophical problems until about 12:30 a.m. Then, finally, I threw myself down on my couch. All my striving during the previous year had been to research whether the following statement by Schelling was true or not: *Within everyone dwells a secret, marvelous capacity to draw back from the stream of time—out of the self clothed in all that comes to us from outside—into our innermost being and there, in the immutable form of the Eternal, to look into ourselves.* I believe, and I am still quite certain of it, that I discovered this capacity in myself; I had long had an inkling of it. Now the whole of idealist philosophy stood before me in modified form. What's a sleepless night compared to that!"

Rudolf Steiner begins communicating with leading thinkers of the day, who send him books in return, which he reads eagerly.

July: "I am not one of those who dives into the day like an animal in human form. I pursue a quite specific goal, an idealistic aim—knowledge of the truth! This cannot be done offhandedly. It requires the greatest striving in the world, free of all egotism, and equally of all resignation."

August: Steiner puts down on paper for the first time thoughts for a "Philosophy of Freedom." "The striving for the absolute: this human yearning is freedom." He also seeks to outline a "peasant philosophy," describing what the worldview of a "peasant"—one who lives close to the earth and the old ways—really is.

1881-1882: Felix Koguzki, the herb gatherer, reveals himself to be the envoy of another, higher initiatory personality, who instructs Rudolf Steiner to penetrate Fichte's philosophy and to master modern scientific thinking as a preparation for right entry into the spirit. This "Master" also teaches him the double (evolutionary and involutionary) nature of time.

1882: Through the offices of Karl Julius Schröer, Rudolf Steiner is asked by Joseph Kurschner to edit Goethe's scientific works for the *Deutschen National-Literatur* edition. He writes "A Possible Critique of Atomistic Concepts" and sends it to Friedrich Theodore Vischer.

1883: Rudolf Steiner completes his college studies and begins work on the Goethe project.

1884: First volume of Goethe's *Scientific Writings* (CW 1) appears (March). He lectures on Goethe and Lessing, and Goethe's approach to science. In July, he enters the household of Ladislaus and Pauline Specht as tutor to the four Specht boys. He will live there until 1890. At this time, he meets Josef Breuer ((1842-1925), the coauthor with Sigmund Freud of *Studies in Hysteria*, who is the Specht family doctor.

1885: While continuing to work on Goethe, Rudolf Steiner reads deeply in contemporary philosophy (Edouard von Hartmann, Johannes Volkelt, and Richard Wahle, among others).

1886: May: Rudolf Steiner sends Kurschner the manuscript of *Outlines of Goethe's Theory of Knowledge* (CW 2), which appears in October, and which he sends out widely. He also meets the poet Marie Eugenie Delle Grazie and writes "Nature and Our Ideals" for her. He attends her salon, where he meets many priests, theologians, and philosophers, who will become his friends. Meanwhile, the director of the Goethe Archive in Weimar requests his collaboration with the *Sophien* edition of Goethe's works, particularly the writings on color.

1887: At the beginning of the year, Rudolf Steiner is very sick. As the year progresses and his health improves, he becomes increasingly "a man of letters," lecturing, writing essays, and taking part in Austrian cultural life. In August-September, the second volume of Goethe's *Scientific Writings* appears.

1888:   January-July: Rudolf Steiner assumes editorship of the "German Weekly" (*Deutsche Wochenschrift*). He begins lecturing more intensively, giving, for example, a lecture titled "Goethe as Father of a New Aesthetics." He meets and becomes soul friends with Friedrich Eckstein (1861-1939), a vegetarian, philosopher of symbolism, alchemist, and musician, who will introduce him to various spiritual currents (including Theosophy) and with whom he will meditate and interpret esoteric and alchemical texts.

1889:   Rudolf Steiner first reads Nietzsche (*Beyond Good and Evil*). He encounters Theosophy again and learns of Madame Blavatsky in the Theosophical circle around Marie Lang (1858-1934). Here he also meets well-known figures of Austrian life, as well as esoteric figures like the occultist Franz Hartman and Karl Leinigen-Billigen (translator of C.G. Harrison's *The Transcendental Universe.*) During this period, Steiner first reads A.P. Sinnett's *Esoteric Buddhism* and Mabel Collins's *Light on the Path.* He also begins traveling, visiting Budapest, Weimar, and Berlin (where he meets philosopher Edouard von Hartman).

1890:   Rudolf Steiner finishes volume 3 of Goethe's scientific writings. He begins his doctoral dissertation, which will become *Truth and Science* (CW3*).* He also meets the poet and feminist Rosa Mayreder (1858-1938), with whom he can exchange his most intimate thoughts. In September, Rudolf Steiner moves to Weimar to work in the Goethe-Schiller Archive.

1891:   Volume 3 of the Kurschner edition of Goethe appears. Meanwhile, Rudolf Steiner edits Goethe's studies in mineralogy and scientific writings for the *Sophien* edition. He meets Ludwig Laistner of the Cotta publishing company, who asks for a book on the basic question of metaphysics. From this will result, ultimately, *The Philosophy of Freedom* (CW 4), which will be published not by Cotta but by Emil Felber. In October, Rudolf Steiner takes the oral exam for a doctorate in philosophy, mathematics, and mechanics at Rostock University, receiving his doctorate on the twenty-sixth. In November, he gives his first lecture on Goethe's "Fairy Tale" in Vienna.

1892:   Rudolf Steiner continues work at the Goethe-Schiller archive and on his *Philosophy of Freedom. Truth and Science*, his doctoral dissertation, is published. Steiner undertakes to write introductions to books on Schopenhauer and Jean Paul for Cotta. At year's end, he finds lodging with Anna Eunike, née Schulz (1853-1911), a widow with four daughters and a son. He also develops a friendship with Otto Erich Hartleben (1864-1905) with whom he shares literary interests.

1893:   Rudolf Steiner begins his habit of producing many reviews and articles. In March, he gives a lecture titled "Hypnotism, with Reference to Spiritism." In September, volume 4 of the Kurschner edition is completed. In November, *The Philosophy of Freedom* appears. This year, too, he meets John Henry Mackay (1864-1933), the anarchist, and Max Stirner, a scholar and biographer.

1894: Rudolf Steiner meets Elisabeth Förster Nietzsche, the philosopher's sister, and begins to read Nietzsche in earnest, beginning with the as yet unpublished *Antichrist*. He also meets Ernst Haeckel (1834-1919). In the fall, he begins to write *Nietzsche, A Fighter against His Time* (CW 5).

1895: May, *Nietzsche, A Fighter against His Time* appears.

1896: January 22: Rudolf Steiner sees Friedrich Nietzsche for the first and only time. Moves between Nietzsche and the Goethe-Schiller Archives, where he completes his work before year's end. He falls out with Elisabeth Förster Nietzsche, thus ending his association with the Nietzsche archive.

1897: Rudolf Steiner finishes the manuscript of *Goethe's Worldview* (CW 6). He moves to Berlin with Anna Eunike and begins editorship of the *Magazin für Literatur*. From now on, Steiner will write countless reviews, literary and philosophical articles, and so on. He begins lecturing at the "Free Literary Society." In September, he attends the Zionist Congress in Basel. He sides with Dreyfus in the Dreyfus affair.

1898: Rudolf Steiner is very active as an editor in the political, artistic, and theatrical life of Berlin. He becomes friendly with John Henry Mackay and poet Ludwig Jacobowski (1868-1900). He joins Jacobowski's circle of writers, artists, and scientists—"The Coming Ones" (*Die Kommenden*)—and contributes lectures to the group until 1903. He also lectures at the "League for College Pedagogy." He writes an article for Goethe's sesquicentennial, "Goethe's Secret Revelation," on the "Fairy Tale of the Green Snake and the Beautiful Lily."

1888-89: "This was a trying time for my soul as I looked at Christianity. . ..I was able to progress only by contemplating, by means of spiritual perception, the evolution of Christianity . . ..Conscious knowledge of real Christianity began to dawn in me around the turn of the century. This seed continued to develop. My soul trial occurred shortly before the beginning of the twentieth century. It was decisive for my soul's development that I stood spiritually before the mystery of Golgotha in a deep and solemn celebration of knowledge."

1899: Rudolf Steiner begins teaching and giving lectures and lecture cycles at the Workers' College, founded by Wilhelm Liebknecht (1826-1900). He will continue to do so until 1904. Writes: *Literature and Spiritual Life in the Nineteenth Century; Individualism in Philosophy; Haeckel and His Opponents; Poetry in the Present;* and begins what will become (fifteen years later) *Riddles of Philosophy* (CW 18). He also meets many artists and writers, including Käthe Kollwitz, Stefan Zweig, and Rainer Maria Rilke. On October 31, he marries Anna Eunike.

1900: "I thought that the turn of the century must bring humanity a new light. It seemed to me that the separation of human thinking and willing from the spirit had peaked. A turn or reversal of direction in human evolution seemed to me a necessity." Rudolf Steiner finishes *World and Life Views in the Nineteenth Century* (the second part of what will become *Riddles of Philosophy*) and dedicates it to Ernst Haeckel. It is published in March. He continues lecturing at *Die Kommenden*, whose leadership he assumes after the death of Jacobowski. Also, he gives the Gutenberg Jubilee lecture before 7,000 typesetters and printers. In September, Rudolf Steiner is invited by Count and Countess Brockdorff to lecture in the Theosophical Library. His first lecture is on Nietzsche. His second lecture is titled "Goethe's Secret Revelation." October 6, he begins a lecture cycle on the mystics that will become *Mystics after Modernism* (CW 7). November-December: "Marie von Sivers appears in the audience...." Also in November, Steiner gives his first lecture at the *Giordano Bruno Bund* (where he will continue to lecture until May, 1905). He speaks on Bruno and modern Rome, focusing on the importance of the philosophy of Thomas Aquinas as monism.

1901:   In continual financial straits, Rudolf Steiner's early friends Moritz Zitter and Rosa Mayreder help support him. In October, he begins the lecture cycle *Christianity as Mystical Fact* (CW 8) at the Theosophical Library. In November, he gives his first "Theosophical lecture" on Goethe's "Fairy Tale" in Hamburg at the invitation of Wilhelm Hubbe-Schleiden. He also attends a tea to celebrate the founding of the Theosophical Society at Count and Countess Brockdorff's. He gives a lecture cycle, "From Buddha to Christ," for the circle of the *Kommenden*. November 17, Marie von Sivers asks Rudolf Steiner if Theosophy does not need a Western-Christian spiritual movement (to complement Theosophy's Eastern emphasis). "The question was posed. Now, following spiritual laws, I could begin to give an answer. . .." In December, Rudolf Steiner writes his first article for a Theosophical publication. At year's end, the Brockdorffs and possibly Wilhelm Hubbe-Schleiden ask Rudolf Steiner to join the Theosophical Society and undertake the leadership of the German section. Rudolf Steiner agrees, on the condition that Marie von Sivers (then in Italy) work with him.

1902:   Beginning in January, Rudolf Steiner attends the opening of the Workers' School in Spandau with Rosa Luxemburg (1870-1919). January 17, Rudolf Steiner joins the Theosophical Society. In April, he is asked to become general secretary of the German Section of the Theosophical Society, and works on preparations for its founding. In July, he visits London for a Theosophical congress. He meets Bertram Keightly, G.R.S. Mead, A.P. Sinnett, and Annie Besant, among others. In September, *Christianity as Mystical Fact* appears. In October, Rudolf Steiner gives his first public lecture on Theosophy ("Monism and Theosophy") to about three hundred people at the Giordano Bruno Bund. On October 19-21, the German Section of the Theosophical Society has its first meeting; Rudolf Steiner is the general secretary, and Annie Besant attends. Steiner lectures on practical karma studies.

On October 23, Annie Besant inducts Rudolf Steiner into the Esoteric School of the Theosophical Society. On October 25, Steiner begins a weekly series of lectures: "The Field of Theosophy." During this year, Rudolf Steiner also first meets Ita Wegman (1876-1943), who will become his close collaborator in his final years.

1903: Rudolf Steiner holds about 300 lectures and seminars. In May, the first number of the periodical *Luzifer* appears. In June, Rudolf Steiner visits London for the first meeting of the Federation of the European Sections of the Theosophical Society, where he meets Colonel Olcott. He begins to write *Theosophy* (CW 9).

1904: Rudolf Steiner continues lecturing at the Workers' College and elsewhere (about 90 lectures), while lecturing intensively all over Germany among Theosophists (about a 140 lectures). In February, he meets Carl Unger (1878-1929), who will become a member of the board of the Anthroposophical Society (1913). In March, he meets Michael Bauer (1871-1929), a Christian mystic, who will also be on the board. In May, *Theosophy* appears, with the dedication: "To the spirit of Giordano Bruno." Rudolf Steiner and Marie von Sivers visit London for meetings with Annie Besant. June: Rudolf Steiner and Marie von Sivers attend the meeting of the Federation of European Sections of the Theosophical Society in Amsterdam. In July, Steiner begins the articles in *Luzifer-Gnosis* that will become *How to Know Higher Worlds* (CW 10) and *Cosmic Memory* (CW 11). In September, Annie Besant visits Germany. In December, Steiner lectures on Freemasonry. He mentions the High Grade Masonry derived from John Yarker and represented by Theodore Reuss and Karl Kellner as a blank slate "into which a good image could be placed."

1905: This year, Steiner ends his non-Theosophical lecturing activity. Supported by Marie von Sivers, his Theosophical lecturing—both in public and in the Theosophical Society—increases significantly: "The German Theosophical Movement is of exceptional importance." Steiner recommends reading, among others, Fichte, Jacob Boehme, and Angelus Silesius. He begins to introduce Christian themes into Theosophy. He also begins to work with doctors (Felix Peipers and Ludwig Noll). In July, he is in London for the Federation of European Sections, where he attends a lecture by Annie Besant: "I have seldom seen Mrs. Besant speak in so inward and heartfelt a manner...." "Through Mrs. Besant I have found the way to H.P. Blavatsky." September to October, he gives a course of thirty-one lectures for a small group of esoteric students. In October, the annual meeting of the German Section of the Theosophical Society, which still remains very small, takes place. Rudolf Steiner reports membership has risen from 121 to 377 members. In November, seeking to establish esoteric "continuity," Rudolf Steiner and Marie von Sivers participate in a "Memphis-Misraim" Masonic ceremony. They pay forty-five marks for membership. "Yesterday, you saw how little remains of former esoteric institutions." "We are dealing only with a 'framework'...for the present, nothing lies behind it. The occult powers have completely withdrawn."

1907:   Further expansion of the German Theosophical Movement according to the Rosicrucian directive to "introduce spirit into the world"—in education, in social questions, in art, and in science. In February, Col. Olcott dies in Adyar. Before he dies, Olcott indicates that "the Masters" wish Annie Besant to succeed him: much politicking ensues. Rudolf Steiner supports Besant's candidacy. April-May: preparations for the Congress of the Federation of European Sections of the Theosophical Society—the great, watershed Whitsun "Munich Congress," attended by Annie Besant and others. Steiner decides to separate Eastern and Western (Christian-Rosicrucian) esoteric schools. He takes his esoteric school out of the Theosophical Society (Besant and Rudolf Steiner are "in harmony" on this). Steiner makes his first lecture tours to Austria and Hungary. That summer, he is in Italy. In September, he visits Edouard Schuré, who will write the introduction to the French edition of *Christianity as Mystical Fact* in Barr, Alsace. Rudolf Steiner writes the autobiographical statement known as the "Barr Document." In *Luzifer –Gnosis*, "The Education of the Child" appears.1906: Expansion of Theosophical work. Rudolf Steiner gives about 245 lectures, only 44 of which take place in Berlin. Cycles are given in Paris, Leipzig, Stuttgart, and Munich. Esoteric work also intensifies. Rudolf Steiner begins writing *An Outline of Esoteric Science* (CW 13). In January, Rudolf Steiner receives permission (a patent) from the Great Orient of the Scottish A & A Thirty-Three Degree Rite of the Order of the Ancient Freemasons of the Memphis-Misraim Rite to direct a chapter under the name "Mystica Aeterna." This will become the "Cognitive Cultic Section" (also called "Misraim Service") of the Esoteric School. (See: >*From the History and Contents of the Cognitive Cultic Section* (CW 264). During this time, Steiner also meets Albert Schweitzer. In May, he is in Paris, where he visits Edouard Schuré. Many Russians attend his lectures (including Konstantin Balmont, Dimitri Mereszkovski, Zinaida Hippius, and Maximilian Woloshin). He attends the General Meeting of the European Federation of the Theosophical Society, at which Col. Olcott is present for the last time. He spends the year's end in Venice and Rome, where he writes and works on his translation of H.P. Blavatsky's *Key to Theosophy*.

1908:   The movement grows (membership: 1150). Lecturing expands. Steiner makes his first extended lecture tour to Holland and Scandinavia, as well as visits to Naples and Sicily. Themes: St John's Gospel, the Apocalypse, Egypt, science, philosophy, and logic. *Luzifer-Gnosis* ceases publication. In Berlin, Marie von Sivers (with Johanna Mücke (1864-1949) forms the *Philosophisch-Theosophisch* (after 1915 *Philosophisch-Anthroposophisch*) *Verlag* to publish Steiner's work. Steiner gives lecture cycles titled *The Gospel of St John* (CW 103) and *The Apocalypse* (104).

1909:   *An Outline of Esoteric Science* appears. Lecturing and travel continues. Rudolf Steiner's spiritual research expands to include the polarity of Lucifer and Ahriman; the work of great individualities in history; the Maitreya Buddha and the Bodhisattvas; spiritual economy (CW 109); the work of the spiritual hierarchies in heaven and on Earth (CW 110). He also deepens and intensifies his research into the Gospels, giving lectures on the Gospel of St. Luke (CW 114) with the first mention of two Jesus children. Meets and becomes friends with Christian Morgenstern (1871-1914). In April, he lays the foundation stone for the Malsch model—the building that will lead to the first Goetheanum. In May, the International Congress of the Federation of European Sections of the Theosophical Society takes place in Budapest. Rudolf Steiner receives the Subba Row medal for *How to Know Higher Worlds.* During this time, Charles W. Leadbeater discovers Jiddu Krishnamurti (1895-1986) and proclaims him the future "world teacher," the bearer of the Maitreya Buddha and the "reappearing Christ." In October, Steiner delivers seminal lectures on "anthroposophy," which he will try, unsuccessfully, to rework over the next years into the unfinished work, *Anthroposophy (A Fragment)*(CW 45).

1910:   New themes: *The Reappearance of Christ in the Etheric* (CW 118); *The Fifth Gospel*; *The Mission of Folk Souls* (CW 121); *Occult History* (CW 126); the evolving development of etheric cognitive capacities. Rudolf Steiner continues his Gospel research with *The Gospel of St. Matthew* (CW 123). In January, his father dies. In April, he takes a month-long trip to Italy, including Rome, Monte Cassino, and Sicily. He also visits Scandinavia again. July-August, he writes the first mystery drama, *The Portal of Initiation* (CW 14). In November, he gives "psychosophy" lectures. In December, he submits "On the Psychological Foundations and Epistemological Framework of Theosophy" to the International Philosophical Congress in Bologna.

1911:   The crisis in the Theosophical Society deepens. In January, "The Order of the Rising Sun," which will soon become "The Order of the Star in the East," is founded for the coming world teacher, Krishnamurti. At the same time, Marie von Sivers, Rudolf Steiner's coworker, falls ill. Fewer lectures are given, but important new ground is broken. In Prague, in March, Steiner meets Franz Kafka (1883-1924) and Hugo Bergmann (1883-1975). In April, he delivers his paper to the Philosophical Congress. He writes the second mystery drama, *The Soul's Probation* (CW 14). Also, while Marie von Sivers is convalescing, Rudolf Steiner begins work on *Kalendar 1912/1913*, which will contain the "Calendar of the Soul" meditations. On March 19, Anna (Eunike) Steiner dies. In September, Rudolf Steiner visits Einsiedeln, birthplace of Paracelsus. In December, Friedrich Rittelmeyer, future founder of the Christian Community, meets Rudolf Steiner. The *Johannes-Bauverein*, the "building committee," which would lead to the first Goetheanum (first planned for Munich), is also founded, and a preliminary committee for the founding of an independent association is created that, in the following year, will become the Anthroposophical Society. Important lecture cycles include *Occult Physiology* (CW 128); *Wonders of the World* (CW 129); *>From Jesus to Christ* (CW 131). Other themes: esoteric Christianity; Christian Rosenkreutz; the spiritual guidance of humanity; the sense world and the world of the spirit.

1912:   Despite the ongoing, now increasing crisis in the Theosophical Society, much is accomplished: *Calendar 1912/1913* is published; eurythmy is created; both the third mystery drama, *The Guardian of the Threshold* (CW 14) and *The Road to Self Knowledge* (CW 16) are written. New (or renewed) themes included life between death and rebirth and karma and reincarnation. Other lecture cycles: *Spiritual Beings in the Heavenly Bodies and the Kingdoms of Nature* (CW 136); *The Human Being in the Light of Occultism, Theosophy, and Philosophy* (CW 137); *The Gospel of St Mark* (CW 139); and *The Bhagavad-Gita and the Epistles of St. Paul* (CW 142). On May 8, Rudolf Steiner celebrates White Lotus Day, H.P. Blavatsky's death day, which he had faithfully observed for the past decade, for the last time. In August, Rudolf Steiner suggests the "independent association" be called the "Anthroposophical Society." In September, the first eurythmy course takes place. In October, Rudolf Steiner declines recognition of a Theosophical Society lodge dedicated to the Star of the East and decides to expel all Theosophical Society members belonging to the order. Also, with Marie von Sivers, he first visits Dornach, near Basel, Switzerland, and they stand on the hill where the Goetheanum will be. In November, a Theosophical Society lodge is opened by direct mandate from Adyar (Annie Besant). In December, a meeting of the German section occurs at which it is decided that belonging to the Order of the Star of the East is incompatible with membership in the Theosophical Society. December 28: informal founding of the Anthroposophical Society in Berlin.

1913:   Expulsion of the German section from the Theosophical Society. February 2-3: Foundation meeting of the Anthroposophical Society. Board members include: Marie von Sivers, Michael Bauer, and Carl Unger. September 20: Laying of the foundation stone for the *Johannes Bau* (Goetheanum) in Dornach. Building begins immediately. The third mystery drama, *The Soul's Awakening* (CW 14), is completed. Also: *The Threshold of the Spiritual World* (CW147). Lecture cycles include: *The Bhagavad-Gita and the Epistles of St. Paul* and *The Occult Foundations of the Bhagavad-Gita* (CW 146), which the Russian philosopher Nikolai Berdyaev attends; *The Mysteries of the East and of Christianity* (CW 144); *The Effects of Esoteric Development* (CW 145); and *The Fifth Gospel* (CW 148). In May, Rudolf Steiner is in London and Paris, where anthroposophical work continues.

1914:   Building continues on the *Johannes Bau* (Goetheanum) in Dornach, with artists and coworkers from seventeen nations. The general assembly of the Anthroposophical Society takes place. In May, Rudolf

Steiner visits Paris, as well as Chartres Cathedral. June 28: assassination in Sarajevo ("Now the catastrophe has happened!"). August 1: War is declared. Rudolf Steiner returns to Germany from Dornach — he will travel back and forth. He writes the last chapter of *Riddles of Philosophy*. Lecture cycles include: *Human and Cosmic Thought* (CW 151); *Inner Being of Humanity between Death and a New Birth* (CW 153); *Occult Reading and Occult Hearing* (CW 156). December 24: marriage of Rudolf Steiner and Marie von Sivers.

1915: Building continues. Life after death becomes a major theme, also art. Writes: *Thoughts during a Time of War* (CW 24). Lectures include: *The Secret of Death* (CW 159); *The Uniting of Humanity through the Christ Impulse* (CW 165).

1916: Rudolf Steiner begins work with Edith Maryon (1872-1924) on the sculpture "The Representative of Humanity" ("The Group"—Christ, Lucifer, and Ahriman). He also works with the alchemist Alexander von Bernus on the quarterly *Das Reich*. He writes *The Riddle of Humanity* (CW 20). Lectures include: *Necessity and Freedom in World History and Human Action* (CW 166); *Past and Present in the Human Spirit* (CW 167); *The Karma of Vocation* (CW 172); *The Karma of Untruthfulness* (CW 173).

1917: Russian Revolution. The U.S. enters the war. Building continues. Rudolf Steiner delineates the idea of the *threefold nature of the human being* (in a public lecture March 15) and the *threefold nature of the social organism* (hammered out in May-June with the help of Otto von Lerchenfeld and Ludwig Polzer-Hoditz in the form of two documents titled *Memoranda*, which were distributed in high places). August-September: Rudolf Steiner writes *Riddles of the Soul* (CW 20). Also: commentary on "The Chemical Wedding of Christian Rosenkreutz" for Alexander Bernus (*Das Reich*). Lectures include: *The Karma of Materialism* (CW 176); *The Spiritual Background of the Outer World: The Fall of the Spirits of Darkness* (CW 177).

1918: March 18: peace treaty of Brest-Litovsk— "Now everything will truly enter chaos! What is needed is cultural renewal." June: Rudolf Steiner visits Karlstein (Grail) Castle outside Prague. Lecture cycle: *From Symptom to Reality in Modern History* (CW 185). In mid-November, Emil Molt, of the Waldorf-Astoria Cigarette Company, has the idea of founding a school for his workers' children.

1919: Focus on the threefold social organism: tireless travel, countless lectures, meetings, and publications. At the same time, a new public stage of anthroposophy emerges as cultural renewal begins. The coming years will see initiatives in pedagogy, medicine, pharmacology, and agriculture. January 27: threefold meeting: " We must first of all, with the money we have, found free schools that can bring people what they need." February: first public eurythmy performance in Zurich. Also: "Appeal to the German People" (CW 24), circulated March 6 as a newspaper insert. In April, *Toward Social Renewal* (CW 23)—"perhaps the most widely read of all books on politics appearing since the war"—appears. Rudolf Steiner is asked to undertake the "direction and leadership" of the school founded by the Waldorf-Astoria Company. Rudolf Steiner begins to talk about the "renewal" of education. May 30: a building is selected and purchased for the future Waldorf School. August-September, Rudolf Steiner gives a lecture course for Waldorf teachers, *Foundations of Human Experience (Study of Man)*(CW 293). September 7: Opening of the first Waldorf School. December (into January): first science course, the *Light Course* (CW 320).

1920:   The Waldorf School flourishes. New threefold initiatives. Founding of limited companies *Der Kommenden Tag* and *Futurum A.G.* to infuse spiritual values into the economic realm. Rudolf Steiner also focuses on the sciences. Lectures: *Introducing Anthroposophical Medicine* (CW 312); *Warmth Course* (CW 321); *Boundaries of Natural Science* (CW 322); *The Redemption of Thinking* (CW 74). February: Johannes Werner Klein—later a cofounder of the Christian Community—asks Rudolf Steiner about the possibility of a "religious renewal," a "Johannine church." In March, Rudolf Steiner gives the first course for doctors and medical students. In April, a divinity student asks Rudolf Steiner a second time about the possibility of religious renewal. September 27-October 16: anthroposophical "university course." December: lectures titled *The Search for the New Isis* (CW 202).

1921:   Rudolf Steiner continues his intensive work on cultural renewal, including the uphill battle for the threefold social order. "university" arts, scientific, theological, and medical courses include: *Astronomy Course* (CW 323); *Observation, Mathematics, and Scientific Experiment* (CW 324); the *Second Medical Course* (CW 313); *Color*. In June and September-October, Rudolf Steiner also gives the first two "priests' courses" (CW 342 and 343). The "youth movement" gains momentum. Magazines are founded: *Die Drei* (January), and—under the editorship of Albert Steffen (1884-1963)— the weekly, *Das Goetheanum* (August). In February-March, Rudolf Steiner takes his first trip outside Germany since the war (Holland). On April 7, Steiner receives a letter regarding "religious renewal," and May 22-23, he agrees to address the question in a practical way. In June, the Klinical-Therapeutic Institute opens in Arlesheim under the direction of Dr. Ita Wegman. In August, the Chemical-Pharmaceutical Laboratory opens in Arlesheim (Oskar Schmiedel and Ita Wegman, directors). The Clinical Therapeutic Institute is inaugurated in Stuttgart (Dr. Ludwig Noll, director); also the Research Laboratory in Dornach (Ehrenfried Pfeiffer and Gunther Wachsmuth, directors). In November-December, Rudolf Steiner visits Norway.

1922:   The first half of the year involves very active public lecturing (thousands attend); in the second half, Rudolf Steiner begins to withdraw and turn toward the society—"The society is asleep." It is "too weak" to do what is asked of it. The businesses—*Die Kommenden Tag* and *Futura A.G.*—fail. In January, with the help of an agent, Steiner undertakes a twelve-city German tour, accompanied by eurythmy performances. In two weeks he speaks to more than 2,000 people. In April, he gives a "university course" in The Hague. He also visits England. In June, he is in Vienna for the East-West Congress. In August-September, he is back in England for the Oxford Conference on Education. Returning to Dornach, he gives the lectures *Philosophy, Cosmology, and Religion* (CW 215), and gives the third priest's course (CW 344). On September 16, The Christian Community is founded. In October-November, Steiner is in Holland and England. He also speaks to the youth: *Youth Course* (CW 217). In December, Steiner gives lectures titled *The Origins of Natural Science* (CW 326), and *Humanity and the World of Stars: The Spiritual Communion of Humanity* (CW 219). December 31: Fire at the Goetheanum, which is destroyed.

1923: Despite the fire, Rudolf Steiner continues his work unabated. A very hard year. Internal dispersion, dissension, and apathy abound. There is conflict—between old and new visions—within the society. A wake-up call is needed, and Rudolf Steiner responds with renewed lecturing vitality. His focus: the spiritual context of human life; initiation science; the course of the year; and community building. As a foundation for an artistic school, he creates a series of pastel sketches. Lecture cycles: *The Anthroposophical Movement; Initiation Science* (CW227) (in England at the Penmaenmawr Summer School); *The Four Seasons and the Archangels* (CW 229); *The Human Being: Symphony of the Creative Word* (CW 230); *The Supersensible Human* (CW 231), given in Holland for the founding of the Dutch society. On November 10, in response to the failed Hitler-Ludendorf putsch in Munich, Steiner closes his Berlin residence and moves the *Philosophisch-Anthroposophisch Verlag* (Press) to Dornach. On December 9, Steiner begins the serialization of his *Autobiography: The Course of My Life* (CW 28) in *Das Goetheanum.* It will continue to appear weekly, without a break, until his death. Late December-early January: Rudolf Steiner refounds the Anthroposophical Society (about 12,000 members internationally) and takes over its leadership. The new board members are: Marie Steiner, Ita Wegman, Albert Steffen, Elizabeth Vreede, and Guenther Wachsmuth. (See *The Christmas Meeting for the Founding of the General Anthroposophical Society* (CW 260). Accompanying lectures: *Mystery Knowledge and Mystery Centers* (CW 232); *World History in the Light of Anthroposophy* (CW 233). December 25: the Foundation Stone is laid (in the hearts of members) in the form of the "Foundation Stone Meditation."

1924: January 1: having founded the Anthroposophical Society and taken over its leadership, Rudolf Steiner has the task of "reforming" it. The process begins with a weekly newssheet ("What's Happening in the Anthroposophical Society") in which Rudolf Steiner's "Letters to Members" and "Anthroposophical Leading Thoughts" appear (CW 26). The next step is the creation of a new esoteric class, the "first class" of the "University of Spiritual Science" (which was to have been followed, had Rudolf Steiner lived longer, by two more advanced classes). Then comes a new language for anthroposophy—practical, phenomenological, and direct; and Rudolf Steiner creates the model for the second Goetheanum. He begins the series of extensive "karma" lectures (CW 235-40); and finally, responding to needs, he creates two new initiatives: biodynamic agriculture and curative education. After the middle of the year, rumors begin to circulate regarding Steiner's health. Lectures: January-February, *Anthroposophy* (CW 234); February: *Tone Eurythmy* (CW 278); June: *Agriculture Course* (CW 327); June-July: *Speech Eurythmy* (CW 279); *Curative Education* (CW 317); August: (England, "Second International Summer School"), *Initiation Consciousness: True and False Paths in Spiritual Investigation* (CW 243); September: *Pastoral Medicine* (CW 318). On September 26, for the first time, Rudolf Steiner cancels a lecture. On September 28, he gives his last lecture. On September 29, he withdraws to his studio in the carpenter's shop; now he is definitively ill. Cared for by Ita Wegman, he continues working, however, and writing the weekly installments of his *Autobiography* and *Letters to the Members/Leading Thoughts* (CW 26).

1925:   Rudolf Steiner, while continuing to work, continues to weaken. He finishes *Extending Practical Medicine* (CW 27) with Ita Wegman. On March 30, around ten in the morning, Rudolf Steiner dies.

INDEX

acid/acidic, 6, 99, 185
Addison's disease, 263
adrenal, 263
  adrenal degeneration, 263
Ahasuerus, 163,
ahrimanic, 97
air, as a component of outer world, 4
alkalies, 6
alkaline, 15, 144, 149, 151, 167, 185
alchemy, 95, 271
allopathic/allopathically, 72, 290-
  291
ammonia salts, 280-281
amoeba, 10
anabolic, 29
analyzing process, in outer world,
  128-129
animal
  development, 219-220
  formative forces, 42-44, 47, 147
  kingdom, 16, 41, 47-48, 59, 83,
    100, 146-147, 162, 202-204,
    215, 219
  nature, 162
  serum therapy, 64
animalizing process, 162, 164, 254
animism, 7
anise, 142
arteriosclerosis, 114
Anthroposophical/Anthroposophy,
  1-2, 17, 52, 70-72, 75, 86, 93,
  95, 100, 102, 123, 130, 142,
  148, 157, 159, 161-162, 173-
  174, 178, 182, 186-188, 191-
  193, 195, 199, 203, 207, 213,
  224, 234, 242, 249, 265, 279,
  284, 288-289, 294
Anthroposophical Society, 1
antimony, 247, 270-276, 292
  crystal-forming forces, 270-271
  flowers of, 271
antipathy, 8, 61, 93, 134, 246
archetypal phenomenon, 232-233

Archimedes, 54
  his hydraulic principle of
buoyancy, 54
archeus, 6-7, 23-24. *See also* etheric
  body
ash formation, 89
arnica, 211
aromatic, 122, 126
arsenic, 172
arteries, 5
artist, 257
astral, 117-121, 125, 211, 219, 253
  super-astral, 19
astral body, 69-71, 76, 93, 102-104,
  108, 110, 117, 119, 145, 173-
  174, 199, 209, 211-212, 217,
  228, 253, 269, 280-281, 288
astronomical factors, 131, 136
atomism/atomistic, 8-11, 94, 175, 242
  view of medicine, 8-11
autopsy, 8-9, 25
autosuggestion, 38-39

bacterium/bacillus, 56, 251, 254,
  256, 291
Behring, von, Emil, 82, 84
belladonna. *See* nightshade, deadly
birch tree. *See* white birch
birds, 55, 62, 215
  blackbirds, 213-215
black gall, 4
black hellebore. *See* Christmas rose
black locust, 41
bladder, 66, 132-135, 175
  as a suction organ, 133
blastema, 9
blood, 4, 19-20, 48-50, 97, 115,
  124, 128, 143-145, 148, 166,
  217, 219
  blood formation, 48-49, 128, 148,
    217, 219, 229, 233, 280-281,
    285-287
  cells, 45

phantom, 278
bones. *See* skeletal system, human
Brahma, days and nights of, 93
brain, 54, 66, 74, 81-82, 125-126,
  217, 287
  disease, 194
  forebrain, 66
breathing process, coal, 161
bubonic plague, 84
buoyancy, 54, 74

calcium carbonate, 75, 90, 134, 149,
  169
  forces, 75
Carbo vegetabilis, 158-159, 161-162,
  164-165, 167, 169, 181, 194
carbon, 53-54, 154, 159, 163-164,
  167, 176, 178, 181, 194
  animal carbon, 181
  plant carbon, 181
carbonates, 149, 151
carbonic acid, 54, 60, 138-140, 154
carbonization, 162
carcinoma, 186, 188, 191, 207
cardiac function, 20-21, 31, 34, 36,
  107, 132-134, 136-137, 175,
  177, 252
cardiology, 19
catabolic, 29
Catholic, 247
cells, 9-10, 112-113
  constantly diseased, 49
  formative forces, 113, 154
  not reproductive, 45, 48
cellular pathology, 10, 112
cerebral fluid, 54
chemical/chemistry, 4-6, 15, 95,
  159, 161, 174-176, 183, 236,
  262-263, 288
  atomic (molecular), 94, 175
  earthly, 15-16
  external, 185
  force, 166, 168
  non-earthly, 15, 24
  organic, 195
chemical zones (forces), 165-170
chicory, 143-144

childhood, 102-108, 114, 182, 233-
  234, 240, 248, 257-258, 260-
  264
chlorophyll, 243-244
cholera
  Huntingdon's, 103
  Sydenham's, 103
Christmas rose, 193-194
circulatory system, 64, 77
clairvoyance/clairvoyant, 5-6, 153,
  179, 200, 203-204, 209, 278
  atavistic (ancient), 3, 8, 30, 64, 66,
  76, 93, 179-180, 270
coal, 161
coffee, 197, 275
  reestablishes rhythm, 275
  releases forces for logic, 197
cognition, 66
colon, 62, 66
color, 230
color therapies, 52, 230-231
combustion process, 99, 122, 125,
  141
concept/conceptualization, 27, 78,
  96, 125-126, 128, 193, 218
consciousness, 7, 70, 178-179, 226-
  228, 230-231, 236, 249-250,
  256, 277
  as laying between soul and spirit, 7
consciousness soul, 7
constipation, 30, 206
contagion, 27
cooked vs. raw food, 148, 150
Copernican, 87
copper, 96, 98, 115-116, 139, 149,
  184, 286
  attribute to Venus, 96
  forces, 115, 149, 172, 286
correspondences, 22-24, 63, 127,
  129, 174, 205
cosmic/cosmos, 4-7, 10-11, 73, 75,
  78-79, 81, 85, 88-89, 92-95, 97,
  100, 102, 112, 149, 151, 153-
  156, 166-167, 215, 219, 224,
  232, 252-253, 260, 266, 276
  balancing, 97, 154
  forces, 4-5, 7, 14-17, 19, 24-25,

172, 182, 189-190, 209, 215, 247, 270
naturopathic, 135, 292
nearsightedness, 70
neoplasms, 188
nerves, 36-37, 44-45, 48-49
  motor nerves, 36-37
  sensory nerves, 36-37
nervous/sensory system, 23, 36-37, 44-46, 53, 63, 77, 144, 225
  only perceptive processes connect, 36
neurasthenia, 25-26, 31, 145
neurons, 44-45
  do not self-replicate, 45, 48
night shade, deadly, 277-278
night sweats, 29-31
null point, 160-161, 227
nux vomica, 284-285, 287

ointments (salves), 185, 186, 194
olfactory nerve, 126
ossification, 105, 114. *See also* sclerosis
oyster shells, 75, 167-169, 276

Paracelsus, 5-7, 23, 35, 64, 139, 156-157, 179
  archeus, 6-7, 23
  as first to distinguish gases from air, 6
paralysis, 145, 259
pathological/pathology, 8-10, 34-35, 40, 52, 56-57, 68, 101, 105, 109, 115, 132, 152-153, 186, 198, 251, 264, 289
  humoral, 3-5, 8-9
  pathological anatomy, 3, 8, 10
pecten, 124
pedagogy, 102
perception, 281
petiole, 41-42
phantom, 200-201, 208, 211
  scaffolding, 201, 209
phosphoric/phosphorus, 167, 232, 236, 281
  principle, 75-77, 81, 83, 90-92, 98-99, 113, 263

contains light internally (light-bearer), 76, 99-100
physics, molecular, 94-95
physis (physical reality), 54
phytogeneric/phytogeny, 246
phytotherapeutic/phytotherapy, 54, 59, 64, 74, 127, 146, 220
pineal gland, 67
pituitary gland, 67
planets, 151, 260
  guest planets, 87
  forces, 87-88, 95
  inner planets, 87, 92, 104, 110-111
    forces of, 88, 151
    influences of, 92
  outer planets, 87, 92, 104, 110-111, 131, 258
    influences of, 92,104
  spiral movement, 86-87
plants
  comparison to animals and humans, 78, 85, 89-90
  development, 218-219, 221
  excretory process, 89
  forces, 79, 94, 122, 146, 153, 155, 191, 218, 222, 252
  formative, 42, 44, 47, 53, 86, 94
  ghost replicas, 121-122
  kingdom, 41, 46-47, 53-54, 77-83, 85, 87-89, 100-101, 116-118, 120-122, 126-127,
  root process, 87-89, 131, 146-147, 166-167, 213, 218-219, 252
  spiral path, 86
  sexual process, 89
platonic year, 92
pleurisy, 107-108, 114
pneumonia, 107-109, 114
poles of human organization (polarity), 22, 24
  equates to a positive image and its negative, 26-27
  as a homeopathizer, 33
  lower, 22-32, 57, 66-67, 74-75, 81-82, 90, 107, 125-126, 139, 162, 194, 197-198, 255, 260, 286